+B+C

+B+C+D →

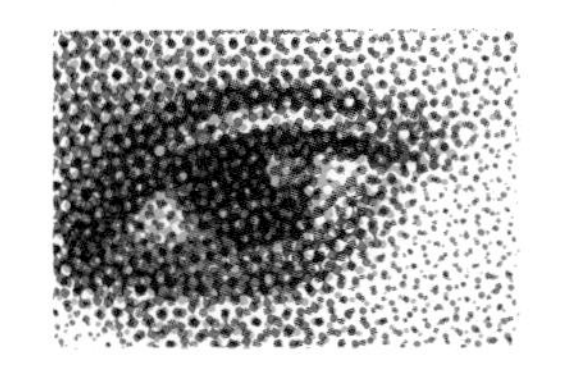

To Hilla

BOOK

A
BALANCE HOUSE
BOOK

MARSHALL LEE

MAKING:

The illustrated guide to design & production

Published by

R. R. Bowker Company

New York

1180 Avenue of the Americas, New York, N.Y. 10036
Library of Congress Catalog Card Number: 65-22380

Manufactured in the United States of America.

SIXTH PRINTING, 1972

Prices in text revised to January 1972

ACKNOWLEDGMENTS

Particular mention is due to Daniel Melcher, who contributed extensive commentaries on the Ms, and made available the material he had assembled for a similar book of his own. Others who read the entire Ms and made valuable suggestions were Ernst Reichl, John Begg, and Chandler Grannis.

Dozens of experts, specialists, technicians, and generally experienced people were consulted to some extent. Some were asked only one question, others were asked for and gave considerable portions of their time. Many of these were of the H. Wolff Book Manufacturing Company, with which the author was associated, but many were with other organizations having special operations and backgrounds. Of the latter, Jack W. White of Graphic Arts Technical Foundation and Leonard Schlosser of Lindenmeyr-Schlosser Paper Corp. were especially helpful. It is impossible to name each one who helped, but to all of them goes our sincere gratitude.

Despite every effort to check the facts, errors have undoubtedly remained in the text. For these, as well as for the judgments expressed, the author takes all responsibility.

Grateful acknowledgement is made also to: McGraw-Hill Book Co. for permission to use or adapt several illustrations from *Printing and Promotion Handbook;* Strathmore Paper Co. for permission to use the papermaking diagrams on pages 132-33; Kingsport Press for permission to reproduce the copyfitting table on page 258; *Publishers' Weekly* for permission to use several pictures from their files; The British Museum for permission to reproduce the manuscript on page 101.

Read this first

The following paragraphs define the terms and explain the concepts and premises on which this book is based.

BOOK DESIGN is the conception, planning, and specifying of the physical and visual attributes of a book.

BOOK PRODUCTION is the execution of the design, i.e. purchasing materials and services, scheduling and routing the work, coordinating the manufacture of the book with distribution requirements, and maintaining records.

Book design and production are not 2 separate functions, but 2 parts of 1 function, i.e. *to transmit the author's message to the reader in the best possible way*. This means creating a product that can be profitably sold, as well as satisfying the requirements of author and reader. The term BOOKMAKING is used to express the whole function.

The word BOOK applies to many different products. As often as possible, the text refers to a specific category of book (text, reference, paperback, juvenile, reprint, etc.) but when the term itself is used alone it may be taken to mean *tradebook*, the conventional hardcover book sold to the general public.

A WELL-DESIGNED BOOK means one that is (a) appropriate to its content and use, (b) economical, and (c) satisfying to the senses. It is not a "pretty" book in the superficial sense and it is not necessarily more elaborate than usual.

ECONOMICAL refers to an efficient use of the graphic and material elements of the book and the money spent for its manufacture. This does not necessarily imply the smallest possible expenditure, but rather the smallest expenditure that will achieve the most successful result.

It is assumed that the importance of being PRACTICAL and ECONOMICAL at all times is understood, so reminders to this effect will remain implied rather than stated.

Each technical or special term is italicized the first time it occurs and usually its meaning is given directly or by the context. At the back of the book is a Glossary-Index, in which every italicized term is listed alphabetically, with a definition when one is needed. In the text are references [(CH.20) etc.] to other chapters in which a term or subject is discussed.

Grammatical usage in the text defers to logic and efficiency more than custom. For example, space and reading time are saved by the use of figures instead of spelled-out numbers and abbreviations for frequently used terms. In punctuation, British practice is followed where it is more logical and no confusion will result. Commas are used wherever they contribute to clarity.

This volume is *an outline of practical information and procedure* for those engaged in planning and producing books, and as such it is quite complete, but no book of this length—or many times this length—could describe in detail *all* the processes, equipment, and materials that go into bookmaking. Part D lists specialized books and other sources of further information on each subject.

Even if everything known about bookmaking was included today there would be something lacking tomorrow, because of the rapid pace of development. Probably, the technological principles on which bookmaking will be based for the coming decade are those in operation now, but there will undoubtedly be improvements and additions in large numbers. Readers of this book are advised to keep informed through trade periodicals.

The book is divided into 4 parts. The first part (A) concerns bookmaking as a profession and should be read, but not necessarily first. The second part (B) gives basic knowledge about methods, materials, and equipment. These chapters are not connected and may be read in any order, but they should be understood before beginning the third part (C), which discusses the procedure of bookmaking and should be read in sequence. The last part (D) contains reference matter only.

We have tried to make this book useful also for those who are not directly concerned with design or production, because of our conviction that everyone in book publishing should know something of each part.

A SPECIAL NOTE ON TERMINOLOGY

Much time (money) and energy are wasted, countless practical and esthetic calamities are caused by misunderstandings due to our lack of a uniform terminology in bookmaking. The problem would not exist if we had a central publishing school teaching one set of terms and signals but, since there is none, perhaps this first comprehensive textbook of American bookmaking can help achieve the much-needed standardization.

Thus, it is urged that the terminology found here be adopted by, and disseminated to, all concerned with bookmaking—including authors, editors, and suppliers. These terms are not necessarily better than others used elsewhere but they are, for the most part, those most generally accepted. After all, it is not so important *which* term is used, but that the term used is understood by all.

Short contents

A THE PROFESSION

B BASIC KNOWLEDGE

C PROCEDURE

D USEFUL INFORMATION

Contents

A THE PROFESSION

B BASIC KNOWLEDGE

C PROCEDURE

D USEFUL INFORMATION

THE PROFESSION

1 | Background

The beginning of books

In its broadest sense, the story of bookmaking goes back to the beginning of graphic communication. The development of writing from the first picture-symbols scratched on stone to the sophisticated alphabets of today is a fascinating study, but, for our purposes, the story begins with the earliest codex, i.e. the first book in the form of bound leaves, as distinguished from the scrolls that preceded it.

No one knows when the first codices were made, but they came into general use in Europe during the 9th century. By that time, paper and printing were known in Asia, and some codices were used, but scrolls were still in favor there. A form of codex was developed by the Aztecs during this period, but only a few later ones survived the systematic destruction of the Spanish conquest. Until

2nd century Egyptian codex covers

the fall of Rome, papyrus had been the common material of books and then it was vellum, the treated skin of animals.

The art of papermaking was brought to the West in the 8th century and was ready to serve that voracious consumer, the printing press, which appeared in Central Europe in the mid-15th century. As far as we know, printing in Europe was invented without reference to the Asian craft that had been in use for hundreds of years—perhaps a thousand years—before Gutenberg.

A book printed in Mexico in 1544.

Many of the conventions of bookmaking originated in the manuscript phase, and the general aspects of page form and binding were quite well established by the time printing began. Indeed, the first printed books were made to look as much like manuscripts as possible, in the hope that the difference would not be noticed!

Whereas a complex alphabet and unfavorable social conditions discouraged a wide use of printing in China, its spread was relatively explosive in Europe. Within 50 years, presses were established in every major country—and by 1535 printing issued in Mexico City from the first press in the New World. However, another century passed before printing came to the North American settlements.

The book in America
1639–1939

From 1639, when the first printing was done in the American colonies, until the 19th century, the printer was publisher and bookseller as well. Working with presses little different from Gutenberg's, he became increasingly involved in the complexities of publishing until it was impractical to operate these functions *and* the craft of printing from one office. Separation began with the advent of the steam-powered press (about 1815), when printing became a major business in itself.

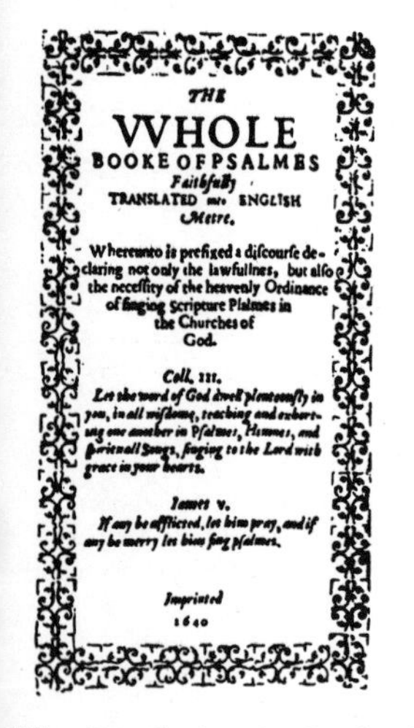

THE
VVHOLE
BOOKE OF PSALMES
Faithfully
TRANSLATED into ENGLISH
Metre.

Whereunto is prefixed a discourse declaring not only the lawfullnes, but also the necessity of the heavenly Ordinance of singing Scripture Psalmes in the Churches of God.

Coll. III.
Let the word of God dwell plenteously in you, in all wisdome, teaching and exhorting one another in Psalmes, Himnes, and spirituall Songs, singing to the Lord with grace in your hearts.

James v.
If any be afflicted, let him pray, and if any be merry let him sing psalmes.

Imprinted
1640

The Bay Psalm Book, the first book printed in the colonies.

The power presses were capable of devouring all the handmade paper produced and more but, fortunately, papermaking machines came along to meet the demand. Then, with the introduction of mechanical typecasting equipment about 1838, mass production of books became possible.

Rapid expansion had an unfortunate effect on typographic development. Where the hand printer was confined to a few basic typefaces (and therefore simple typography), the machine-age printer had types of every description—and many that defied description. The result, beginning at mid-century, was typographic chaos. About 1890, a reaction set in against machine-made monstrosities. In England, William Morris revived the handcrafts of medieval bookmaking. In America, a few scholar-printers, notably DeVinne, Updike, and Rogers, restored the typography of the 17th and 18th centuries. Although no more inventive than Morris's this movement introduced the mature traditions of printing to machine technology—and had a far greater effect.

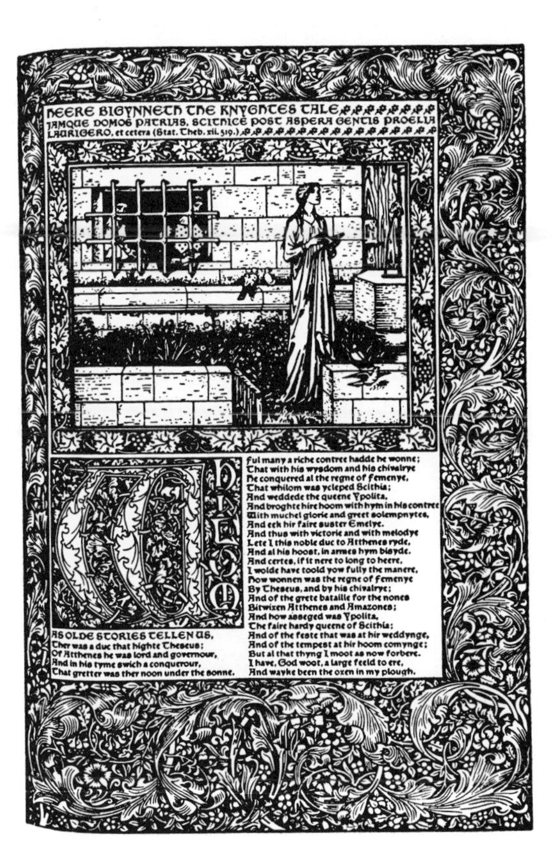

HEERE BIGYNNETH THE KNYGHTES TALE
JAMQUE DOMOS PATRIAS, SCITHICE POST ASPERA GENTIS PROELIA LAURIGERO, et cetera (Stat. Theb. xii. 519.)

WHILOM AS OLDE STORIES TELLEN US,
Ther was a duc that highte Theseus;
Of Atthenes he was lord and governour,
And in his tyme swich a conquerour,
That gretter was ther noon under the sonne.
Ful many a riche contree hadde he wonne;
That with his wysdom and his chivalrye
He conquered al the regne of Femenye,
That whilom was ycleped Scithia;
And weddede the queene Ypolita,
And broghte hire hoom with hym in his contree
With muchel glorie and greet solempnytee,
And eek hir faire suster Emelye.
And thus with victorie and with melodye
Lete I this noble duc to Atthenes ryde,
And al his hoost, in armes hym bisyde.
And certes, if it nere to long to heere,
I wolde have toold yow fully the manere,
How wonnen was the regne of Femenye
By Theseus, and by his chivalrye;
And of the grete bataille for the nones
Bitwixen Atthenes and Amazones;
And how asseged was Ypolita,
The faire hardy queene of Scithia;
And of the feste that was at hir weddynge,
And of the tempest at hir hoom comynge;
But al that thyng I moot as now forbere.
I have, God woot, a large feeld to ere,
And wayke been the oxen in my plough.

William Morris page

Bruce Rogers page

THE CENTAUR. WRITTEN BY MAURICE DE GUÉRIN AND NOW TRANSLATED FROM THE FRENCH BY GEORGE B. IVES.

Was born in a cavern of these mountains. Like the river in yonder valley, whose first drops flow from some cliff that weeps in a deep grotto, the first moments of my life sped amidst the shadows of a secluded retreat, nor vexed its silence. As our mothers draw near their term, they retire to the caverns, and in the innermost recesses of the wildest of them all, where the darkness is most dense, they bring forth, uncomplaining, offspring as silent as themselves. Their strength-giving milk enables us to endure without weakness or dubious struggles the first difficulties of life; yet we leave our caverns later than you your cradles. The reason is that there is a tradition amongst us that the early days of life must be secluded and guarded, as days engrossed by the gods.

My growth ran almost its entire course in the darkness where I was born. The innermost depths of my home were so far within the bowels of the mountain, that I should not have known in which direction the opening lay, had it not been that the winds at times blew in and caused a sudden coolness and confusion. Sometimes, too, my mother returned, bringing with her the perfume of the valleys, or dripping wet from the streams to which she resorted. Now, these her home-comings, although they told me naught of the valleys or the streams, yet, being attended by emanations therefrom, disturbed my thoughts, and I wandered about, all agitated, amidst my darkness. 'What,' I would say to myself, 'are these places to which my mother goes and what power reigns there which summons her so frequently? To what influences is one there exposed,

ANNALS

OF THE

CITY OF KANSAS:

EMBRACING FULL DETAILS OF THE

TRADE AND COMMERCE

OF THE

Great Western Plains,

TOGETHER WITH

STATISTICS OF THE

AGRICULTURAL, MINERAL AND COMMERCIAL RESOURCES

OF THE COUNTRY

WEST, SOUTH AND SOUTH-WEST,

EMBRACING

WESTERN MISSOURI, KANSAS, THE INDIAN COUNTRY, AND NEW MEXICO.

BY C. C. SPALDING.

KANSAS CITY:
VAN HORN & ABEEL'S PRINTING HOUSE.
1858.

Victorian title page

The last basic bottleneck in printing was eliminated by the perfection of typesetting machinery in 1886. By this time, machinery had been introduced into the bindery, although some operations are only now being mechanized.

The separation of printer and publisher which had begun at the start of the 19th century was far advanced at its end. Where an association remained, it was generally a publisher who owned a printing plant rather than a printer who published books.

New distribution methods created the need for protective wrappers, which developed rapidly from plain paper to the modern full-color jacket. While books changed little in 400 years, jackets evolved entirely during the first quarter of the 20th century.

At the beginning of the second quarter, a distinction between printer and typographer/designer took form. By then, technical developments permitted a wide enough range of expression in book design to attract some full-time designers. The names of T. M. Cleland, W. A. Dwiggins, Merle Armitage, Ernst Reichl, John Begg, and others became known in the next decades. This was the period that saw book design emerge as a recognized department of publishing. Book design courses, the Fifty Books shows, clinics, and other activities of the American Institute of Graphic Arts (AIGA) grew in influence, and the publishing trade journal, *Publishers' Weekly,* began a monthly department devoted to design and production.

1939–

World War II interrupted the progress of bookmaking as it did every other activity. The principal effects in this field were a shortage of personnel and materials and the suspension of technical advances other than military, although one important development in bookmaking did come out of military needs. This was the technique of high-speed production of paperbacks—which paved the way for the postwar expansion of paperback publishing.

The years between 1946 and the Korean War were marked by inflation, gradually disappearing shortages, and renewed attention to technical improvements. With the end of the Korean War, a period of expansion commenced. Prices stabilized and business picked up. Book publishing increased greatly and began to strain the manufacturing facilities of America. At the same time, European bookmaking revived and a trend to importation began.

An important new element entered the picture in the '40s when paperbacks began to be distributed through magazine outlets. This made possible very large printings, thus enabling greatly reduced costs and low retail prices. At first, these books were handled like magazines and, like the pulp magazines they virtually drove off the stands, they tended toward Westerns and mysteries—with maximum pictorial appeal on the outside and relatively little attention

mass market paperback covers of the 1940s

trade paperback covers of the 60s

to design inside. Gradually, the publishers and magazine distributors began to treat titles of more enduring interest as if they were books, and the better lines began to find their way into bookstores. An important breakthrough occurred when the *Anchor* books, a line of higher-priced paperback reprints of serious titles, demonstrated that the college market could absorb enough books of this kind to justify their publication. Similar lines followed, thereby creating a whole new segment of publishing. The design of these "quality", or "trade", paperbacks got off to a good start and has been in the main excellent, although their inside pages tend to be neglected.

By the 1950s, books showed definite signs of responding to the visual esthetics of the 20th century. Significant stabs in this direction were made in the first quarter of the century and great progress was seen in the second quarter. The design of jackets and paperback covers led the way, chiefly because they are closer to advertising and are often the work of designers whose training and experience were in that field. (A critical survey of individual designers and their work is outside the scope of this book—see "Sources of information" in Part D for further reading.)

It was not until after World War II, however, that publishers generally began to recognize the visual problem posed by a generation accustomed to the dynamic graphics of advertising, magazines, and television. The most marked development has been in the textbook and children's book fields, where rapidly expanding markets and keen competition drove publishers to heavy use of color and illustration. At first, the competition was mainly in the *amount* of graphic effects used, but gradually the quality of design has become the selling point.

There is still considerable adherence to convention in American publishing, but it is becoming weaker. The change is good where meaningless and impractical conventions are dropped, but the blessing is not unmixed. Too many young designers have cast themselves loose from conventional forms without having developed better alternatives. On the whole, however, it seems preferable to allow the possibility of creative design than to remain locked within rigid and outworn rules.

2 | Function

Relationships

DESIGN TO PRODUCTION

Ideally, responsibility for bookmaking—design and production—is vested in 1 person who is well qualified in both aspects, and there are a few successful examples of such an arrangement in publishing houses. Generally, however, the function is divided, and an imbalance results. Because of its economic role and seniority, the production department almost invariably has a dominant relationship to design. Planning tends to originate in the production department, and often the designer is brought in only after the main decisions are made. This arrangement does not usually bring the best results, although a great deal depends on the particular production manager.

Some publishers have added an "art director" to their staffs. This arrangement is effective where the art director has some authority, but in many houses he is simply foreman of the design department, with about the same relationship to the production manager as the designer had before.

The proper relationship of designer to production manager is comparable to that of architect to builder. The architect (designer) plans the practical and esthetic aspects of the structure and the builder (production manager) carries out the plans. However, no matter how good the builder, the result will not be successful unless the architect has a thorough mastery of the materials and techniques of construction. From this it is apparent that the designer must be expert in production or become merely a "layout artist".

Production people should, of course, learn as much as they can about design, but their role is primarily purchasing and coordination of schedules.

BOOKMAKING TO EDITORIAL

In practice, some of the principal decisions affecting design and production are made by editors. This is inevitable and proper because the editor represents the interests of publisher and author. The weakness of this arrangement, unfortunately, is that the editor often does not know production or understand design well enough to make the best decisions.

Publishing books is a complex and deeply interrelated operation, in which specialization can easily be carried too far. Each member of the staff must know his job extremely well, but each should have a working knowledge of all the other operations. The editor functions somewhat like the director of a play, supervising and coordinating the various elements. But, where the theatrical director is expected to be qualified to supervise acting, staging, scenery, costumes, lighting, and music, few editors are sufficiently educated or experienced in the making of books. This is due in great part to the lack of a publishing school in America—a deficiency which, it is hoped, this book will help overcome.

BOOKMAKING TO SALES

The bookmaker has 2 basic tasks:

(a) To facilitate communication between author and reader.

(b) To make the book a successful commercial product.

This book will deal directly with both problems, but for a proper understanding of their background, it is necessary to know something of the way books are sold and distributed and the economics of publishing.

There are various kinds of publishing—direct mail, textbook, technical, medical, law, music, paperback, etc.—and each kind has its own economics, with unique problems requiring special considerations of design and production. As it is obviously impossible to explain every kind of operation here, this discussion will deal only with tradebooks. The particular problems of other kinds will be taken up in other chapters.

Publishers often have cultural or personal objectives when they accept a book for publication, but the object of publishing as a business is to sell books. However, it is only in the profit motive that book publishing resembles any other business. It is much more informal, complicated, and hazardous than most.

A toothpaste manufacturer, for example, hires people to create a few products to his desire (after considerable market research), standardizes their manufacture, and turns them out in large quantities year after year. He can advertise and promote his products as much as he likes, knowing that his campaign will take effect sooner or later. He can concentrate his money and effort on a single campaign that is good for years. His products are sold in stores accessible to virtually everyone and his production can be geared to his sales—or at least to an estimate of sales based on thorough research. Most important, a satisfied customer is likely to *continue* buying the same product.

The publisher, on the other hand, must sell perhaps a hundred entirely different products in 1 year, each one a unique creation by an independent individual who has determined for himself what the product shall be. There is no way of knowing how many buyers there will be, so (except in rare cases) the product must be made in an uneconomically small quantity. The amount of money and effort spent on promoting the book will be disproportionately high if there is only 1 printing (as usually there is), and the campaign must be immediately effective, because most books are highly perishable, like vegetables, and become almost worthless if not sold quickly. To sell his books, the publisher has only a few thousand outlets in the cities, of which only a few hundred are really bookstores. Even when he sells his products to the stores he is not necessarily ahead, because the stores can return the books if they don't sell them. Worst of all, the sale of a book to a reader doesn't mean that the same person will remain a customer of the publisher's, except perhaps for another book by the same author—which may not come in for years, if at all. To survive, the publisher must have other kinds of outlets—libraries, book clubs, etc.—each of which requires special handling and attention.

The sales and distribution problems of publishing are discouraging enough, but the economics are positively forbidding. Of the book's retail price, about 42% is the (combined) wholesaler's and retailer's discount, and at least 10% is the author's royalty—with the figure going to 12% or 15% under some circumstances. Of the 48% retained by the publisher, about 20% goes for making the book, about 7% must go into sales and advertising and 3% for storing and shipping. A share of the cost of editorial work, bookkeeping, and other salaries, as well as the rent, electric bills, and other items of overhead must be carried by each title—and 18% of the retail price is considered a realistic figure. With a little arithmetic you will see that 100% of the book's price has been accounted for and no profit has been mentioned. The picture is *this* bright only because we are assuming that all the books printed will be sold—which is rarely the case. Indeed, there are numerous copies—sometimes hundreds—given away for review and promotion, and some of the expenditures mentioned above are incurred even on books not sold.

Obviously, every item of cost must be held to a minimum. As the manufacture accounts for 20% of the retail price, it can be seen that even 1 penny in this cost is significant, since it means 5¢ in the retail price—or a cash loss of $10 for every 1000 books bound but unsold. From this, incidentally, it can be seen that one of the most important decisions the publisher makes is the size of the first printing. If he makes too few books, the unit price will be too high; if he makes too many, to keep the unit cost down, he will be left with many unsold books.

There are 3 factors which may lighten this otherwise black picture of publishing as a business: (a) one soothing procedure is to charge less than 18% of the receipts to overhead, and call the rest profit. This benefit is only temporary, however, and could result in bankruptcy unless 1 of the other helpful factors materializes. These are: (b) a sellout of the first printing and the necessity of a second (and more) to meet the demand and (c) a sale of subsidiary rights to the book—reprint rights, translation rights, foreign rights, serial rights, book club distribution rights, television, radio, dramatic and movie rights, etc.

What then is the relationship of book design to the book's sale? It is to be found in the complex of elements affecting the public's reaction to a particular title. This reaction is not only unpredictable, it is usually impossible to rationalize even after it is known.

There are at least a dozen factors that influence sales of a book:

(a) Intrinsic quality
(b) Reputation of author
(c) Reviews
(d) Advertising
(e) Promotion and publicity
(f) Current events
(g) Efficiency of distribution
(h) Price
(i) Jacket design
(j) Local interest
(k) Competition
(l) Availability
(m) Size and weight

A commercial success may be attributed almost entirely to 1 of these elements, or it may be due to 2 or more of them. Except in the most dramatic cases—such as the almost unanimous and simultaneous rave reviews that made Anne Frank's diary an immediate best-seller, the obvious impact that Pasternak's refusal of the Nobel Prize had on the sale of *Dr. Zhivago*, or the obvious effects of the names of major authors, such as Hemingway or Steinbeck, on a new title—the reasons for any book's sale are almost impossible to identify.

The first factor named—intrinsic quality—includes those qualities of the book itself that generate enthusiasm in the reader or browser. This is believed by many to be the most influential single factor because it results in the kind of "word-of-mouth" advertising that begins with "You *must* read . . ." and ends with sales. It is within this area that the book's design operates as a cause of sales.

The importance of the design can vary from *vital*, in the case of the "coffee table" books which are meant to sell as impressive gifts, to *insignificant*, in the case of books which have an appeal of a special, and nonvisual, kind (lurid novels, for example). Between these extremes lies a vast and uncharted area in which design has an unmeasurable but definite effect on sales.

The general public's reaction to book design is, in most cases, subconscious. Except where the visual aspect is spectacular, the nonprofessional browser is aware of only a general sense of pleasure or satisfaction in the presence of a well-designed book and a vague feeling of irritation when confronted by a badly designed one.

While it is impossible to isolate the reaction to design from the other elements of a book's appeal, it is probably safe to say that good design is in many cases influential and, where a buyer is undecided, this influence, small as it may be, can tip the balance in favor of a purchase. This is particularly true in the case of expensive gift books and nonfiction that competes with similar titles. It is also effective in the sale of schoolbooks, where competition among several titles of almost identical content is common.

There are 2 ways in which good book design psychologically aids sales: (a) it gives the buyer an impression that the book is highly regarded by the publisher and (b) it tends to make the book look more expensive than it is.

The importance of design in book publishing has much increased in the past decades as movies, magazines, and television have heightened the competition for public attention, sharpened the public's appetite for visual excitement, and conditioned its taste. During this period, incidentally, it has become apparent that the public tends to *follow* leadership in matters of taste rather than insist on its own preferences. The soundest policy then—both esthetic and practical—is to do what seems *best*, without trying to guess what the public will like.

BOOKMAKING TO MANAGEMENT

The truth is that many books are created by editors, production managers, designers, and sales managers, each of whom knows little of the work of the others.

In the early days of book publishing this problem never arose. The publisher himself was editor, printer, and designer. Today, the publisher functions more like the producer of a play. He hires the principal members of his staff and makes the major decisions on matters they bring to him, but he is usually not equipped (by time, talent, or training) to direct their work. Most of the directing functions of management have been shifted to editors.

Publishers are coming to regard book designers as industrial designers who can be of help in creating salable products, and they regard production managers as experts who can help them operate economically and profitably. This is a far cry from the time (not so long ago) when the "manufacturing man" was little more than a clerk who sent manuscripts to the printer, and the designer was a luxury to be used only for fancy editions.

Schools of design

There is a continuing controversy over the relationship of design to the book. There are 2 distinct points of view:

(a) Book design is concerned only with making an economical, tasteful choice and disposition of the material and visual ingredients of the book.

(b) Book design is a problem in communications, of which the above is only a part.

The proponents of (a) contend that the designer should not interpret the content of the book. He should keep his work as neutral as possible, so that it will not "interfere" between author and reader. The other school (to which the author, frankly, belongs) feels that such neutrality, even if it were desirable, is impossible. A book inevitably has graphic and tactile characteristics, and these should be organized to the advantage of author and reader. It is foolish to ignore the reader's senses when the thoughts of the writer are being transmitted to him through a physical book which can and does affect these senses.

The full powers of visual design are as properly brought to bear in a book as they are in a play or a building. It is true that the essential qualities of a play or the shelter of a building can be enjoyed without sight, but they are certainly better appreciated when seen *unless* they are badly designed.

Here lies the crucial point. The books of the "neutral" school are often poorly done but they are rarely offensive. On the other hand, a clumsy or tasteless attempt to use the full range of graphic effects in a book can be monstrous. This is not an insignificant point, but more important is the fact that a book produced by a skillful and sensitive designer can rise far above a work that aspires only to be neutral.

3 | Requirements

Talent

PRODUCTION

"Talent" refers to innate capacities rather than acquired skills. The talent required by a production worker is primarily a sense of organization and secondly a superior ability to learn and retain facts. The successful production manager is one who knows the vast array of technical data, material specifications, prices, sources, processes, and equipment that go into the manufacture of books and can organize this knowledge in a smooth and efficient operation. A third talent he needs is a knack for getting cooperation from a variety of people. In his capacity as coordinator, the production manager must extract copy from editors, specifications from designers, materials and production from suppliers—always in competition with numerous conflicting demands.

Patience and calmness under pressure may not properly be called talents, but whatever they are, the production worker needs them.

DESIGN

Failure in production is revealed by late schedules, broken budgets, and faulty manufacture, but a poorly designed book goes unnoticed in the great flood of bad book design. This doesn't mean that it is easier to design books than to produce them, it is simply easier to get away with incompetence.

Fifty years ago the limited possibilities of book design made few demands on the designer. Today, particularly in textbooks and increasingly in tradebooks, the graphic and technical resources available require the highest level of competence in the designer. He (or she) must (a) be definitely talented in the disposition of form, space, color, and texture, (b) be especially perceptive and analytical, and (c) have some natural ability to assimilate technical knowledge.

In the fullest sense, the designer is a partner (albeit a minor one) of the author and must be capable of analyzing and interpreting the author's intentions. This is most apparent in the creation of textbooks and other books of exposition in which the graphic part of the presentation is vital, if not equal to the verbal part. This relationship is not as well understood in connection with other books, but it is no less valid.

A talent for graphic representation (and mastery of graphic techniques) is not absolutely necessary because the book designer, like the architect, specifies work that others carry out, but it helps to be able to draw well.

One can design books without even a talent in visual art, but the possibilities are definitely limited. If a book designer need not be a craftsman, he should be an artist. Book design without art is like building without architecture. However, don't give up if you have never thought of yourself as an "artist". Talent exists in many persons, unknown to themselves or to others.

Background & training

The *ideal* background for a production manager is to have worked for at least some time in shops doing: hot and cold composition, photoengraving, letterpress, lithographic, and gravure printing, and paper manufacturing. It would help also to have had a stint in an art studio as well as in the sales, editorial, shipping, promotion, and accounting departments of a publishing company. College courses in engineering, math, physics, chemistry, and statistics would come in handy.

It isn't *necessary* to have this work experience and education to run a production department successfully, but the equivalent of a large part of it is very desirable. Most of it can be picked up on the job by reading books and trade publications, taking courses, visiting plants, and asking questions. A good production manager aims to know almost as much about the work of his suppliers as they know themselves.

The perfect background for a designer would include all of the above, plus a liberal arts education heavy on English and Literature, a couple of years at a good art school, and at least a year's apprenticeship to a first-class designer. An extremely valuable experience for *anyone* in publishing is selling in a bookstore. This can provide insights not obtainable any other way.

A 4-year college program geared to prepare for either production or design work might begin with 2 years of liberal arts, with English as the major subject and the fundamentals of graphic arts and publishing as minors. The second half might concentrate on technical theory and practice, business administration, and design. During the last year, production students would stress administration and science while the design students would emphasize design and literature. Such a curriculum, larded with field trips to plants and summer work in publishing houses, could radically improve the quality of American publishing.

A number of schools offer courses along these lines, some more extensive than others, some leaning more toward technical training, others emphasizing the esthetic side. The programs vary from time to time, but at present the most notable are those at Carnegie and Rochester Institutes of Technology, Simmons College, Radcliffe College, Yale University, and Pratt Institute. At New York University there is a strong program of evening professional courses. (An attempt to establish a Graduate Institute for Book Publishing at N.Y.U. was discontinued in 1963 after a few years of operation, when promised financial support failed to materialize.) Other courses of value are given at various institutions in all parts of the country.

4 | Opportunities

Kinds of jobs

The nature of each kind of job varies according to the size and organization of the company. In the smaller houses, usually 1 person does all of the production work and directs, or actually does, the design. In the very smallest operations, the proprietor himself may handle these functions, although this is possible only when the list is small (a dozen books or fewer per year), and the service departments of other publishers or of manufacturers and other suppliers are used.

In medium-sized houses (30 to 100 titles per year) there is usually a production manager and from 1 to 3 assistants. In such situations, the manager or one of the assistants may do most of the design—giving out only the complicated and "special" books to freelance designers. Some rely almost entirely on the design services of manufacturers.

In the larger companies (100 to 150 titles) the production department may consist of a half dozen persons, or more, and 1 or 2 designers. The largest houses (150 titles and up), of which there are about 10, may employ up to 50 people in design and production. In some, there is a separate design department under an art director or chief designer; in others, the designers work within the production department. There is often considerable specialization in the large production departments.

Besides the size of the company, the nature of its operation is significant. Textbook and reference book publishers require more help in their art departments than tradebook publishers of comparable size. The same is true of children's book publishers, although most "flats" for small children are created by author, illustrator, and editor, without the use of a designer. In mass-appeal paperback houses, design is emphasized less than direction of the cover art, which is handled by editors except in large houses where art directors are employed.

The design of jackets is usually given to freelancers in the smaller and medium-sized companies—unless the production manager is also a designer. In the largest houses, many of the jackets are designed by the staff.

Another source of jobs is the book manufacturer who employs people not only to handle the production of his various departments, but to coordinate production problems of the publishers with those of the plant. This work is excellent preparation for a good production job in publishing. Some of the larger manufacturers maintain design departments as well.

Finally, there is a handful of independent production and design services that employ assistants.

Futures

Evaluating the ultimate rewards of each kind of job is a highly personal matter. From the standpoint of money, the maximum can be obtained by working through smaller production jobs to becoming head of production in a giant company. Such jobs pay (roughly) from $25,000 to $50,000 per year, and often include a vice-presidency with stock-options and other financial benefits.

The production manager of a small company cannot expect to earn more than $22,000, but he will usually have the satisfaction of intimate participation in company affairs. How satisfying such an arrangement will be depends to a large extent on the personalities involved. There is little difference in pace and pressure, whether 30 or 300 books are produced each year. Much more depends on the efficiency of the operation than on its size.

A production assistant can expect to start at about $140 per week and work up to $250. At this point, one either stays on in anticipation of eventually replacing the boss or moves on. The production trainee—who will keep records, file, etc. while learning—starts at about $110.

For the designer, the ultimate—both financially and in terms of satisfaction—is to become head of bookmaking for a large firm. The same position in a medium-sized company brings less money, but usually more creative opportunity. As art director of a large company, the salary is from $20,000 to $30,000 per year—and the satisfaction depends on the compatibility of the management. As head of both design and production, the pay is probably about the same as indicated above for production managers. The staff designer can expect to start at $175 per week and work up to $350.

In manufacturing companies, salaries are roughly equivalent to those in publishing houses.

How to get a job

Book publishing being what it is, a large proportion of its positions are filled in accidental ways. There is no school from which candidates can be drawn and there is no organized pool of applicants. People drift into jobs by knowing someone or by being in the right place at the right time. Paradoxically, book publishing is one of the most desired (glamorous) fields in the world, but many of its jobs go to those who are willing to take unusually low pay.

To get a first job in production, unless you have worked in a suppliers' shop or know someone who is willing to take you in spite of your lack of experience (either to save money or to train you), you will probably have to start in some relatively subordinate position in the company. As a stenographer, wrapper, clerk, or even messenger, you have a better chance than someone outside. In a small firm it doesn't matter where you work, but in a large one, try to get into the production department, because it is sometimes harder to move from one department to another than to get in at all. If you show yourself intelligent, diligent, and interested, there is a good chance that you will be given a production job in time.

If you live outside the main publishing areas, look around for a nearby university press before rushing to the city. The university presses have few jobs and pay the poorest of all, but they give good experience and are certainly no harder to crack than any other. The same is true of local printers, compositors, etc. Once you have even a little experience it is much easier to get a job.

Experience with a printer or manufacturer is, rightly, highly regarded as preparation for a production job in a publishing company. A period spent working in the shops and plants where books are made will pay big dividends in better jobs and higher pay later on.

The first design job is in some ways easier and in some ways more difficult to get. You can show tangible evidence of your ability, but you are then trying for one of relatively few positions. Also, it is almost essential that you have a considerable amount of knowledge if you are to be given any responsibility.

It is not a bad idea to start by working at any job you can get in a production or design department, with the hope that you can move over into design work later (as suggested for getting into production). Whether you do this or attack the job directly, the best thing you can do is to assemble a portfolio of layouts and sketches that show (a) that you know what you are doing and (b) that you have real talent. Leave out the lovely but unprofessional collages and figure sketches from art school and, after studying this book, make a series of sketches *with specifications* of all the parts of at least 1 book, and preferably 3 or 4. Be realistic in terms of commercial production, but let your imagination have a bit of play, too. A truly impressive portfolio of this kind will be almost as effective as a bagful of printed books. If you have previously done any graphic work that could conceivably be related to practical book work—

such as illustration in woodcut, pen and ink, etc., or your own printing—put in some of this, provided that it shows ability of specific value.

Buy or borrow a copy of *Literary Market Place* and look up the names and addresses of the publishers. It is much more likely that you will get started in a large house than a small one, so try these first. The listings show the number of books published by each company. Start with those over 100. It probably does some good to get in to see the top man, but it really isn't necessary. If the firm is looking for someone, they are just as anxious to find you as you are to find them. In the smaller companies, it is a good idea to look for the name of the production manager or art director in the *LMP* listing (get the latest edition) and call or write to him for an appointment.

From this point on, the rules are the same as for getting any other job. Be prompt, neat, reserved, but pleasant—and don't stay too long.

There are specialized employment agencies in this field, but they are more likely to help you find your second job than your first.

Freelancing

Freedom, like peace, is wonderful. The idea of coming and going as you please with no grouchy old boss to be nice to is very attractive. But, before you decide to freelance, remember that a lot of others like freedom just as much as you do—and the grouchy old boss comes through with a paycheck *every* week.

A fair amount of freelance design work is done by relatively inexperienced people, particularly in jackets, but there are a great many such people competing and as book publishing gets more professional this kind of work diminishes. Generally, the smaller, routine jobs are done in the house, while the more demanding and special ones go outside. These go, of course, to the designers of experience and reputation.

In freelance production work, there is really no room for any but the expert. The large publisher, if he gives out production work at all, will do so only for a special book that requires more attention than he can give it or involves a special circumstance. In either case he wants an experienced hand. The small publisher who has production work done on a freelance basis to avoid hiring someone on a salary, does not feel safe unless he deals with a competent and reputable person.

Generally, it is best to have a number of years of experience before freelancing. For those who want to try this method, the following scale of prices will be useful.

▪ *Book design*—The range is from about $150 for an unillustrated book of uncomplicated narrative text to thousands of dollars for a large picture-and-text book. The prices paid vary considerably according to the publisher and the standing of the designer.

- *Jacket and paperback cover design*—Prices run from about $200 to $500, again depending on the publisher and designer involved.
- *Production work*—This is done on either a brokerage basis—in which case the publisher pays a certain amount over the cost of manufacture (about 10 to 20%) for the service—or on a fee basis—whereby he pays a flat sum for the service, either over a period of time or for a specific number of books. Either way, the amount paid by the publisher should equal a proportionate share of what his production department costs, or would cost if he had one.

B

BASIC KNOWLEDGE

5 | Composition

Not so long ago, "composition" could have been defined as the assembly of individual metal type characters into words, lines, and pages. Today, if we are to encompass the great variety of composition methods, we might say that composition is *the transformation of original copy into a form suitable for printing or for making printing plates*. This would cover the 4 present methods:

(a) setting metal type by hand,
(b) setting metal type by machine,
(c) typewriter composition, and
(d) photographic composition.

Machine composition—metal type, typewriter, and photo—is now being produced with the application of various electronic aids: punched and magnetic tapes, computers, etc. While these radically affect speed and efficiency, the typesetting operation and the product remain the same, so we still have 4 basic methods. There are, however, developments in progress which will be, when ready, sufficiently radical to represent a new method.

In this chapter, each operation will be explained and the various machines will be discussed. However, the standards of measurement of typography are the same for all methods and must be learned first.

Measurement & terminology

MEASUREMENT

Printers measure type and spaces by *points*. One point is .01384″, and 72 pts. equal almost exactly 1″. (Actually, 12 x 72 pts. falls 4 pts. short of equaling 12″.) For an exception, see CH.16.

One *pica* is equal to 12 pts., so there are approximately 6 picas to 1 inch. Picas and half-picas are used to measure the width and

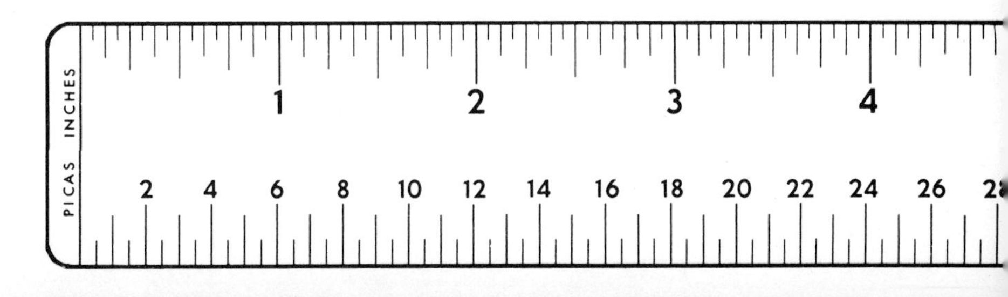

depth of pages or columns, and other distances of 1 pica or more. Dimensions are given in multiples of picas plus a half-pica when applicable, or plus the appropriate number of points. For example: 22 picas, 24 ½ picas, 17 picas 4 pts. Dimensions up to about 6 picas are sometimes expressed in points, i.e. 14 pts., 28 pts., 42 pts., 53 pts., etc.

Note that paper, illustration, and margin measurements are given in inches. In general, measurements *within* the type page are given in points and picas, those outside in inches.

Another unit of type measurement is the *em*, which is the square of the type size; i.e. the em of a 10 pt. type is 10 pts., of a 12 pt. type 12 pts., etc. (An exception to this is in *Linotype* and *Intertype**, where the em is often slightly more or less than the type size, depending on the design of the particular typeface.) An *en* is half an em. Ems and ens are used as units of horizontal measurement, such as indentions, sentence-, word-, and letter-spacing, and dashes. In writing, the em may be expressed as M or □. The en is either N or M. In speech, printers call an en a "nut" to avoid confusing it with an em.

3 em quad

2 em quad

1 em quad

2 em space

3 em space

4 em space

5 em space

Horizontal spacing is further divided into multiples and fractions of the em. The multiples are called *quads*. In *Monotype* and in hand-set type there are, in addition to em quads and en quads, 2-em and 3-em quads. The fractions are called *spaces*. One fifth of an em is called a 5-em space, one fourth a 4-em, and one third a 3-em. There is also a *hair space*, which is a strip of copper about ½ pt. thick. In Linotype the only spaces available on the keyboard are the em, the en, and a 4-em space called a *thin space*. (This sometimes causes confusion, as the hair space is sometimes referred to as a "thin" space.) There are also ¼, ½, and 1 pt. spaces, but they must be inserted by hand. Spacing with *spacebands* on the Linotype machine will be explained later in this chapter.

The *type size* refers to the distance from top to bottom that includes the highest and the lowest points in an alphabet. For example, in a 10 pt. type there will be a distance of 10 pts. from the top of, say, the "f" to the bottom of the "y". In another 10 pt. face the highest point may be the top of the capitals or the lowest may be the bottom of the "g". In any case, the size refers to the overall measurement. (In large sizes, the face of the type is sometimes a little less than the nominal type size. For example, a 36 pt. type may measure only 32 or 33 pts., although the *body* [see below] is 36. In small sizes there is occasionally a minute variation.)

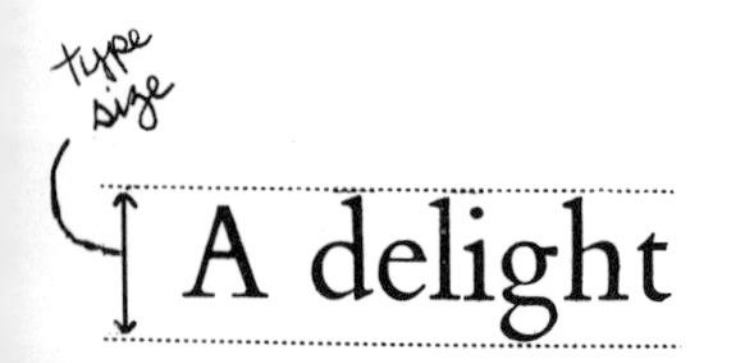

Note that the apparent size of the characters may vary considerably among faces of the same type size. The height of the lower-

* The Linotype and Intertype machines are virtually identical. When this kind of machine is referred to hereafter, only the term *Linotype* will be used.

case letters exclusive of *ascenders* or *descenders* is called the *x height*. While this is not used as a unit of measurement itself, it is often referred to in the specification of distances. The x height of two 10 pt. typefaces may be quite different.

nylon nylon

10 pt. Granjon 10 pt. Electra (enlarged)

Alphabet length is the measurement in points of a complete lower-case alphabet in any type face and size. This in itself is not a particularly useful figure, except in comparing the relative width of various typefaces, but it is the basis for determining the average *characters per pica*—an important unit of measurement in typography (CHS.6,17, Part D).

In metal type, the *body size* refers to the metal on which the type is cast, both height and width. A 10 pt. type is usually cast on a 10 pt. body, but it may be cast on one 11 pts. or even 9 pts. high. Type may be cast on a larger body in order to provide extra space, or *lead*, between the lines. This page is set in 10 pt. type on a 13 pt. body. (The additional 3 pts. are at the bottom.) This is expressed as 10 on 13, or 10/13. If there is no extra lead added to the body, it would be *solid*—10/10. (Lead is pronounced *led*).

The body width of a piece of individual metal type is usually the width of the character itself—i.e. a "w" is cast on a wider body than an "i", although some types are designed with a little wider body on some characters, to provide more space between them and others.

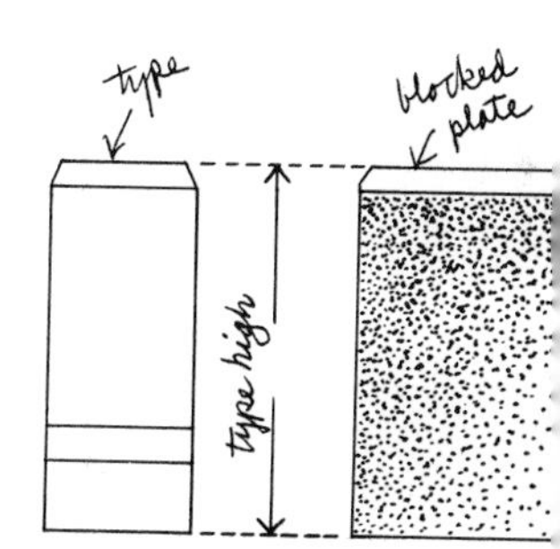

Metal type is 3-dimensional, and the third dimension is the height of the type from the surface on which it stands to the printing surface. This distance is *type-high*, which is a uniform dimension in the United States (almost an inch, .918 to be exact) but differs slightly from this in many parts of the world. All *plates* (CH.7) which print with type must be secured to blocks of wood or metal so that their printing surfaces will be type-high.

Leading is the vertical spacing between lines. It is measured in points. In metal type, spaces of 1, 2, and 3 pts. are made with strips called *leads*, although a lead is understood to be 2 pts. unless 1 or 3 is specified. Spaces of 6 and 12 pts. are made with *slugs*. All spacing between lines is made with combinations of these 5 sizes. For spaces of less than 1 pt., strips of cardboard are used. Leading, like horizontal spaces, is made less than type-high, so that it will not print.

1 Point

2 Point

3 Point

6 Point

12 Point

The *measure* of a line is its width in picas. To give the measure to which a particular type and size is to be set (and include the leading also) one says, for example, 10 pt. Electra on 13 by 25 picas. This may be expressed as Electra 10/13 x 25. *Full measure* means that the line is set the full width of the type page, without any indention.

Spacing type

These lines of 24-point Caslon have been set with type-high spaces and leads to show how spacing is done. One lead (2 points thick) was inserted between each two lines.

The paragraphs are indented one em. Between words is the normal "3-em space" (3 to the em). Additional spaces were used as necessary to make the lines come out even.

Some 1½-em and 2-em "quads" were used at the ends of paragraphs. Here is some l e t t e r - s p a c i n g.

TERMINOLOGY Most of the terms discussed here are defined in the Glossary-Index, but it is particularly helpful to have a knowledge of these in reading this chapter and the next.

The parts of type are described with various terms—some of which relate to the printed image and some only to the metal itself. The adjacent illustration shows and names the parts. There are

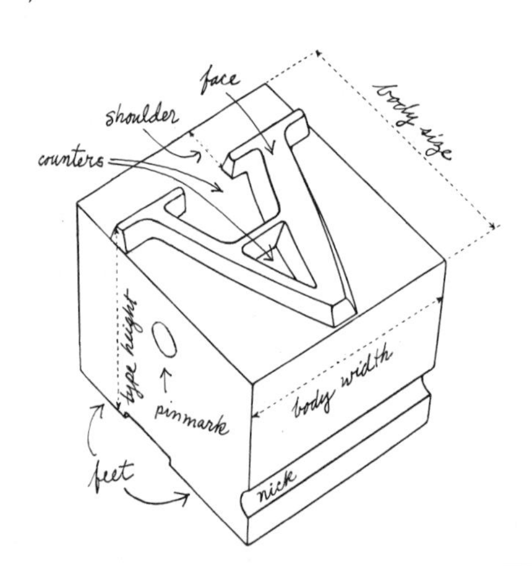

numerous terms which refer to variations in the design of a particular typeface. For example, *expanded, wide,* or *extended* means that the letters are made wide in proportion to their height. Exceptionally narrow type is called *condensed* or *elongated.*

EXPANDED

CONDENSED

A *font* is a complete assortment of types of one face and size including capitals, small capitals, lower-case letters, numbers, punctuation marks, etc. Each item in a font is called a *character,* i.e. a capital M, a comma, a 5, are each characters. *Small capitals* (*small caps* or *s.c.*) are x height, but are not made in every typeface. Numbers are called *figures,* and may be *lining,* i.e. the height of the capitals (approx.), or *old style,* which means that the 1, 2, and 0 are x height, the 3, 4, 5, 7, and 9 descend below the *baseline* [the bottom of the capitals] and the 6 and 8 extend above the *x line* [the top of x height]. Almost all fonts have an *italic* [slanted] variation, and most have a *bold,* which is a heavier weight of the typeface. Capitals are called *upper case* and the other (small) letters are called *lower case.* (These terms come from the arrangement of *cases* or trays of type in the old printing offices. The case with caps was placed above the case containing the small letters.) Words of small letters beginning with caps are referred to as *upper and lower case* (*ulc*).

ABCDEFGHIJKLMNOPQR
STUVWXYZ&
abcdefghijklmnopqrstuvwxyz
1234567890$ Qu ct
. , : ; - ‘ ’ ! ? [ ] fi fl ff ffi ffl Æ Œ

ABCDEFGHIJKLMNOPQRS
TUVWXYZ&
abcdefghijklmnopqrstuvwxyz
A B C D E G J K L M N P Q
R T U W Y & *hkvwz*
1234567890$ *. , : ; - ’ ! ? fi fl ff ffi ffl st*

Font proofs of 24 pt. Caslon 337 and Caslon 337 italic. Note the swash *[decorative] characters in the italic font.*

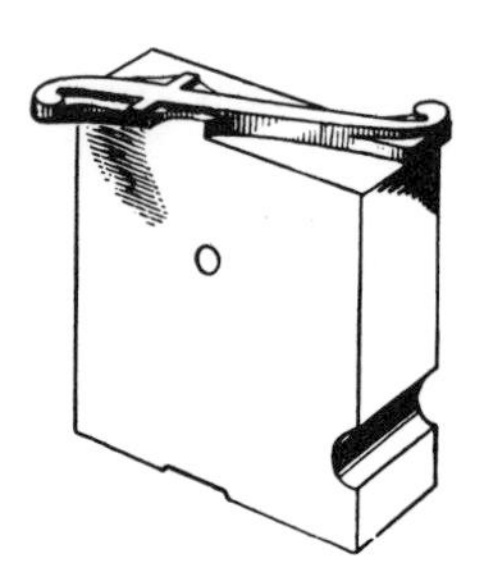

A *kern* is a part of a character which extends beyond the body of the type, overlapping another character. These occur most frequently in scriptlike typefaces. *Kerning* is fitting type to improve the spacing of standard characters that occur in an awkward sequence—such as a cap A following a cap F. Such kerning, or fitting, is usually accomplished by *notching* or *mortising* [cutting away a part of the type metal].

Slugs, besides being 6 and 12 pt. spaces, are the lines of type cast on a single piece of metal, as on Linotype, Intertype, and *Ludlow* machines, which are referred to as *slug-casting* machines (discussed later in this chapter).

A *matrix* (or *mat*) is a mold in which type is cast. Originally used to refer to the casting of individual pieces of type, the term has come to be used in connection with the Linotype slug-casting operation, and even with the photocomposition machines in which no type is cast at all. Today, the term refers to any model from which a type character is produced.

Rules are elements of typography such as straight or decorative lines, usually used as borders or separators. They may contain 1 unit of design or a repeated series of units. In metal type, a large number of straight line rules are available in thicknesses ranging from hairline to 72 pts., in any length up to 144 picas.

Ornaments are individual decorative or illustrative type elements. With a few exceptions, these are not part of type fonts, but are available separately.

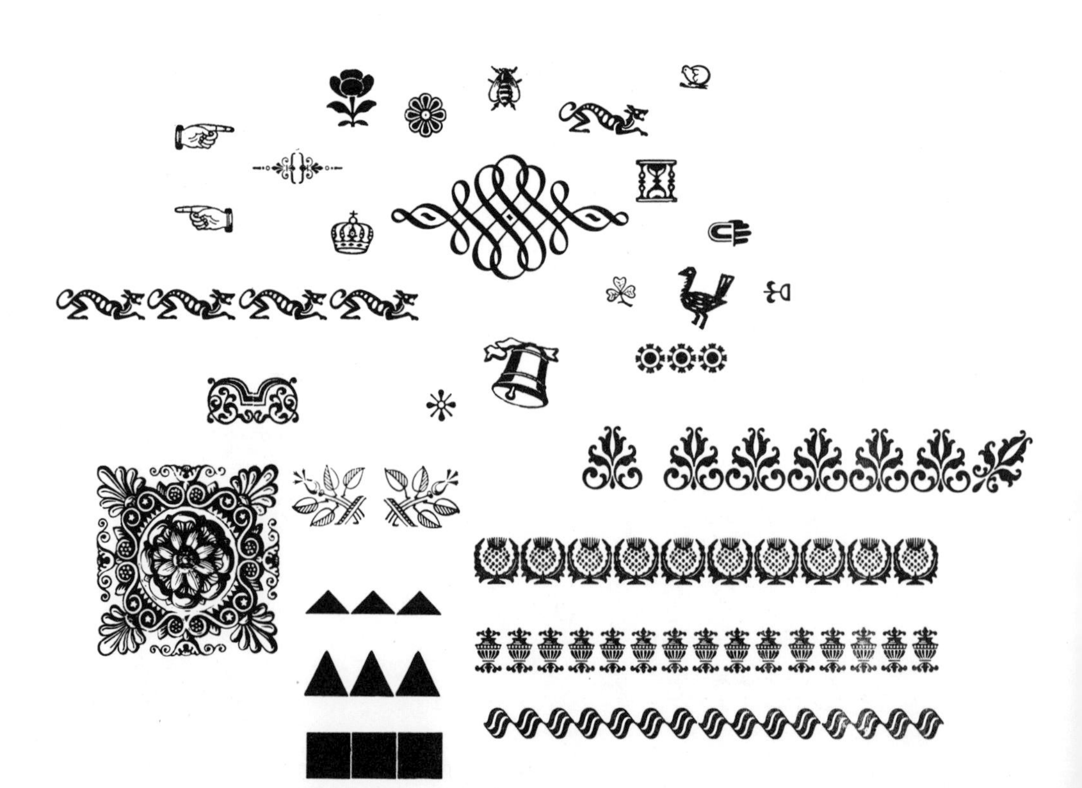

Hairline

¼ Point

½ Point

¾ Point

1 Point

1½ Point

2 Point

3 Point

4 Point

6 Point

8 Point

10 Point

12 Point

18 Point

24 Point

30 Point

36 Point

At left, *ornaments*; above, *rules*; below, *ornamental brackets*; at right, *straight rules*.

Justified lines are those in which the word and sentence spacing are varied to achieve uniform measure (as these), as opposed to *unjustified* or ragged lines, which are set with uniform word spacing and uneven lengths (see page 50).

The *type page* is the area containing all of the printed elements on a page. The term is used mainly in reference to books whose text pages have a uniform overall width and depth. The type page includes the text itself, the *folio* [page number] and any heading, marginal notes, or other elements on the page.

Emage is the area of the text page expressed in terms of ems of the type size of the text, and is used as the basis for pricing most composition (CH.12).

Sinkage is the distance down from the topmost element on the type page, *not* from the edge of the page itself.

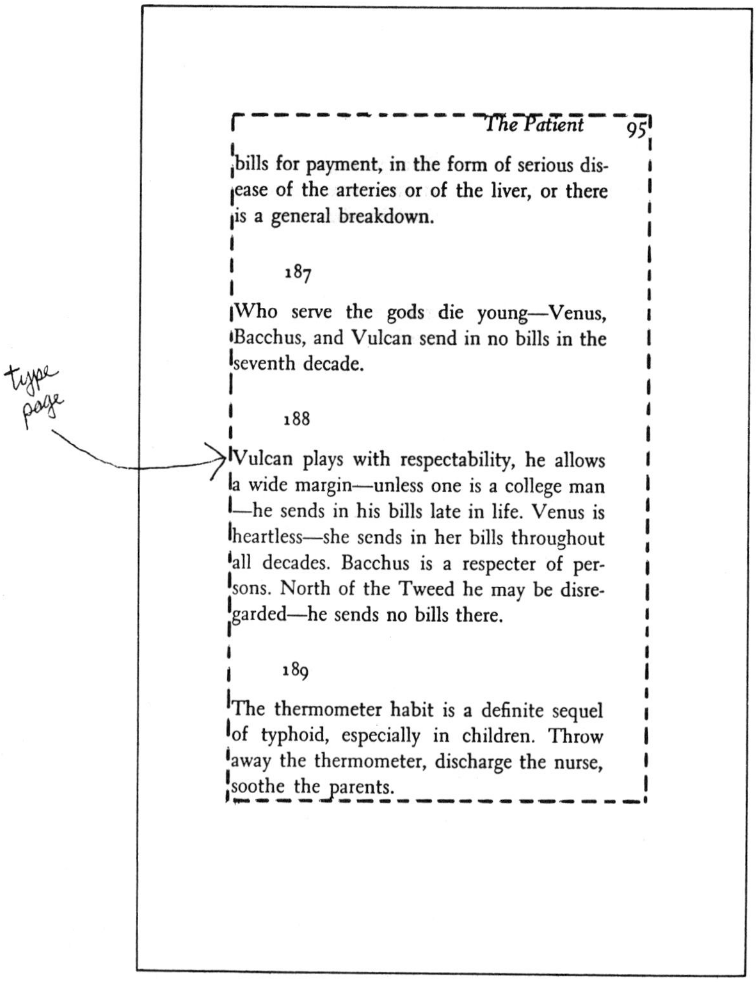

type page

The Patient 95

bills for payment, in the form of serious disease of the arteries or of the liver, or there is a general breakdown.

187

Who serve the gods die young—Venus, Bacchus, and Vulcan send in no bills in the seventh decade.

188

Vulcan plays with respectability, he allows a wide margin—unless one is a college man —he sends in his bills late in life. Venus is heartless—she sends in her bills throughout all decades. Bacchus is a respecter of persons. North of the Tweed he may be disregarded—he sends no bills there.

189

The thermometer habit is a definite sequel of typhoid, especially in children. Throw away the thermometer, discharge the nurse, soothe the parents.

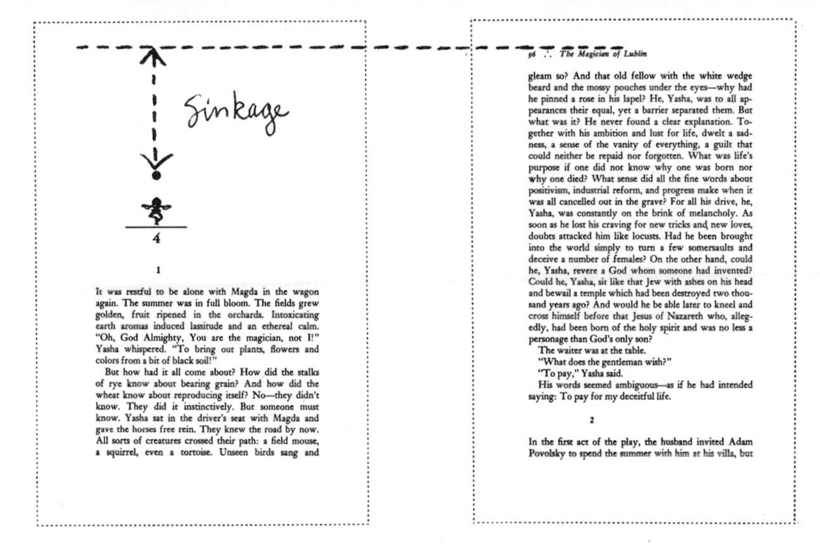

4

1

It was restful to be alone with Magda in the wagon again. The summer was in full bloom. The fields grew golden, fruit ripened in the orchards. Intoxicating earth aromas induced lassitude and an ethereal calm. "Oh, God Almighty, You are the magician, not I!" Yasha whispered. "To bring out plants, flowers and colors from a bit of black soil!"

But how had it all come about? How did the stalks of rye know about bearing grain? And how did the wheat know about reproducing itself? No—they didn't know. They did it instinctively. But someone must know. Yasha sat in the driver's seat with Magda and gave the horses free rein. They knew the road by now. All sorts of creatures crossed their path: a field mouse, a squirrel, even a tortoise. Unseen birds sang and

96 ∴ *The Magician of Lublin*

gleam so? And that old fellow with the white wedge beard and the mossy pouches under the eyes—why had he pinned a rose in his lapel? He, Yasha, was to all appearances their equal, yet a barrier separated them. But what was it? He never found a clear explanation. Together with his ambition and lust for life, dwelt a sadness, a sense of the vanity of everything, a guilt that could neither be repaid nor forgotten. What was life's purpose if one did not know why one was born nor why one died? What sense did all the fine words about positivism, industrial reform, and progress make when it was all cancelled out in the grave? For all his drive, he, Yasha, was constantly on the brink of melancholy. As soon as he lost his craving for new tricks and new loves, doubts attacked him like locusts. Had he been brought into the world simply to turn a few somersaults and deceive a number of females? On the other hand, could he, Yasha, revere a God whom someone had invented? Could he, Yasha, sit like that Jew with ashes on his head and bewail a temple which had been destroyed two thousand years ago? And would he be able later to kneel and cross himself before that Jesus of Nazareth who, allegedly, had been born of the holy spirit and was no less a personage than God's only son?

The waiter was at the table.

"What does the gentleman wish?"

"To pay," Yasha said.

His words seemed ambiguous—as if he had intended saying: To pay for my deceitful life.

2

In the first act of the play, the husband invited Adam Povolsky to spend the summer with him at his villa, but

Proofs are printed examples of type and/or illustrations. *Reproduction proofs* are carefully printed to achieve the best quality of image. They are photographed for making printing plates of various kinds (CH.7).

The "proof" of a photographic film is a print made by one of various processes (explained later in this chapter). These are called *blueprints, whiteprints, Ozalids, vandykes, Brunings,* etc.

The person who actually sets the type is a *compositor*, and the typesetting is done in a *composing room.*

Type specification

In order to have type set as it is wanted, specifications of certain kinds must be given for every line or character. More often than not, one or more of the necessary instructions is missing from the copy received by printers. These omissions result in delay and expense and should be avoided. Layouts should be used to supplement, not substitute for, specifications.

Here is the information required for *each* item:

(a) typeface,

(b) type size,

(c) whether caps, small caps, cap and lower case, lower case, or caps and small caps,

(d) whether italic or roman,

(e) letterspacing, if any,

(f) vertical position (sinkage, or distance to next item above or below),

(g) leading (if more than one line),

(h) measure (if set on justified lines or to a particular width),

(i) horizontal position (flush left or right, indented, centered, etc.).

The specifications should be written legibly in the margin of copy or layout with a sharp pencil of a different color than used elsewhere.

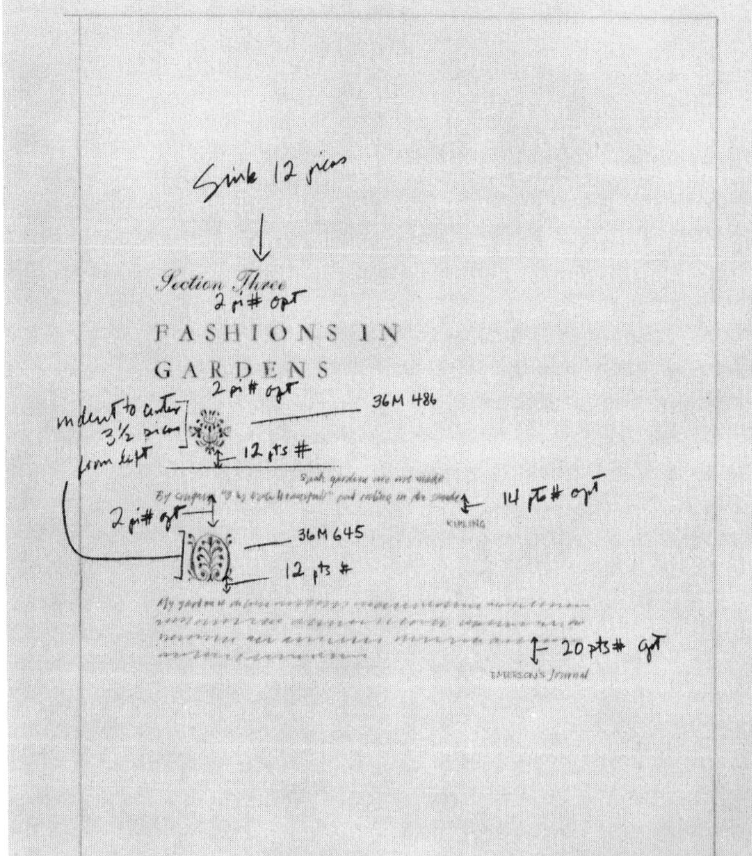
Sink 12 picas
Section Three
2 pi # opt
FASHIONS IN
GARDENS
2 pi # opt
36M 486
indent to center
3½ picas
from left
12 pts #
14 pts # opt
KIPLING
2 pi # opt
36M 645
12 pts #
20 pts # opt
EMERSON'S Journal

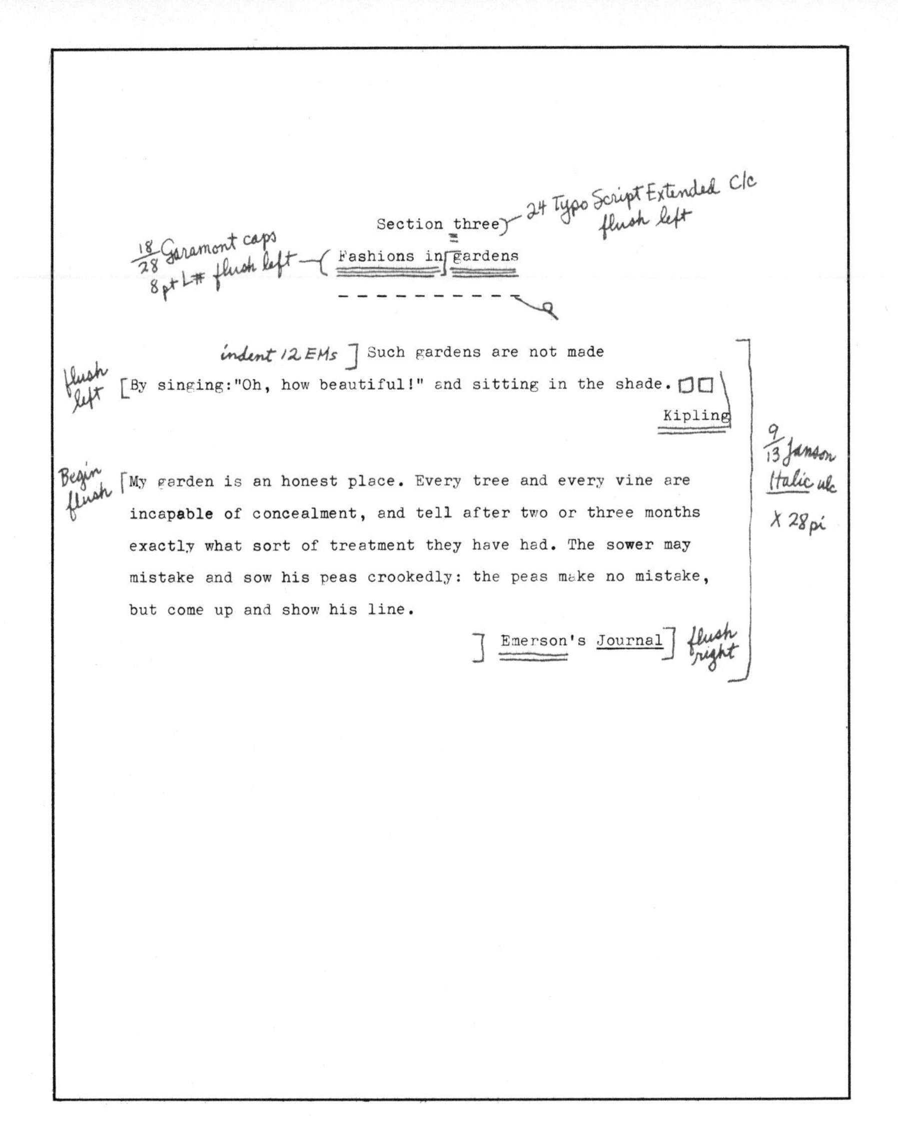

Section three — 24 Typo Script Extended C/c flush left

18/28 Garamont caps 8 pt L# flush left — Fashions in gardens

indent 12 EMs — Such gardens are not made

flush left — By singing: "Oh, how beautiful!" and sitting in the shade.

Kipling

Begin flush — My garden is an honest place. Every tree and every vine are incapable of concealment, and tell after two or three months exactly what sort of treatment they have had. The sower may mistake and sow his peas crookedly: the peas make no mistake, but come up and show his line.

Emerson's Journal — flush right

9/13 Janson Italic u/c X 28 pi

When specifying leading or the space between lines, it is necessary to indicate whether the space is to be *actual* or *optical,* i.e. whether you want the compositor to insert spacing material in the amount indicated or to insert only enough material to give the *appearance* of the space indicated. Remember that most metal type is made the full depth of the type size, including the ascenders and descenders. In a line of capitals, for example, there will be a nonprinting area of metal underneath the line. Your specifications must take this into account. When you indicate spacing, it is taken to mean actual spacing material. If you want optical spacing, the word "optical" or the abbreviation "opt." (sometimes *visual* is used) should be written after the amount.

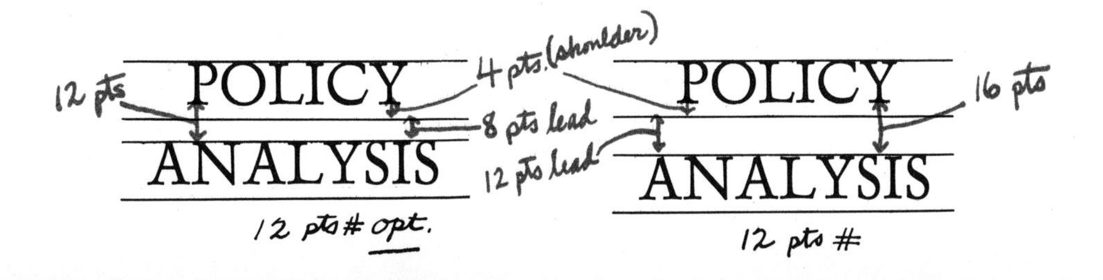

In letterspacing, where a single line is involved, it is usually better to have the line letterspaced to a specific width rather than to indicate the amount of spacing. This prevents disappointment. In specifying letterspace for a number of small-cap lines that will vary in length (subheads, etc.), give the amount of spacing wanted, preferably in units of standard machine spaces.

Chapter titles, subheads, etc. may be set in lower case with caps beginning either (a) all important words or (b) only the first word and proper nouns. The copy should be typed or marked with the capitalization desired (a vertical line through a cap makes it lower case; 3 lines under a letter makes it cap) and the specifications should indicate that this is to be followed. However, it is helpful to have a symbol for each style. Some use *Clc* for "cap all important words" and *ulc* for "cap first letter and proper nouns only". If you use these designations, be sure that your compositor understands what you mean by them. This usage is not widely known, but it would be very good to have it generally adopted, since there is no other for the purpose.

When giving type specifications for printed copy, it is useful to know the standard proofreaders' marking system. This is shown in the section on "Marking proofs" later in this chapter.

Hand composition

Typesetting is no longer done by hand, letter by letter, as it was before the invention of typesetting machines, except to set *display type* (usually larger than 18 pt., see CH.6) and occasional small blocks of text. Nevertheless, a knowledge of hand composition is fundamental because much of the practice and terminology of machine composition is based on the original method. Even the most advanced composition systems do not entirely abandon some concepts of metal typesetting by hand.

Like most hand operations, hand composition is relatively expensive. The cost of setting a line of display type by hand may range from $1.50 to $5 or more, depending on the typeface and size used, the length of line, the spacing requirements, who does the setting and for what purpose. The cost of hand setting is based on the time required, plus the cost of the type if it must be obtained for the job. While much more type can be set in the same time by machine, it should be remembered that setting up a machine takes time also, and it is often cheaper to set a few lines by hand.

HAND-SET TYPE

Hand composition may involve any one of 3 kinds of type: (a) Foundry, (b) Monotype, and (c) Ludlow.

▪ *Foundry type*—The type cast in relatively hard metal by *type founders* such as ATF, Bauer, Stempel, Stephenson-Blake, etc. and sold to compositors.

- *Monotype*—Individual characters are cast in a softer metal on the Monotype machine, usually by the compositor himself.
- *Ludlow*—This type is actually cast on a slug in the Ludlow machine, but is considered hand composition (for pricing) because the mats from which the type is cast must be assembled by hand.

Foundry type is sold by the fonts or by the pound. The fonts usually have a standard assortment of characters based on normal frequency of occurrence, i.e. there will be many of the common letters such as "e" or "a" but comparatively few such as "q" or "z". The type is stored in wooden trays called cases, each character having a compartment of its own, in a size and position also based on frequency of use.

There are several problems connected with foundry type. It is relatively expensive, particularly the more decorative faces. Being expensive, it is rarely used for printing except to *pull* [print] reproduction proofs. An alternative is to make duplicate *plates* (CH.7) or else to incorporate the foundry type in a page which is then plated.

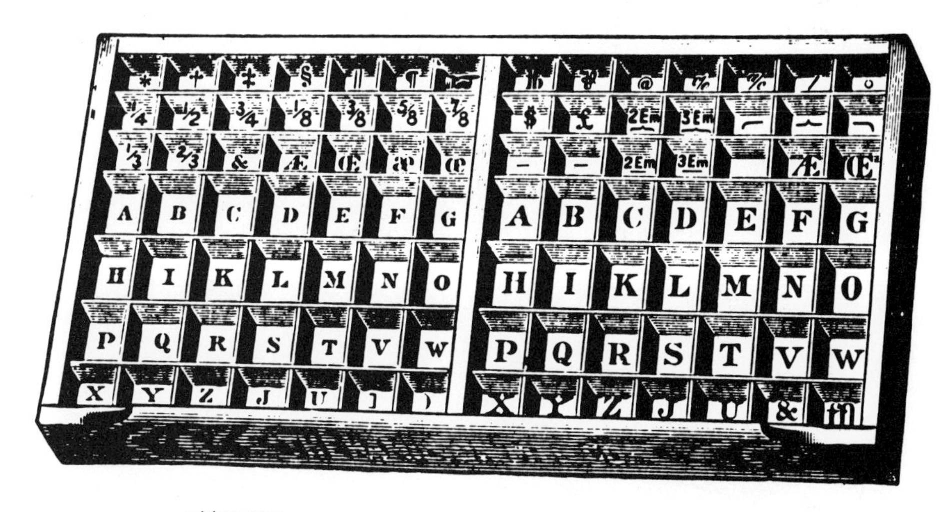

upper case

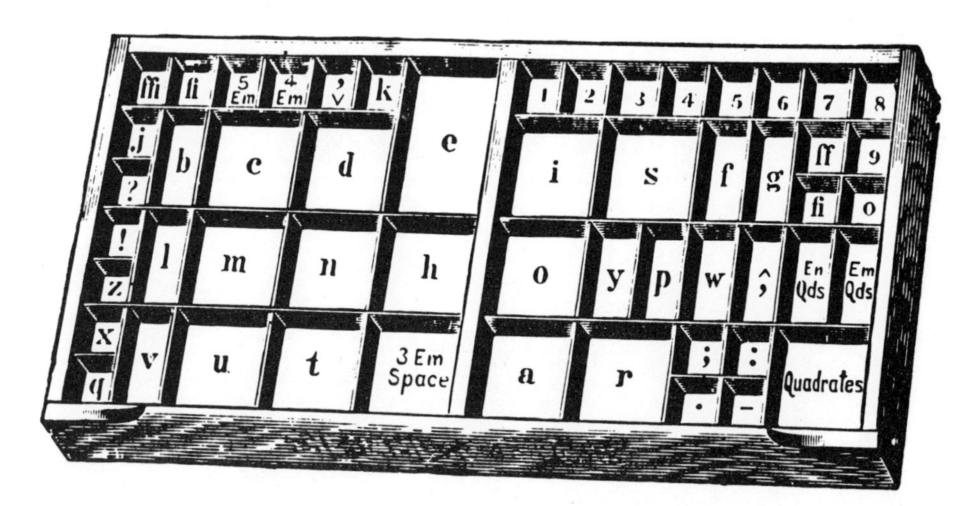

lower case

Any of these operations involves considerable cost. Then, too, the type must be *distributed* [each character returned to its compartment] after use, an expensive hand operation.

Monotype is much less expensive to buy and it need not be stored in cases at all if the printer has his own casting machine. It is almost as cheap to melt down Monotype after 1 use and recast it as needed as it is to save and distribute it each time. Also, there is then less need for storage space and the type will always be fresh and sharp.

Ludlow composition (CH.6) is used primarily for newspaper headings, for which the machine was designed. The maximum width is 22½ picas and the typefaces available are mainly those used in newspaper heads and ads. There are, however, a few faces suitable for book composition, and the width may not present a problem. The advantage of Ludlow is in the relative ease of handling a solid slug. On the other hand, there is the inconvenience (and cost) of having to reset the entire line to make corrections.

SETTING TYPE BY HAND

The compositor begins by holding in his left hand a small metal tray called a *stick*, into which he places the type taken from the case. The stick has an adjustable bracket to control the length of line. The type is arranged (upside down) in lines, with spacing inserted as desired. When the stick is full—it holds about 10 picas in depth—the bracket is released and the type is transferred to a *galley*, which is an oblong metal tray with an edge about ½″ high. This process is repeated until the hand composition is finished. In

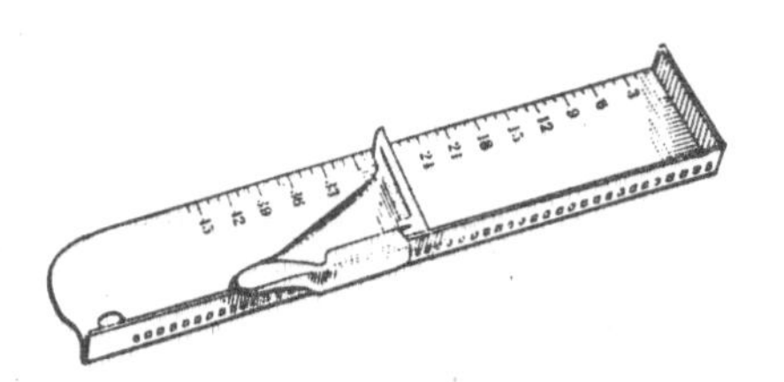

Type being assembled in galleys on the bank. Note storage of galleys at right. Cabinet at left holds strips of wooden spacing material called furniture.

the galley, the lines are assembled with other type and/or cuts belonging together, and the elements are arranged with proper sequence and spacing. This is done on a table or cabinet called a *bank.*

Machine composition—metal type

All mechanical methods of setting metal type are basically the same—the copy is typed out on a keyboard and another device casts the type in accordance with the keyboarding. The use of tape controls and computers have speeded the process, and in some cases the keyboard is separated from the caster to the extent that it may not even be in the same city; nevertheless someone must tap a key for each character and the type must be cast. There are machines that can produce a coded tape by electronically scanning a typescript page, but even here a keyboarding must provide the copy to be scanned.

There are 2 kinds of metal type set by machine: (a) individual type characters and spaces assembled into lines—the Monotype method—and (b) entire lines consisting of a single bar of metal (slug) on the face of which the characters appear—Linotype, Intertype, and (for display) Ludlow. Slug composition is the fastest, and therefore the least expensive, way of setting large amounts of metal type. Being the least expensive it is by far the most widely used method for book composition, although in Europe most typesetting was done on the Monotype until very recently and a large amount still is today. Monotype has certain advantages over slug composition—it is more practical for setting complicated material, it can be corrected by hand, its typefaces are generally better designed, and its metal is harder—but it is more expensive for straight, uncomplicated composition.

Ludlow is mentioned here although it is mechanical only in the casting element. The Monotype caster is used also for setting display sizes of type for which the mats are hand assembled, and there is a special Linotype machine—the *All-Purpose Linotype* (APL)—which casts large sizes and extralong slugs. However, when one speaks of machine composition what is meant is the mechanical production of *text type* (CH.6).

LINOTYPE & INTERTYPE

The Linotype and Intertype machines are virtually identical and interchangeable, so that whatever is said here about Linotype is also true of Intertype. The only significant point of difference is in their typefaces. Even here there is little involved, as the mats are interchangeable. A Linotype face can be set on an Intertype machine and vice versa.

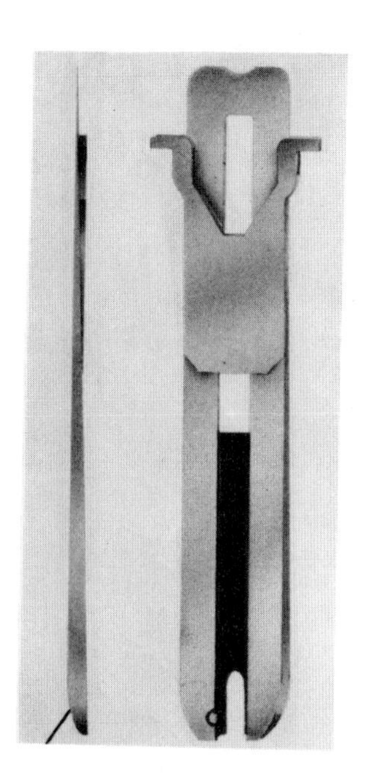

The Linotype machine combines keyboard and caster. Their link is the *magazine*, a flat metal box containing the mats. Each mat (and there are several of each kind in the magazine) is in a separate *channel* or slot. When the operator taps a key, the appropriate channel is opened and the mat drops into position in a rack called a *rail*, on which the desired width of line (in picas) is set. The consecutive mats drop into place until the line is almost filled. At the end of each word, a key is struck to drop in a *spaceband* [a thin metal wedge]. The operator stops when he sees that he cannot fit another full word or syllable on the line *and* have enough space between the words and sentences. At this point he sends the row of mats to the casting element, where the spacebands are pushed up until the line is wedged out to full width (justified). Hot type metal is then injected into the molds on the face of the mats, and the slug is formed. It is trimmed to size by knives and ejected onto a tray similar to a galley.

Sometimes an awkward situation occurs at the end of a line and the operator may have to reset several lines to get better breaks. The evenness, and therefore the quality, of Linotype composition depends on how judiciously the problem of justification is handled.

While the slug is being cast, the mats are lifted onto a *distributor bar* which drops each one back into its own channel. This is accomplished by notching the edge of each mat in an individual pattern (as on a latch key) so that it can fit into its own channel and no other.

Each mat has 2 characters on it. They are usually the roman and italic form of the same letter, although some fonts have a boldface instead of the italic, and in a few instances the mats have 2 different typefaces on them. Even where the font has roman with italic, some of the mats have other combinations, such as two punctuation marks, or a small cap and a number. Sizes of 16 pt. and larger have only 1 character on each mat. To change from one character on the mat to another (say, roman to italic) the operator moves a lever which raises the mats to bring the lower characters into posi-

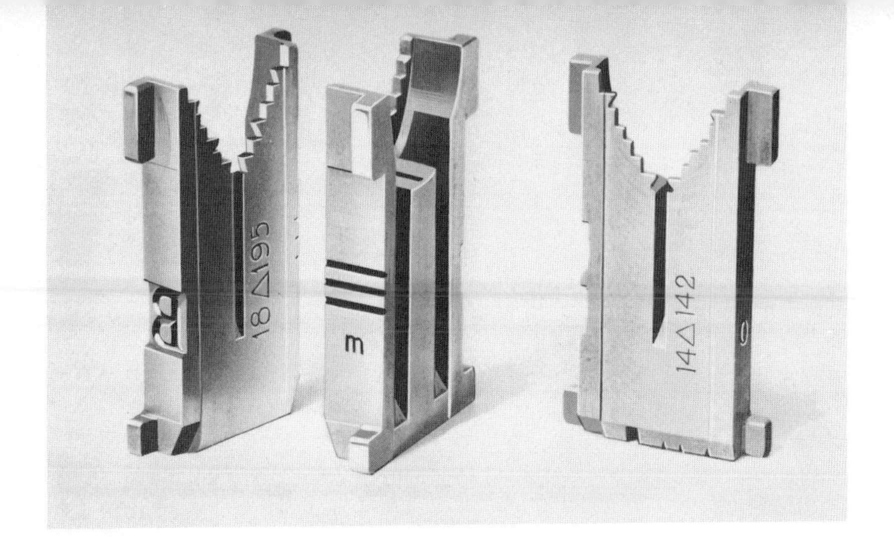

At left, *Linotype spaceband*; above, *Linotype mats (edge views of 1-letter mat and side view of 2-letter mat)*; below, *a line of mats assembled with spacebands between words.*

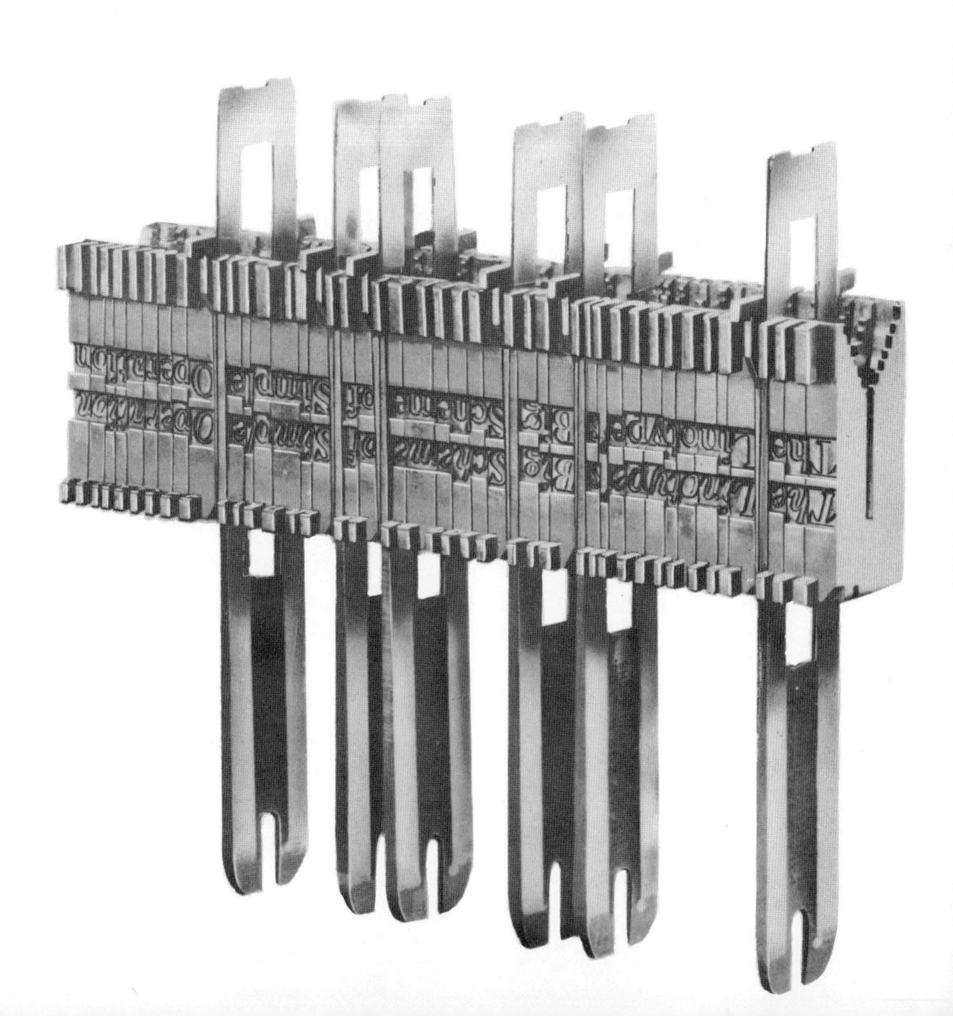

Newly ejected slug being examined by operator.

tion to be cast. This is like the shift key on a typewriter, which enables typing the capital or other alternate character on the key.

As there cannot be more than 2 characters on a mat, it is not possible to have roman, italic, *and* bold on the same line with only 1 magazine. On the standard Linotype machine it is not practical to change magazines frequently while setting. However, a Linotype *Mixer* enables the operator to set from 2 magazines (a new model has 4), with only a shift of a lever needed to change from 1 face or size to the other. Use of the Mixer is, of course, more expensive than the regular machine.

The standard Linotype machine cannot set a slug longer than 30 picas. For longer slugs, up to 42 picas, a special machine must be used. One can set wider than 30 picas with the regular machine by setting each line on 2 slugs and *butting* them together. Intertype has a model which produces 42 pica slugs.

Any requirement that slows an operator increases the cost of setting. It is more expensive to set a great many italic or small cap words interspersed with roman, due to the frequent shift from upper rail to lower and vice versa. Setting a large number of centered lines involves more time unless the lines are set with a *quader*, which automatically centers. Other causes of additional expense are the use of hand spacing, and the use of *pi mats* or *side sorts*. These contain special characters (such as brackets, accented letters, etc.) that do not run in the magazine, and must be picked out of a special box on the machine and inserted in the line by hand. Pi mats are automatically returned to the *pi box* after use.

A Linotype magazine holds 90 different mats, providing 180 different characters. The number of characters available may be doubled (or quadrupled) by using a Mixer, and some machines are fitted with an auxiliary keyboard and magazine providing 34 more

Diagram showing operation of Linotype machine.

1. *Keyboard*
2. *Magazines*
3. *Mats dropping out of channels*
4. *Mats and spacebands on rail*
5. *Line at caster*
6. *Ejected slug*
7. *Line elevated after casting*
8. *Mats being lifted to distributor bar*
9. *Mats dropping back into magazine*

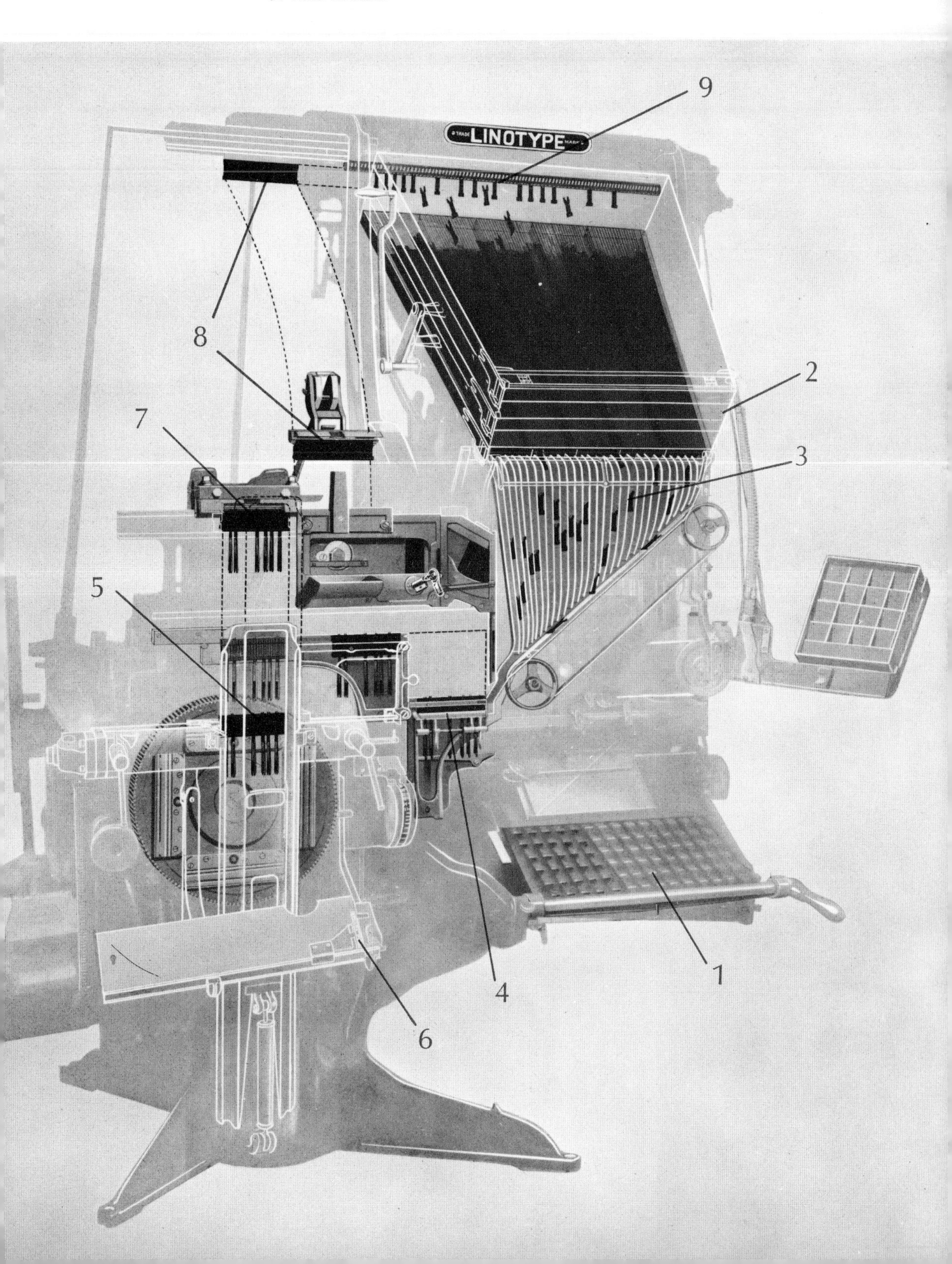

M M

characters. If the machine is a Mixer, 2 side magazines may be used, increasing the number of characters to 424, plus whatever pi mats are used.

Characters of different point size can be set on the same slug, but they will align at the top rather than at the bottom.

Both Linotype and Intertype have models which can be operated by coded tapes produced on a separate keyboard machine.

MONOTYPE

In Monotype, the keyboard and the casting machine are entirely separate. Instead of the keyboard arranging mats directly, as in Linotype, it produces a perforated roll of paper (which is actually a coded tape) which is then "played back" in the casting machine.

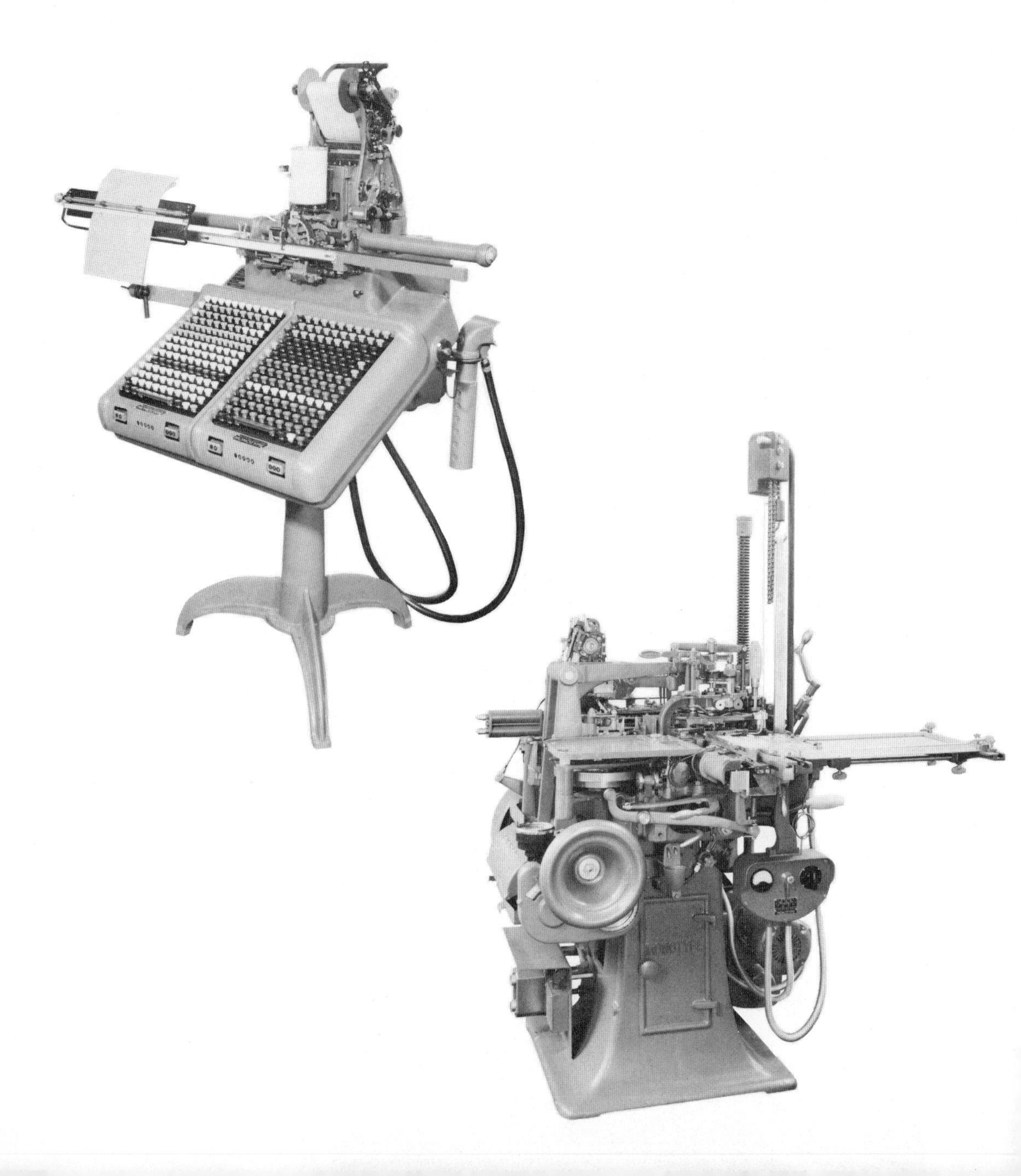

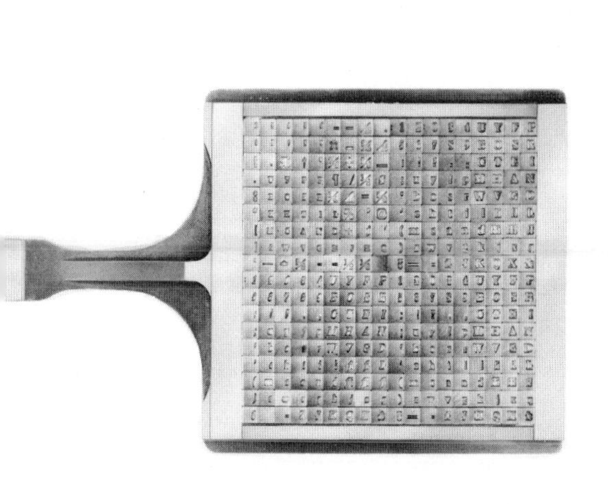

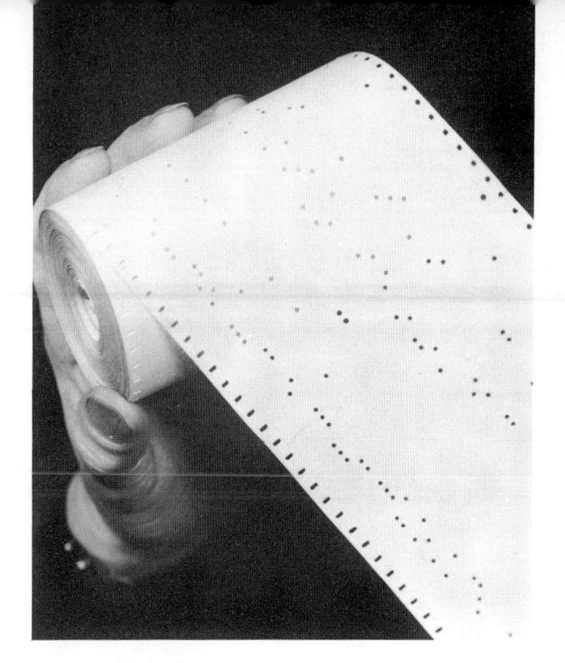

The mats, which are contained in a rectangular frame (*matrix-case*), are moved into place according to the pattern on the roll and then are cast in individual characters. Each character is sprayed with a fine mist of oil to hold it in place. The completed lines are ejected onto a galley.

Justification is accomplished by a means somewhat similar to the Linotype spaceband system. The keyboard machine indicates when the line is nearly full and how much is needed to make it full. The operator presses a button and the word spaces are automatically divided evenly into the remaining space. When the tape is fed through the casting machine it begins at the end, so that the spacing indication, which was the last to be keyboarded, is the first to be received by the composing element.

The Monotype system is based upon units of width, so that it is possible to keyboard an entire book for one typeface and then cast the type in a different face using the same tape, provided the 2 typefaces have the same *set width*.

There are a maximum of 225 mats available at one time on the Monotype caster, so it is possible to set roman, italic, and bold on 1 line or to mix typefaces without the additional handling required for such work in Linotype. For this reason, some complicated

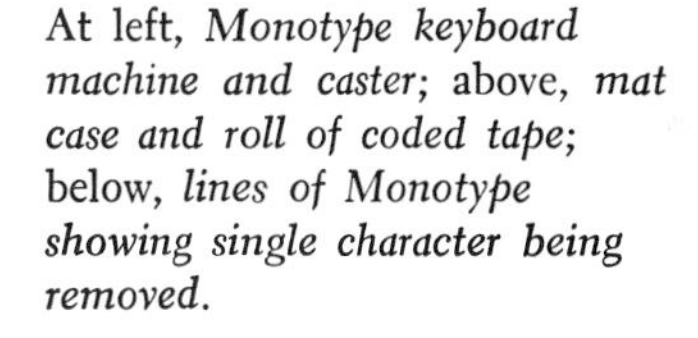

At left, *Monotype keyboard machine and caster*; above, *mat case and roll of coded tape*; below, *lines of Monotype showing single character being removed.*

books can be set at less cost by Monotype. Also, the Monotype machine will cast lines up to 60 picas in length without any difficulty. One model, the *Monomatic,* has 289 mats.

It is possible to use a much harder metal in casting Monotype than is used for Linotype. In Europe it is customary to print most books directly from Monotype and then make duplicate plates only if the success of the first printing indicates re-runs. In the United States it is more usual for a softer metal to be used and duplicate plates made immediately. The cost of the plates is offset partly by the lower cost of printing from, and storing, plates. Where reprints do justify making plates, there is a saving because the first printing is made from plates rather than type. (In Europe this does not apply since the rates are higher there for printing from plates.)

There is an English as well as an American Monotype company. Their products are almost identical but are not interchangeable. The English mats will not cast in the American machines or vice versa. Some typefaces made by the English company are cut to run in American equipment, but not all. American machines can be modified to take English mats.

LUDLOW

The brass mats are assembled in a special frame similar to a compositor's stick. When 1 line has been arranged and spaced, it is locked in place and the stick is inserted into the casting machine. A lever is pulled and molten metal is injected into the mats, casting the line as a solid slug. Duplicate slugs can be cast by repeatedly pulling the lever.

The caster will handle type from 6 to 96 pt. and can be adjusted to take up to 240 pt. The slug itself is either 6 pts. or 12 pts. thick depending on the type size, and all type larger than the slug thickness hangs over on both sides equally, forming a T-shaped end view. Ludlow slugs are all either 21 or 22½ picas wide. Multiples of these widths can be produced by the machine, which joins the slugs end to end. Odd widths must be cut on a saw.

While Ludlow composition is not much used for book work, there are occasions when it is very helpful. Since it can produce line

slugs in any quantity with display sizes of type, it makes certain things practical which would not be so otherwise as, for example, a display-size running head.

ELROD

The *Elrod* caster is not really a typesetting machine since it has no keyboard or other arrangement for composition. However, it is a mechanical means of producing some metal type material. Special brass molds are inserted into the machine to cast *strip material* (leads, slugs, and some rules). The length of an Elrod strip is 24″. Shorter lengths are cut from the strips by saw.

Machine composition—typewriter

The impulse behind development of typewriter composition was economy, but it was the simultaneous development of (photo-) *offset lithography* printing (also originally an economy measure, see CH.7) that provided a practical basis. The hot-metal typesetting machines produce type from which high-quality proofs (repro proofs) must be made in order to provide copy for the litho camera. The typewriter, with the same keyboarding, produces camera copy directly. Not only is the repro proof step eliminated, but the cost of keyboarding is greatly reduced by the use of less-skilled operators than are needed to handle Linotype or Monotype machines. In addition, the machines cost very much less and take up much less space.

The product of typewriter machines—a positive proof on paper—can be used to make photomechanical plates for letterpress printing, and more of this is now being done, but it is very doubtful that the typewriter method would have been commercially feasible were it not for the ever-wider use of offset lithography.

When practical typewriter composition machines first appeared in the late 1940s, the term *cold type* was coined to distinguish this method from *hot-metal* typesetting. This term (or *cold composition*) is still used, but it now applies generally to any method of composition that involves no casting of metal type.

The chief characteristic distinguishing typewriter composition from other mechanical means is the absence of any step between the keyboard and the product. The operator strikes a key which prints a character of reproduction quality on a sheet of paper. This is accomplished by impressing metal type on paper through a carbon ribbon, as in an ordinary typewriter. Composing typewriters differ from standard machines mainly in that they produce a higher quality impression, are capable of more variation in typeface and arrangement, and are capable of justification, with a special attachment.

The primary virtue of typewriter composition is still economy, its quality being generally inferior to either hot-metal or photographic composition. Besides the savings already mentioned there are other economies. The relative simplicity of the operation makes possible: (a) *faster production* due to a simpler and easier keyboard, and absence of the production quotas that limit the output of union hot-metal operators, (b) *lower correction costs* due to the operator's ability to see the work as it progresses, thereby catching errors that show up only on proofs in Linotype, and (c) *easier composition of complicated work* such as tables, mathematical equations, chemical formulas, etc. due to the ease of spacing both horizontally and vertically. Another economy is the negligible cost of storing proofs as against holding metal type, but the largest savings result when setting copy that requires no justification (directories, poetry, etc.).

Justification is the most difficult technical problem in typewriter setting. It is accomplished by keyboarding the copy 2 times, once manually and once automatically, or by using a special attachment which justifies the lines after they have been set on the keyboard. Although this work is presently being done by relatively unskilled labor, the extra operation eats up much of the possible savings. This is one of several reasons why typewriter composition is not cheaper than other methods unless used in appropriate situations.

Proofs also pose special problems in this method. First, only 1 or 2 carbon copies can be obtained. Additional copies must be made by some other (and usually more expensive) method. Second, proofs taken from the typewriter will smudge unless fixed by spraying or baking. This is important, as these proofs must be read, corrected, and pasted up into pages before going before the camera —when they should be in sharp, clean condition.

delight to meet
ot ready to go on
B.O. says he can't
enclosing my
ler took it in place
h, Mr. Pixie, we
something fierce.

This method is used today mainly for noncommercial publications (theses, scientific papers, government publications, etc.), for limited-interest books of university presses, for pamphlets, workbooks, and other ephemeral printing, and for reference books in which the composition may be done much more cheaply than by any other method.

The use of typewriter composition *must* be warranted by economy, as it is severely limited typographically. The typefaces available are generally inferior to those of metal type. Although these types are not always limited to the single body-width of the standard machines, they are restricted (at this time) to a maximum of 5 different widths, as opposed to Monotype's 18 and the unrestricted variation in Linotype. On most machines, there are no italics, small caps, or boldface available without a change of font.

Another problem is maintaining uniformity of impression. Not only must the pressure of type on paper be even, but the carbon ribbon, which is changed after each use, must be fresh since the carbon tends to gray with age. It is most important to find the best combination of ribbon, paper, and pressure and maintain it.

The most economical composing typewriter is probably the IBM *Executive*. It is, in fact, merely a superior office machine with a few special features which enable it to serve as a composing machine, providing its limitations are acceptable. Its economy derives from its low price (about $800) relative to other machines and the ease and speed with which it can be operated with little special training. Because the operator is paid hardly more than a typist, the final typing of the manuscript and the composition may be economically combined—thus saving 1 complete keyboarding. This saving could offset the additional operation needed to justify.

The IBM Executive has more than 15 typefaces available, but the one chosen when the machine is purchased cannot be changed, except for a few special characters, and there is only 1 size. The faces are relatively well designed and have more proportional spacing than any other such machine.

Two other composing machines are the *Varityper* and the *Composaline*, both made by the Coxhead Company. The Varityper, although it offers several sizes of type, uses the single-width body, whereby narrow and wide characters are designed to fit the same space, just as in the standard typewriter. This is considered a handicap by typographers accustomed to conventional Roman type design. But if one regards the matter pragmatically, it really is much more useful to have all characters the same width, and therefore the type should be designed to look well within this system. Instead, we have gone to a great deal of trouble to devise systems that will accommodate our present type design. This is turning design backward, creating a practical problem to fit an esthetic solution. In the same vein, tremendous sums are being spent to achieve justification of lines on composing machines of all kinds, when there is really no value in justified composition.

: From an esthetic standpoint, unjustified lines are preferable because word-spacing can be made uniform. Even such a conservative designer as Eric Gill advocated unjustified composition, and so set his own essay on Typography. Readability is improved by the elimination of word-breaking as well as by more even spacing. The only possible argument in favor of retaining the squared-up page* is that we are accustomed to it; but then, we are also accustomed to the unjustified lines of typescript and few, if any, editors complain of difficulty in reading typewritten pages. It is unfortunate that at this technological turning point in bookmaking we missed the opportunity to discard an unnecessary convention. And what a price we are paying to preserve it!

: The Composaline is an extremely versatile machine, which not only offers characters of 3 different widths, but has a large number of typefaces available. Changes from roman to italic and to other fonts can be made quite quickly. On the other hand, considerable skill is required to use the machine most effectively, keyboarding is relatively slow, and the cost of equipment is about triple that of the IBM Executive.

: One of the most practical uses for typewriter composition is the setting of directories and similar listings. For this purpose some machines are adapted to handling cards, on each of which 1 item is typed. The cards may then be arranged in the desired order for page makeup. With the type placed near the upper edge of each one, the cards can be "shingled" so that the items are directly under each other. Adhered or held in position, they are photographed as page units. There are several machines—*Fotolist*, *Listomatic*, *Composalist*, etc.—which will rapidly photograph the individual cards and automatically arrange them in galley form on film. The cards can be punch-coded like IBM cards for automatic sorting. This can save months of time otherwise required for getting the copy prepared for composition.

: There are a number of other composing typewriters on the market and others coming on, all with advantages and disadvantages. There are also several machines available, such as *Justigage* and *Marginator*, which can be used with typewriters to justify the lines.

Machine composition—photographic

There are advantages in phototypesetting which would have warranted its development in any case but, as in typewriter composition, the basic impulse behind its rapid flowering is the

* This book was planned for squared-up pages (except for this one) because the machine on which it is set favors justified lines.

growing use of offset lithography. Here the connection is closer yet. In a photocomposing machine the keyboarding produces an image ready to photograph or a *film* ready for use in making a *photomechanical plate* (CH.7). It is true that photocomposition produces a sharper image than even the best reproduction proofs, that the photocomposing machine is more flexible and versatile than its hot-metal counterpart and is capable of faster production; nevertheless, its primary value is in elimination of the repro-proof *and camera* stages in making plates for litho and gravure printing (CH.7).

Theoretically, this efficiency should result in an overall economy, but it often does not. Part of the reason is the relatively high cost of inserting corrections and page makeup, but there are other factors involved that may outweigh any savings.

Photocomposition can compete economically with Linotype on jobs suited to its capabilities and limitations. For instance, most photo machines are at their best when used for books that can be set directly into pages, i.e. indexes and other line-for-line copy that can be divided into columns or pages of a specific number of lines without concern for awkward breaks. Here it is important to remember that it is not possible to change leading in photocomposition once the type is set. In general, photocomposition is suited to the same kind of material as typewriter composition but one has the advantage of being able to enlarge or reduce the type as it is being set. However, the economics of book composition are so varied and complex that the relative cost of each method must be estimated for each job, or at least each kind of job, to determine which is lowest. When considering photo against typewriter composition, however, the vast difference in quality is usually a major consideration.

THE MACHINES

A popular photocomposition machine is the *Fotosetter,* made by the Harris-Intertype Corporation. Its operation is very similar to the hot-metal machines of the same company. The keyboard, the magazines, the mats, and the mechanics of bringing the mats into position are substantially the same. But instead of casting metal slugs from mats containing a mold of the character, the Fotosetter projects an image of the character, a negative of which is embedded in the mat, onto a photographic film. This film is then developed and may be exposed directly on a litho or gravure plate (CH.7). Film may be positive or negative depending on the photomechanical procedure used in makeup, or a positive image on paper may be produced.

The regular Intertype typefaces are available and the image produced is of the highest quality. Because the process is a photographic projection, the same mats can be used to set type in any size from 4 to 36 pt., and some models can range from 3 to 72 pt.

Line widths up to 51 picas can be set and justified. With no metal in the way, photoset characters may be fully kerned to achieve optimum fitting.

When an error is made, a rectangle of film containing the faulty line is punched out. A corrected line is set and taped into the punched-out space, with register achieved by a row of register holes along the sides of the film.

A newer machine made by this company, the *Fototronic*, has 2 parts—a keyboard to produce a punched tape and a photographic unit driven by the tape. There is also a tape-operated model of the *Fotosetter* called the *Fotomatic*.

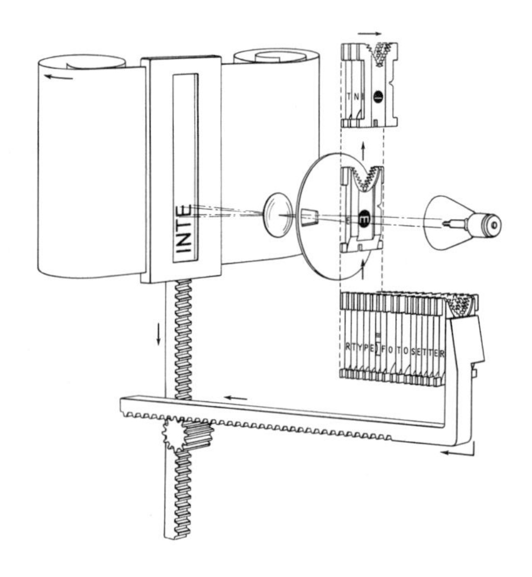

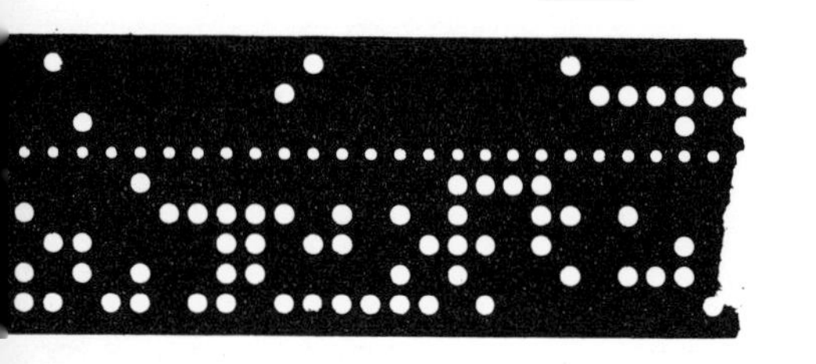

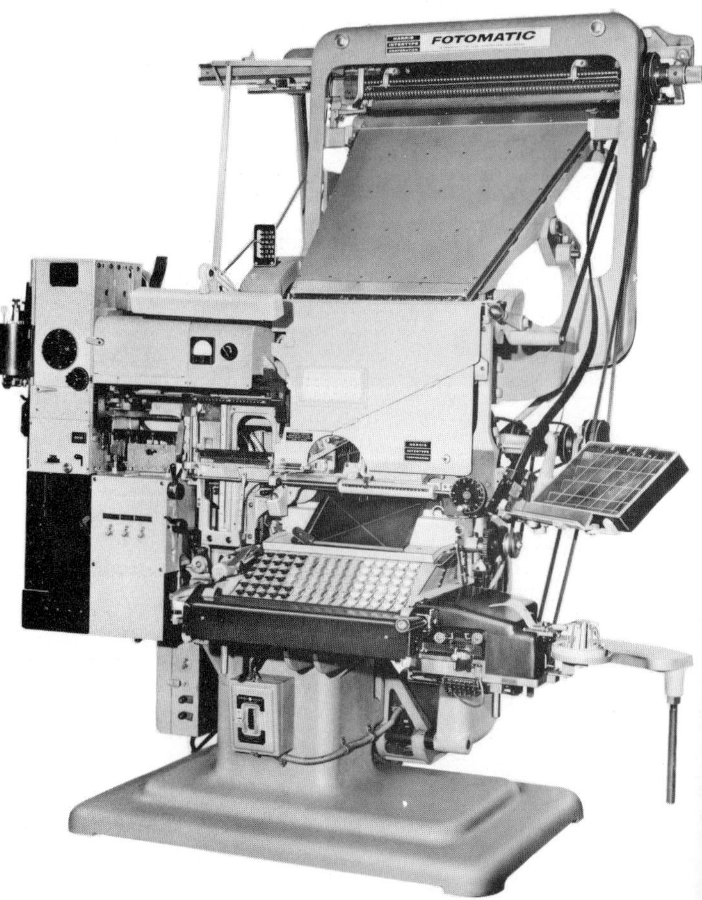

Photon 713

Photon matrix disc

Another machine, the *Photon*, attains great speed of production by using a continuously spinning disc on which the character negatives are carried. When an entire line has been keyed, an electronic "memory" system uses previous instructions from the keyboard and justifies the line. Then a button is pressed and an extremely fast lightbulb flashes at the precise moment that each character in the line appears in front of the lens. This projects the characters onto a film. As the operator works, the machine produces a positive proof (*hard copy*) of his composition, so that errors may be seen as they occur. Errors can be erased by the machine and corrections substituted—either by line or by character. By catching errors immediately the operator can prevent a large percentage of the corrections required with other methods.

The Photon consists of a rather complex keyboard and a photographic unit, which contains the electronic justifying device, in 1 machine. It is possible to bypass the keyboard and compose according to punched or magnetic tape or cards coded by another keyboard.

A Photon disc carries 16 alphabets of 90 characters each. The typefaces are versions of the standard text faces (CH.6). Several faces may be included on 1 disc and may be set in 1 line. Sizes may be mixed also. To switch from one font to another the operator merely presses a button. The entire disc can be changed in a few minutes. Sizes from 5 to 72 pt. can be produced.

The Photon company has produced another machine called the "*Zip*", which operates on a somewhat different principle at a much higher speed. This machine can perform more complex operations too, such as setting pages of 2 or 3 columns on 1 film. The computer functions required are extremely complicated and use of the equipment system involved is too expensive for most typesetting operations.

The *Linofilm*, produced by the makers of Linotype, and the *Monophoto*, made by the Monotype company, both operate like the hot-metal Monotype. A keyboard machine produces a perforated paper type which activates a separate photographic unit. Both machines use a gridlike matrix containing all the character negatives but, whereas the Monophoto grid moves to place the character in position between light, lens, and film, the Linofilm grid is stationary, each character having a tiny shutter that opens on signal to expose the film.

Linofilm sets 6 to 36 pt. up to 42 picas wide. Monophoto sets 6 to 24 pt. up to 60 picas wide. Both offer many of the same typefaces as their respective hot-metal machines. Linofilm produces a positive proof in operation, Monophoto does not.

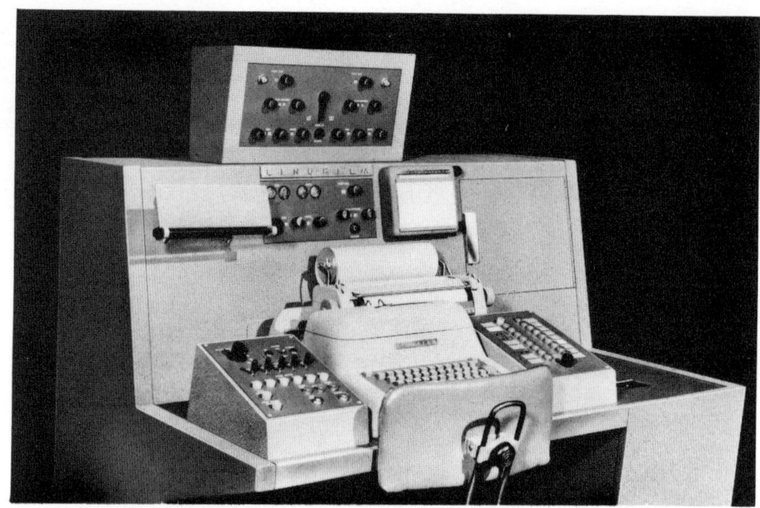

Linofilm photo unit
keyboard
font grid

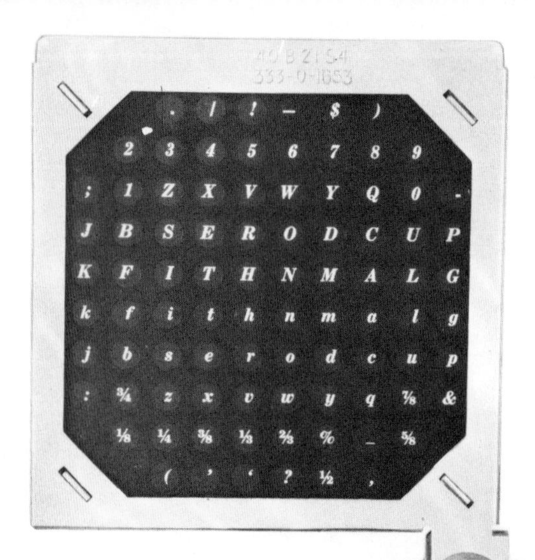

Monophoto keyboard, photo unit

The ATF *Phototypesetter* is a relatively compact system consisting of 2 elements: a keyboard unit which produces a punched tape and a photographic unit which produces either a photoprint or a film according to the coded tape. Each unit is hardly larger than a standard typewriter. The keyboard unit produces a hard copy as the tape is being punched, and corrections can be made quite easily.

A disc, somewhat similar to that of the Photon, contains 2 fonts with a total of 168 characters. Sizes available are 5 to 14 pt. and the maximum width is 44 picas. Discs can be changed quickly.

ATF Phototypesetter keyboard, photo unit

Another relatively simple and inexpensive machine is the *Alphatype*. This has 2 elements also; a typewriter-like keyboard machine and a somewhat larger unit that turns keyboard-produced tape into positive proof or film.

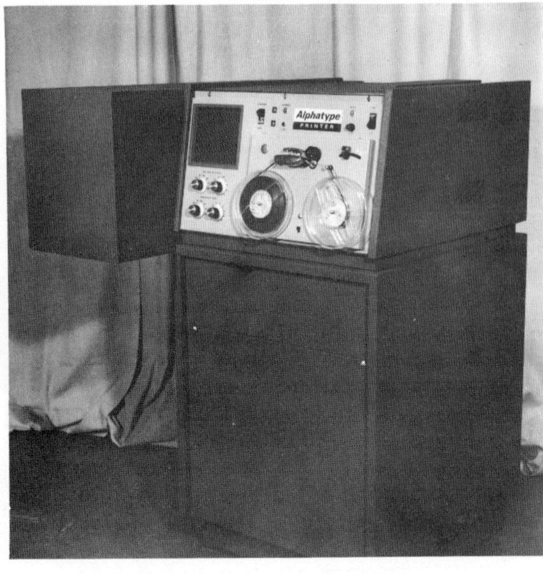

Alphatype

A number of photographic machines have been produced to set display type only. Generally, these have the essential features of Ludlow, i.e. the assembly of characters is more or less manual, while production of the result is (photo) mechanical. The *Protype* is most like Ludlow in operation, while others, such as the *Filmotype, Hadego, Headliner*, etc., use various systems of levers, dials, and other mechanical aids to facilitate composition. In all cases, the product is a strip of film or photographic paper on which the image appears. These machines were designed for advertising use, and the typefaces available are generally of the more flashy kind, but some are perfectly good. By using special lenses, some of these machines can distort type to virtually any degree. The *photolettering* services make these distortions available by the word or line. Curving, undulating, tapering, shivering, and slanting type are all possible. The use of such facilities in books is limited, but it is useful to know that they exist.

CARBON WEB

For Men and Women

PURE
SHORTENING
ARTIFICIALLY COLORED
HYDROGENATED VEGETABLE OILS AND MEAT FATS;
AND DI-GLYCERIDES ADDED; WITH NOT MORE
HYDROXYANISOLE ADDED AS A PRE-
CAROTENE.

Diatype, a photosetting machine for display.

New photocomposing machines and improvements on existing ones are coming along rapidly. Between this writing and your reading there will undoubtedly be developments of this kind and there will be more later, but a knowledge of the machines described here will be a helpful base for keeping abreast of those to come.

Computers in composition

At this time, computers do not do composition in the sense that they "transform original copy into a form suitable for printing or for making printing plates". They are used now mainly to automatically produce justification of lines at a much faster rate than can be accomplished manually. An operator must still keyboard the manuscript as he would in operating a linecasting or photosetting machine, but does nothing about justification. The keyboard produces a punched coded tape which is fed into the computer. A hard copy of the keyboarding is produced by the computer before it begins justifying.

A problem arises in reading proofs of computerized composition. The *printout* of present computers is unjustified lines of a relatively crude, typewriter-like type, containing various symbols for the instructions to be given the typesetting machine. Besides being

```
bF$*ATHERS OF THE CHURCH$%*$/23C*OLLECTIVE BIOGRAPHY, $BR*1705‡
bP*ATROLOGY, $BR*60-67$4**&
bH*ERE ARE ENTERED WORKS ON THE LIFEAND THOUGHT OF THE $@@F*ATH
RS OF THE $C*HURCH,@@ A TERM THAT EMBRACES THE LEADERS OF THE E
RLY CHURCH TO THE TIME OF $G*REGORY THE $G*REAT IN THE $W*EST A
) $J*CHN OF$D*AMASCUS IN THE $E*AST.$%*$O*CCASIONALLY, ESPECIAL
/ IN COMPREHENSIVE WORKS, THIS TIME LIMIT HASNOT BEEN STRICTLY
3SERVED.*&
bW*ORKS ON THE WRITINGS OF THESE MEN ARE ENTERED UNDER THE HEAD
NG $C*HRISTIAN LITERATURE, $E*ARLY.*&
```

Controlled Type

Controlled Type

Controlled Type

Controlled Type

Controlled Type

confusing to the unaccustomed eye, this kind of copy creates an uneasiness in the minds of authors when they realize that there will be an additional step before the actual type is produced. The computer printout can be bypassed and only the type proofs read, but this means foregoing the economy of correction in an early stage. A compromise procedure is to have the printer's proofreader check the printout and the author read the type proofs. In time, computers will be designed to deliver a readable, justified printout comparable to the proofs of typesetting machines.

The economic advantage of high-speed computer justification is limited by the relatively slow speed of the keyboard operator. Keyboard machines can now produce much faster than any human could possibly operate them, so the only way of utilizing the capacity of computer justification is to have several keyboards feeding each computer. On the other end, it takes many typesetting machines to use the output of one computer.

A function of perhaps more economic importance is *merging*. Corrections are made and keyboarded onto another tape which is also fed into the computer. The 2 tapes are automatically merged inside the machine, and out comes a third tape (either punched or magnetic) which can activate a typesetting machine so as to produce justified lines with the corrections included.

Linofilm tape combiner

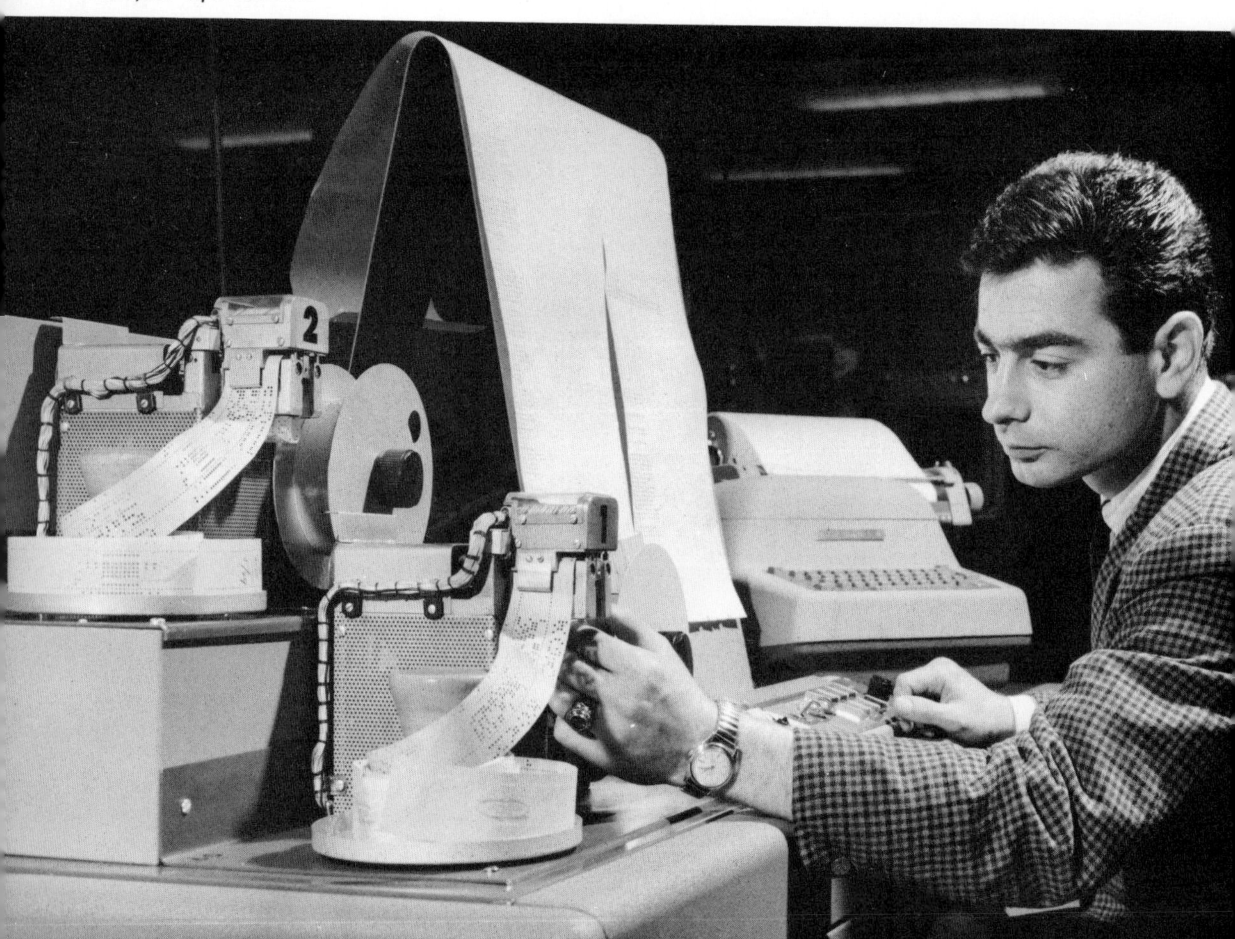

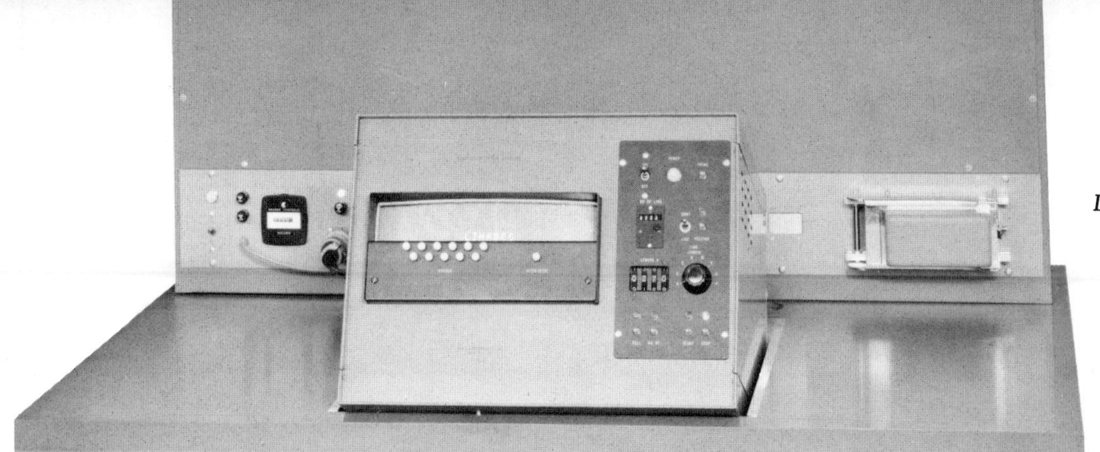

Linasec

Justification in itself is a very simple accomplishment for a computer. There are a number of small, relatively inexpensive, desk-top machines (such as *Linasec*, *Tapetron*, etc.) which will take a keyboard-produced tape and justify the lines at a fast clip—*provided* a human monitor is present to cope with the problems of word division. There are also computers (RCA 301, IBM 1620, etc.) capable of fully automatic justification, *including* word division, but most of these are very large and enormously expensive. The IBM 1130 is a relatively low-priced machine having full capabilities in word division.

There are several possible systems of achieving word division (*whatever* system is used will be considered wrong by a large number of the grammarians, who are hopelessly split on whether syllables should be based on etymology or pronunciation), but all of them involve building tremendous memory capacity into the machines—in some cases whole dictionaries are stored away (!). The computer manufacturers have tried to simplify the problem by adopting a single standard of hyphenation, but no system is guided entirely by rules, so a large number of exceptions must be memorized. The effort and expense put into solving this problem is particularly appalling in view of the fact that there is no real value in justification, and without justification there would be little, if any, need for word division.

A somewhat more promising area of computer operation is in the rearrangement of material and merging of copy from different sources. These are functions performed very much more quickly by machine than by hand. Manuscripts can be edited by feeding into a computer (*input*) original copy plus copy to be added or deleted, and the *output* [the product] will be a single tape with all the changes made. Very complex operations of this kind can be performed with extreme rapidity and consequent savings—*provided* that preparation of the copy and *programming* [instructing] the machine are not so involved that the time gained in 1 place is lost in another. A computer can be made to do almost anything, but it must be instructed what to do, and it can take a person as long to prepare the instructions as it would take to do the job himself. From this it can be seen that it is necessary to choose very carefully *which* jobs are to be put on the machine. The saving may be eaten up, also, if much extra typing is required to punch the necessary tapes.

The latter problem may be eased by several machines in development which can produce a punched or magnetic tape by electronically *scanning* a typewritten or printed page. The drawback here (besides the very high cost of the equipment) is the unlikely prospect of getting a perfect manuscript from an author. If the Ms isn't perfect (without corrections and errors), it would have to be retyped—and this keyboarding could just as well be used to produce the coded tape. This may seem like caviling, but the problem is a human one, and there is no indication that humanity (least of all a writer!) is going to change fast enough to accommodate technology.

Another human factor tends to limit the economic benefits of computer programming. When 1 programming can be applied to numerous titles or editions, or to a very large amount of copy (as in newspapers) the economy is substantial. But this situation is relatively rare in book publishing, with its inherent multiplicity and diversity of products. Except in some textbook and reference book areas, the author is not part of the team—he is a lonely individual producing a unique manuscript according to his own needs and inclinations. By and large, the publisher produces the book as written. This diversity, which gives book publishing its strength and charm, has defeated much standardization in book manufacturing and will probably limit efficient application of computers to the field.

Computers are expensive, so the time savings they produce must be major to warrant the investment (and maintenance). Yet, studies have shown that book composition is made up of numerous operations, no 1 of which represents more than 10% of the cost. Thus, speeding up 2 or 3 operations may result in a large saving in those steps, but would mean a very small reduction in the overall cost of composition—which is, in turn, only part of the total production price of a book. Any hope for a major economy, therefore, must come from radically new systems, in which some steps are eliminated and the rest combined.

Several machine-manufacturing companies have produced *systems* which tend in this direction, but they are really just groupings of standard equipment. For example, the Linofilm system contains a keyboard unit, a photographic unit, a correcting unit which splices corrected film into the original, and a machine called a *Composer*, which combines film (this will be discussed under "Makeup," which follows). All of these are photomechanical rather than computer operations.

The future direction of composition research is concerned rather with the manipulation of code symbols within a computer, so that all the operations described above would be performed before any product is delivered, i.e. a program including typesetting, correcting, merging, and makeup instructions would be set up before any copy is put into the machine, then all of the functions would be computed and completed in 1 operation. Made-up pages or even a complete *form* [all the pages being printed on 1 side of the sheet at one time] could be produced merely by feeding the resultant tape (or tapes) into photographic machines. The obvious weakness here would be the necessity of having an absolutely perfect plan at the start—which is rare enough. However, such a device could probably deliver proofs at various stages and could handle corrections made on them. Certainly, such a system would be very efficient in resetting a new edition from printed copy as, for example, a paperback reprint.

The U. S. Government has contracted for manufacture of a system which would perform not only these operations but would handle line and halftone illustrations as well. All the material—words and pictures—with coded instructions for their size, position, etc. will be fed into the machine on a combination of magnetic and video tapes, and the output will be made-up pages on film, ready for platemaking. The name of this system is *Lexical-Graphical Composer-Printer* (*LGCP*).

Makeup

Makeup is the assembly of all elements of a page in their proper relationships. This may mean the arrangement of metal type and cuts, the arrangement of proofs and illustrations, or the arrangement of film negatives or positives of the various parts. In terms of metal type, makeup is a stage of composition and the work is done in the composing room. Much or all of the makeup done for litho or gravure printing may be done in an art studio, in the publisher's office, or in the printer's shop. The procedure varies considerably and so does its position in the production schedule, but makeup is a fundamental phase in bookmaking which must take place one way or another—even when it is called by another name.

METAL TYPE

Makeup begins when the *castoff* (CH.20) has been made to determine how many lines should be on the text page. This information, with the *sample page* specifications (CH.18), will provide the information on which makeup will be based. All corrections are then made, and *running heads* [book, part, chapter titles, etc. repeated on text pages] and folios are set. At this point the compositor's *makeup man* will take the galleys of type from the bank and insert the space necessary to arrange all the elements properly.

Each page is measured to be sure that it is the proper depth. Theoretically, every page has the same number of lines of text (except, of course, the beginnings and ends of chapters), so the makeup should be very simple. Actually, there are several complications.

▪ *Widows*—The most common cause of difficulty is the *widow* [a line of less than full width occurring at the top of a page]. In a page of justified lines, widows do give a ragged appearance, and it is a typographic custom to eliminate them by one means or another. A short line of conversation is not usually considered a widow, but the end of a paragraph is. Some printers will allow a widow of ⅘ of a line, others will tolerate ¾, but purists insist on a full line. Granted that a *very* short line at the top of a squared-up page looks awkward, it is doubtful that the not-quite-full line warrants the effort required to remove it. (Of course, if we did not insist on justified lines there would be no widow problem at all.)

The simplest way (from the printer's standpoint) to correct a widow is to have the editor or author add words to fill out the line, or delete words to eliminate the line. Sometimes this is possible, sometimes not—for example, in reprints. Otherwise, the usual procedure is to take the previous line from the bottom of the last page and make it the first line of the new page, instead of the widow. This creates a short page. The solution then is to make the facing page 1 line short also. Here the plot thickens. If the offending widow occurs on a right-hand page (*recto*), all that is needed is to leave that page 1 line short and it will match the previous left-hand page (*verso*) from which the rescue line was taken. If, however, a left-hand widow occurs, the 2 previous facing pages must be made a line short, thus providing 2 full lines over the widow—that is, if the 2 previous lines are full width. If not, the complications extend further back. If making the adjustment necessary to eliminate the widow creates a widow on another page, a half-dozen or more pages may become involved.

Facing short pages may be left that way, or they may be *carded*, [strips of thin cardboard are inserted between the slugs to fill the pages out to full depth]. This practice is frowned upon because the lines do not then back up those on the other side of the page. Considering that the average page has about 36 lines, and the lines are about 12 pts. deep, only ⅓ pt. is added to each line. On the facing pages themselves this is imperceptible to almost anyone, and the misalignment on backup can scarcely be observed.

An even naughtier practice is to card only the 1 short page so as to leave the facing page undisturbed. Here the misalignment may be detected by an expert, but considering that this much or more misalignment generally results from inaccurate folding or sewing, the imperfection is not likely to be noticed at all.

These remarks may sound like incitement to the lowering of standards, and in a sense they are. But the relatively meaningless refinements insisted upon by some, at the cost of considerable efficiency, seem a waste of good intentions, when there is so much improvement needed in spacing, presswork, binding, and engraving —where the faults are glaring and only a little care is required for relief.

When the type fits very tightly into the desired number of pages, the makeup may be ordered with facing pages a line *long*, instead of short, to avoid widows. Too many short pages may result in added pages at the ends of chapters in which the last page is full, or almost so.

The widow problem—and makeup problems in general—are eased when the book contains many subheads, illustrations, and other opportunities to adjust space. When the "opportunities" are so numerous that they create their own problems, a *dummy* is made by pasting up rough proofs on pages of correct size and number (CH.21). This avoids taking expensive composing room time and gives designer and editor a chance to experiment with the arrangement. Once the dummy is turned over to the makeup man, the problem of makeup is purely mechanical—provided the dummy is accurate.

▪ *Run-in breaks*—Another problem inherent in page makeup is what to do when subheads, *spacebreaks* [1- or 2-line spaces in text] or *run-in chapters* [chapter openings that occur on the same page as the end of the preceding chapter] (CH.16) fall at the bottom, with insufficient room for a minimum number of text lines underneath. It is best to settle these questions in advance. Neither schedule nor budget fare well if the printer must phone for instructions while the makeup is underway. The considerations involved are discussed in CHS. 20 and 24.

▪ *Running heads and folios*—Practices of inserting running heads and folios (CH.18) vary. Sometimes they are set separately even if they appear on the same line. Other compositors prefer to set them on 1 slug. The difference affects design to some extent. A standard Linotype slug should be at least 2½ picas long in order to include enough *ribs* to give stability, so, if folios are set on separate slugs, their relationship to the running heads will be affected by the minimum slug length. Some compositors, however, now have molds which cast slugs that are solid for the first 3½ picas on one end, so the minimum length may not be required.

Running heads can be set in advance on the basis of the castoff and dropped in as the galleys of type are divided into pages, except where the running heads refer to the content of each page, as in dictionaries, directories, and other reference works. Here, pages are made up first and the running heads are set and inserted later.

■ *Heads in text*—Captions, subheads, and chapter heads not already in the galleys are also set in advance and dropped in place as the pages are made up. All type (except hand-set display) is set on slugs the width of the text, so that the horizontal position of each element on the page is controlled by its position on the slug (centered, flush left or right, or indented). Typographic arrangements that involve cutting and fitting slugs slow the makeup considerably.

■ *Narrow cuts*—The inclusion of *cuts* [engravings, see CH.7] narrower than text involves cutting and inserting spacing material, since the entire rectangle of the type page must be filled with solid material. This usually means metal, but wooden blocks and bars (*furniture*) are used sometimes to fill large areas. The work of *cutting-in* cuts is eliminated by having them mounted on blocks the exact width of the text. (This means that the engraver must position them properly on the blocks—which may equal or exceed the cost of cutting-in.)

■ *Odd-depth spaces*—When all pages must be made up to the same depth, problems may arise when spaces other than full lines are used. For example, the use of half-line spaces above and below poetry causes trouble when the poetry begins on one page and ends on another. Each half-line space must be increased to a full line or eliminated entirely, unless some lines are carded to take up the other half-line of space. The problem is usually complicated by the odd space resulting when the poetry is set on a body size different from that of the text.

Before makeup begins, it must be known whether the book is to be printed from (a) the type itself, (b) plates made by molding the type, or (c) plates made by photographing repro proofs made from the type (CH.7). When the type is used for printing or for pulling repros, all spacing material must be lower in height than when plates are being molded, and the blank ends of slugs with short lines must be sawed down to the lower height (*low-slugging*). This is done to prevent picking up ink in blank areas and transferring it to the paper. On the other hand, the high spacing material facilitates platemaking by molding, and the open areas can later be *routed* [cut away by a revolving cutter similar to a drill] on the plate.

Low-slugging can be, and sometimes is, done after the pages are made up, but the more practical time is before.

In *metal-type pasteup* the bottom of the type or slug is sawed off, leaving only the face and a thin layer of metal shoulder. These flat strips are arranged according to a layout and adhered to a plastic or metal base. This method is sometimes used for complicated makeup with large sizes of type, as in newspaper ads.

MAKEUP WITH PROOFS

When the book is to be printed by a process using photomechanical plates (most often lithography), the final form of the pages before photographing is usually black-on-white (positive) proofs adhered to a white board or heavy paper, with all elements in correct position relative to each other and relative to the edges of the page.

This is called a *mechanical* and the preparation of it (CH.11) is the equivalent of makeup. Very often, when the mechanical is made with repros of metal type, part of the makeup is done in type before the repros are pulled. It is much easier to adjust spacing around subheads, etc. or to insert folios and running heads with slugs than with proofs—which must be cut apart, squared up, aligned, and adhered. The difference in hourly *cost* between a makeup man and a pasteup man is very large (about 3 to 1) so the choice must be carefully considered.

A principal reason for printing by lithography being the lower cost of reproducing illustrations and handling complicated makeup, most mechanicals involve both these elements. To the extent that the page arrangement is formal and uniform, the makeup problems are the same as in metal type. When complicated layouts are involved, a dummy with rough proofs is prepared first and the position of each elements is specified on it (CH.21). The mechanical simply follows these instructions (CH.7).

MAKEUP WITH FILM

The product of photocomposing machines may be positive paper proofs suitable for mechanicals, but mostly it is positive film, i.e the type is black. When such film is exposed in contact with unexposed film, the result is a negative.

Makeup with positive film is done page by page in the same way as a mechanical, except that pieces of film are *stripped in* [taped in position] on a sheet of transparent film instead of proofs being adhered to an opaque board. When an entire form is made up, it is exposed to a single sheet of light-sensitive film and a negative is made. Negatives of the illustrations are then stripped in and the whole form is exposed against the plate (CH.7).

One advantage of this method is the ease of inserting rules for tables and charts. These may be made by *scribing* [scraping off the emulsion with a pointed tool] or by setting the rules on the machine and superimposing this film over the film of the type.

In general, makeup with film is likely to be more precise than mechanical pasteup but, again, the cost per hour is much higher. Against this may be weighed the saving in camera work. As in most comparisons of cost, there are many variables, so the particular conditions of each job must be considered.

MAKEUP WITH COMPUTERS

Since the main hope for substantial economy in computer composition lies in the perfection of integrated systems that automatically produce corrected, made-up pages from *typescript* copy, and it is already possible to produce corrected and justified typesetting by computer, the logical next step is development of machines with automatic makeup capability.

Such machines do in fact exist, in the sense that a computer can be programmed to code the required procedures, and machines are available which will manipulate various elements of film and place them into position according to instructions. Among the latter is the Linofilm Composer, which not only places pieces of film as directed by an operator, but can enlarge or reduce any part of the copy. This machine is used now primarily for making up newspaper ads, but it could be used for book page makeup. It is not, however, an automated process, as it cannot be activated by coded instructions.

Makeup instructions (including illustrations, etc.) could be programmed, and machines like a Linofilm Composer could be modified to operate from a coded tape instead of manually, but the problem of programming could be very formidable. Simple matters, such as the placement of running heads and folios in uniform position, would present no difficulties, but in a complicated book with irregular layouts on every page, the trouble of programing might be economically prohibitive. Certainly, the difficulties would have to be considered in relation to the particular circumstances of each

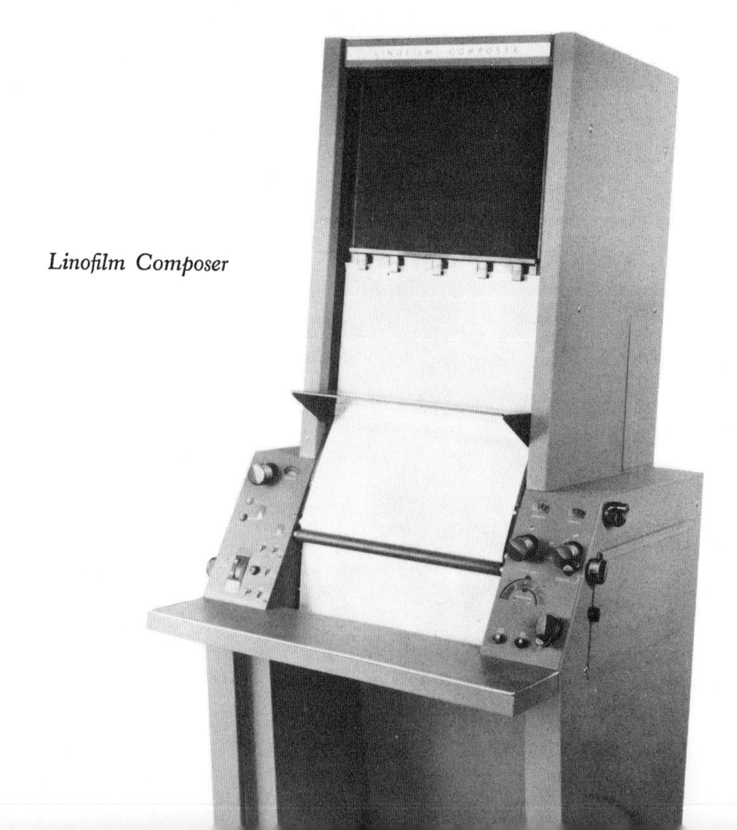

Linofilm Composer

job. Whether the overall utility of computer makeup would warrant the cost remains to be seen; it is likely that the programing involved would require a large, expensive machine. (The LGCP described earlier—which includes typesetting functions as well as makeup—is costing the government $4,000,000 for 2 systems.)

Proofs

The discussions of galley, page, book club, foundry, plate, and repro proofs which follow refer to metal typesetting practice. Proofs of cold composition are discussed separately, after the others. This section deals with the purpose and production of proofs. Proofreading methods are explained later in this chapter. For a discussion of the use of proofs, see CHS. 20 and 24. Color proofs are covered in CH.7.

GALLEY PROOFS

When the galleys on the bank are ready to be filed in a cabinet, a *galley proof* is pulled on a *galley press* or *proof press*. The galley is set on the bed of the press, with the type held firmly by wooden wedges. An inked roller called a *brayer* is passed over the type and then a sheet of galley paper—usually a fairly smooth stock—is placed on top of the type. An *impression cylinder* then passes over the paper, applying enough pressure to transfer the ink from type to paper.

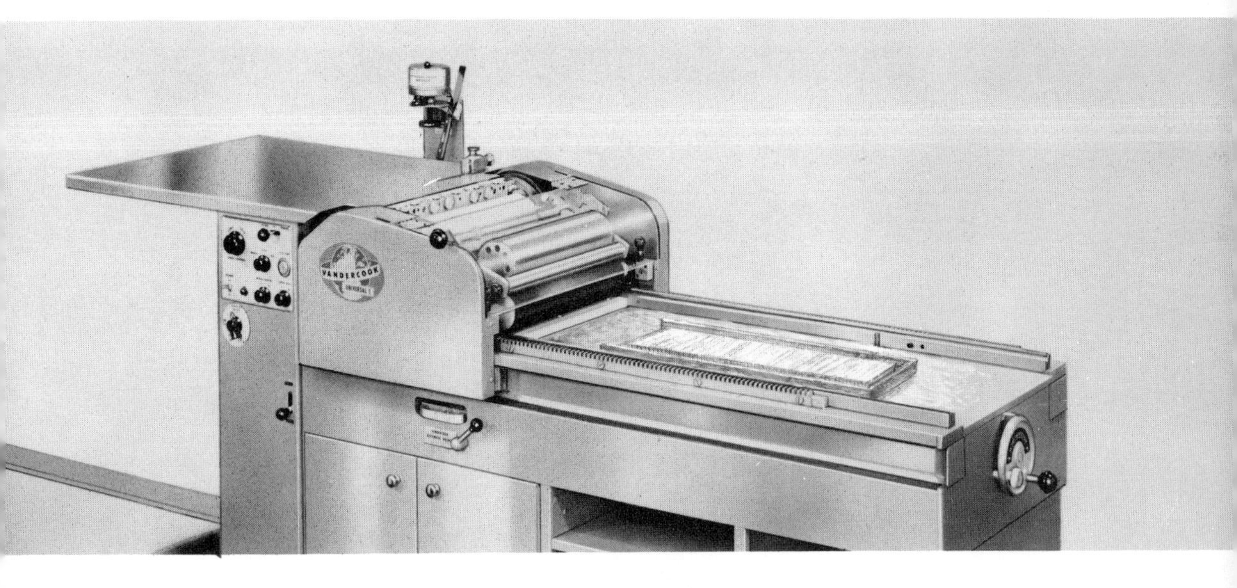

Vandercook proof press

The purpose of the galley proof is to enable authors, editors, and designers to check for typographic errors and to make minor corrections in copy, spacing, etc. The printing should therefore be clean, but need not be of high quality.

PAGE PROOFS

After the corrections indicated on the galley proofs have been made and makeup completed, *page proofs* are pulled, usually on the same proof press as the galleys. The type is still in the galleys, with pieces of furniture separating the made-up pages. Normally, 2 or 3 pages fit on 1 galley.

In England, it is customary to print page proofs on large sheets *imposed* [arranged for printing, see CH.7] as they would be in the finished book. The sheets are then bound in paper covers. This is a pleasant and practical way to handle page proofs—particularly for the designer, who can see how the pages will look while there is still a chance to make changes. Alas, the custom has never been adopted in the United States.

The purpose of page proofs is to enable the checking of galley corrections and the accuracy of the makeup. Not only the corrected lines themselves, but the sequence of lines must be checked, as there is sometimes a transposition of slugs during the makeup. Remember, too, that this is the first reading of running heads and folios. As with galley proofs, page proofs are not necessarily well printed. Corrections in pages are much more expensive than in galleys.

galley proof

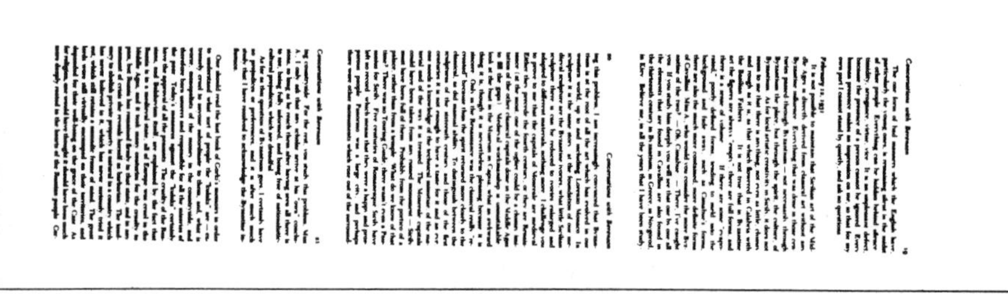

page proof

BOOK CLUB PROOFS

Publishers submit books for consideration of the various book clubs as soon as possible, in order to get a decision before the book goes to press. A book club edition will usually be printed with the regular run, but sometimes the original publication schedule is changed entirely.

Occasionally, a manuscript is submitted, but the clubs prefer the convenience of handling printed and bound copies. This is arranged by pulling special proofs of the galleys (sometimes called *BOM proofs* because they were first used for Book-of-the-Month Club) on each of which half the galley appears. This relieves the judges of handling awkwardly long galley sheets and yet minimizes extra work and expense. The proofs are then given a paper cover with a printed label and bound with a plastic, spiral wire, or other *mechanical binding* (CH.10).

Book club proofs are printed on the proofpress except when the publisher wants a large number to use for promotional purposes, when they may be duplicated by some photo-reproduction process —often by a service company engaged specifically in making such copies.

FOUNDRY PROOFS

If a book is to be printed from type, page proofs are the last ones submitted before the job goes to press. Ordinarily, there are few corrections on pages and the publisher is sent corrected proofs of only those pages involved. When *electrotype plates* (CH.7) are to be made, *foundry proofs* are pulled after pages are corrected.

Pages are grouped into 6- or 8-page forms and locked in a *chase* [a steel frame]. The pages are separated by furniture and surrounded by type-high *bearers* [steel bars about a pica wide] which protect the type during plating. (Foundry proofs are easily identified by the heavy black lines made by the bearers.) The type is held in the chase by double steel wedges called *quoins*. This procedure is called *foundry lock-up*. Proofs are then pulled on a *flat-bed cylinder press* (CH.7) called a *foundry press*. It is special only in that it is designed to take the size chase used for foundry forms. The man who does foundry lockup is called a *stonehand*.

foundry proof

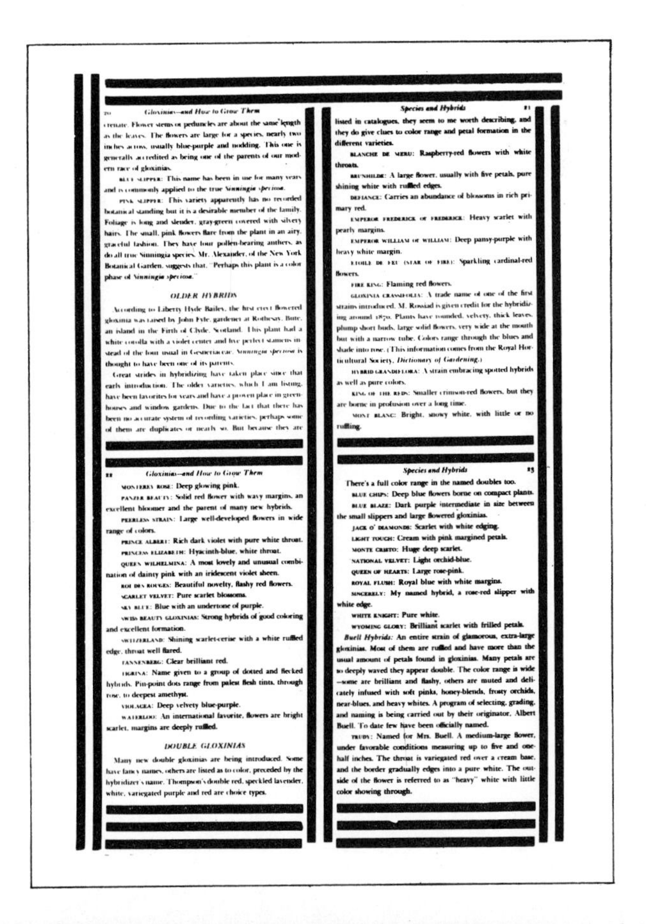

20 *Gloxinias—and How to Grow Them*

crenate. Flower stems or peduncles are about the same length as the leaves. The flowers are large for a species, nearly two inches across, usually blue-purple and nodding. This one is generally accredited as being one of the parents of our modern race of gloxinias.

BLUE SLIPPER: This name has been in use for many years and is commonly applied to the true *Sinningia speciosa*.

PINK SLIPPER: This variety apparently has no recorded botanical standing but it is a desirable member of the family. Foliage is long and slender, gray-green covered with silvery hairs. The small, pink flowers flare from the plant in an airy, graceful fashion. They have four pollen-bearing anthers, as do all true Sinningia species. Mr. Alexander, of the New York Botanical Garden, suggests that, "Perhaps this plant is a color phase of *Sinningia speciosa*."

OLDER HYBRIDS

According to Liberty Hyde Bailey, the first erect flowered gloxinia was raised by John Fyfe, gardener at Rothesay, Bute, an island in the Firth of Clyde, Scotland. This plant had a white corolla with a violet center and five perfect stamens instead of the four usual in Gesneriaceae. *Sinningia speciosa* is thought to have been one of its parents.

Great strides in hybridizing have taken place since that early introduction. The older varieties, which I am listing, have been favorites for years and have a proven place in greenhouses and window gardens. Due to the fact that there has been no accurate system of recording varieties, perhaps some of them are duplicates or nearly so. But because they are

Species and Hybrids 21

listed in catalogues, they seem to me worth describing, and they do give clues to color range and petal formation in the different varieties.

BLANCHE DE MERU: Raspberry-red flowers with white throats.

BRUNSHILDE: A large flower, usually with five petals, pure shining white with ruffled edges.

DEFIANCE: Carries an abundance of blossoms in rich primary red.

EMPEROR FREDERICK or FREDERICK: Heavy scarlet with pearly margins.

EMPEROR WILLIAM or WILLIAM: Deep pansy-purple with heavy white margin.

ETOILE DE FEU (STAR OF FIRE): Sparkling cardinal-red flowers.

FIRE KING: Flaming red flowers.

GLOXINIA CRASSIFOLIA: A trade name of one of the first strains introduced. M. Rossiad is given credit for the hybridizing around 1870. Plants have rounded, velvety, thick leaves, plump short buds, large solid flowers, very wide at the mouth but with a narrow tube. Colors range through the blues and shade into rose. (This information comes from the Royal Horticultural Society, *Dictionary of Gardening*.)

HYBRID GRANDIFLORA: A strain embracing spotted hybrids as well as pure colors.

KING OF THE REDS: Smaller crimson-red flowers, but they are borne in profusion over a long time.

MONT BLANC: Bright, snowy white, with little or no ruffling.

22 *Gloxinias—and How to Grow Them*

MONTEREY ROSE: Deep glowing pink.

PANZER BEAUTY: Solid red flower with wavy margins, an excellent bloomer and the parent of many new hybrids.

PEERLESS STRAIN: Large well-developed flowers in wide range of colors.

PRINCE ALBERT: Rich dark violet with pure white throat.

PRINCESS ELIZABETH: Hyacinth-blue, white throat.

QUEEN WILHELMINA: A most lovely and unusual combination of dainty pink with an iridescent violet sheen.

ROI DES ROUGES: Beautiful novelty, flashy red flowers.

SCARLET VELVET: Pure scarlet blossoms.

SKY BLUE: Blue with an undertone of purple.

SWISS BEAUTY GLOXINIAS: Strong hybrids of good coloring and excellent formation.

SWITZERLAND: Shining scarlet-cerise with a white ruffled edge, throat well flared.

TANNENBERG: Clear brilliant red.

TIGRINA: Name given to a group of dotted and flecked hybrids. Pin-point dots range from palest flesh tints, through rose, to deepest amethyst.

VIOLACEA: Deep velvety blue-purple.

WATERLOO: An international favorite, flowers are bright scarlet, margins are deeply ruffled.

DOUBLE GLOXINIAS

Many new double gloxinias are being introduced. Some have fancy names, others are listed as to color, preceded by the hybridizer's name. Thompson's double red, speckled lavender, white, variegated purple and red are choice types.

Species and Hybrids 23

There's a full color range in the named doubles too.

BLUE CHIPS: Deep blue flowers borne on compact plants.

BLUE BLAZE: Dark purple intermediate in size between the small slippers and large flowered gloxinias.

JACK O' DIAMONDS: Scarlet with white edging.

LIGHT TOUCH: Cream with pink margined petals.

MONTE CRISTO: Huge deep scarlet.

NATIONAL VELVET: Light orchid-blue.

QUEEN OF HEARTS: Large rose-pink.

ROYAL FLUSH: Royal blue with white margins.

SINCERELY: My named hybrid, a rose-red slipper with white edge.

WHITE KNIGHT: Pure white.

WYOMING GLORY: Brilliant scarlet with frilled petals.

Buell Hybrids: An entire strain of glamorous, extra-large gloxinias. Most of them are ruffled and have more than the usual amount of petals found in gloxinias. Many petals are so deeply waved they appear double. The color range is wide —some are brilliant and flashy, others are muted and delicately infused with soft pinks, honey-blends, frosty orchids, near-blues, and heavy whites. A program of selecting, grading, and naming is being carried out by their originator, Albert Buell. To date few have been officially named.

TRUDY: Named for Mrs. Buell. A medium-large flower, under favorable conditions measuring up to five and one-half inches. The throat is variegated red over a cream base, and the border gradually edges into a pure white. The outside of the flower is referred to as "heavy" white with little color showing through.

The purpose of foundry proofs is to show what went into the electrotype foundry. They enable the electrotyper to identify the forms, and establish a basis for determining any damage done to the type during plating. Foundry proofs are usually sent to the publisher for checking of corrections made in pages, but it is not anticipated that any further corrections will be made, and the plating proceeds unless the compositor is specifically ordered to wait for an O.K.

PLATE PROOFS

When plastic plates are made, "foundry" proofs—actually corrected page proofs—are pulled, but are usually not sent to the publisher. However, proofs of the finished plates are sent out. The main purpose of these proofs is to check the quality of the plates, but they are also used to check page corrections. Obviously, any changes requested on these proofs involve recasting the plate. Proofs of electrotype plates are usually provided to the compositor, but they are not ordinarily sent to the publisher.

Plate proofs should have a higher level of quality than earlier ones, because the printing surface of the plate is being checked. They are usually pulled on a very smooth stock, so that imperfections can be seen.

REPRO PROOFS

After pages have been corrected, if repros are wanted, the pages are locked up, usually 4 or 6 in each form, and printed on a *repro press*—which is a fine, electrically operated press with all the adjustments necessary to do first-class printing. The repro press is, in fact, really a miniature of those on which books are printed (CH.7).

Coated paper, either glossy or dull (CH.8), is used, and it may have a pressure-sensitive adhesive backing for convenience in making mechanicals. For special circumstances, usually where a second color is involved, repro proofs may be pulled on transparent plastic sheets, either with or without adhesive backing.

Repro proofs should give a perfect image of the type, which means a perfect impression, perfect inking, perfect choice of ink and paper—perfect everything. This perfection is, of course, impossible to achieve, and even the closest thing to it is very difficult to obtain. Certainly, the images produced by photocomposition are sharper than any printed proof can be, but a *good* repro proof is quite satisfactory for any printing requirement.

COLD-TYPE PROOFS

Cold-type proofs are required at the same stages of composition as in metal typesetting, but they take different forms and are produced by different methods.

Typewriter machines produce a positive proof on paper. Photocomposing machines deliver either positive photographic prints on paper or images on film. These may be positive or negative and may be either *right-reading* or *wrong-reading,* i.e. the type on the emulsion side reads properly from left to right or runs backward (as in a mirror) from right to left. It is important to think the whole job through in advance, so as to order the product best suited to the plate-making process being used. In most cases, any product *could* be used, but the object is to reduce the number of steps between composition and the finished plate.

The considerations involved are: (a) with what kind of illustration or type material will the product be combined and (b) what method of makeup will be used? For example, if halftones are involved, it might be best to make wrong-reading negatives which could then be stripped up with negatives of the halftones. If same-size line illustrations or repro proofs of display type are to be included, a mechanical with right-reading positives on paper would be preferable.

“I will pick up
You will see s
Two things. A

right-reading

he hook.
mething new.
d I call them

wrong-reading

The cold-composition machines generally deliver only 1 proof (some typewriters can make a few copies), so additional copies must usually be produced by another process. This is not really a disadvantage in relation to hot-metal composition if the duplicating is considered equivalent to pulling proofs of the metal type, and the metal type is equated with the film or paper print.

■ *Blueprints*—The most direct method of obtaining a proof from film is to make a blueprint, or one of its variations. The blueprint is actually a contact print of the film. It is less accurate (and less expensive) than a photoprint, but is adequate for proofreading purposes. Blueprint paper is treated chemically so that when a strong light strikes it through the transparent (or translucent) part of the film, the blue color becomes fixed. The paper is then passed through a chemical bath and the blue is washed away where no light came through. This gives a negative image of the film. When a negative film is used, the blueprint is, of course, a positive. The paper shrinks irregularly when it is washed, which makes it unreliable for checking sizes and register. A vandyke print is brown instead of blue.

The whiteprint is an improvement in that it makes a positive from a positive (the *un*exposed parts are fixed) and it is developed by ammonia fumes instead of a liquid wash, so it does not shrink or warp. Whiteprints are also known as Ozalids, from a machine on which they are made.

■ *Duplicating*—The blueprint or whiteprint methods are relatively cheap if only a few prints are needed, but they are not well suited to quantity production. For large numbers of proofs, a duplicating machine such as the *Multilith* or *Davidson Duplicator* must be used. These are primarily office machines but they are actually small offset lithography presses (CH.7). In the hands of good operators they can produce results comparable to much larger presses but, in any case, can turn out any number of very satisfactory proofs of type. These machines generally use a paper plate, which can be made from the film copy.

■ *Photocopying*—Duplicating machines are the answer also for larger numbers of proofs from typewriter composition. For a few copies, a photocopying machine, such as Xerox (CH.7), is practical. These machines require no film and are best suited to making copies from positive proofs and other *reflective copy* [not transparent or translucent].

Costs of cold-composition proofs are likely to be higher than those from metal type. The main difficulty arises when they must be sent to another shop to be made. Not only inconvenience but another profit is involved.

KEYBOARD & COMPUTER PROOFS

Proofs from tape-punching machines are unjustified and of limited value, for the composition is subject to further error in the justification process. Their main purpose is to enable the operator to catch and correct errors before the tape goes into the next machine.

The printout from computers was discussed earlier in this chapter under "Computers in composition".

Proofreading & style

PROOFREADING CUSTOMS

The first reading of any set of proofs is done by proofreaders employed by the compositor. Their notations are marked on the *Author's Proof*, or master proof, and include printer's errors, queries carried over from the Ms or the previous proofs, and editorial corrections such as spelling, punctuation, grammar, or even factual errors.

The Author's Proof and at least 1 duplicate are sent to the publisher, who sends the duplicate to the author for reading. Sometimes proofreaders' queries are transferred to the duplicate set so that the author can answer them, and occasionally the Author's Proof is sent to him, but this is a dangerous practice. Not only might this master set become lost, but it may be spoiled by incorrect marking. Many authors do not take the trouble to learn proofreader's marks.

With the proofs to the publisher go the Ms and the previous proofs (*foul proofs*), if any, for checking. These are sent back to the compositor with the corrected Author's Proof to enable him to determine which corrections should be charged to printer's error (*PE*) and which are author's alterations (*AA*), chargeable to the publisher.

Some publishers rely on the compositor's proofreader and are satisfied to have the author check the proofs with a final once-over by the editor. Other houses insist on all proofs being checked carefully by their own copy-editor. It certainly seems true that no matter how many times a set of proofs is read, more errors can be found.

Whatever is done about reading proofs, the final results are clearly marked on the Author's Proof. Conflicting instructions are resolved, proofreaders' queries are answered, corrections are collected from all copies and combined. There should be no omissions or ambiguities. Only 1 set of proofs should be returned.

Whether or not previous instructions exist, it is a good practice to include, with any proofs, instructions as to the next step. If revised proofs are required, this and the number of copies should be indicated. If the next step is makeup, indicate the number of page proofs required, etc. In the absence of specific orders, the compositor will send the regular number of copies—which may be fewer than you need. In any case, include *some* orders—don't send back an unaccompanied set of proofs.

PROOFREADING PROCEDURE

It is possible to read proofs alone, and this is the practice of almost all authors and editors, but the only way to be at all sure that the proof contains what is in the copy is to have a second person read the copy aloud. This is the way professional proofreading is done (the person who reads the copy is called a *copyholder*).

Reading the proofs alone enables you to determine whether or not the type as set is satisfactory, but it doesn't reveal omissions or changes. For example, an entire word, sentence, or even paragraph may not have been set, and, unless the person reading the proof remembers the copy or finds the omission disturbing enough to check the copy, the omission will go undetected.

To catch errors in spelling, punctuation, typography, etc. it is necessary to read character by character. This is quite the opposite of techniques taught for general reading, in which whole phrases are taken in at a glance. This is why the most obvious errors often escape 2 or 3 readers. Proofreading requires either complete quiet or very intense concentration (preferably both) and very good light. Don't read proofs when you are very tired.

MARKING PROOFS

You may boast about your illegible handwriting, but don't use it on proofs. Clarity is the first requirement of corrections and any delays caused by unclear writing are inexcusable. Use a writing tool with a fine point—a sharpened pencil is good if it is not too soft and is *kept* sharp, and the ballpoint pen is ideal—if you are not inclined to change your mind.

Use a color different from any other markings on the proof—particularly the proofreader's. Initial each proof in the color used.

All marks must be at least partly, and preferably entirely, in the margins, as markings entirely within the text might be overlooked.

The location of a correction is indicated in the text usually with a *caret* [a small wedge ∧], a line, or a circle, but instructions are written in the margin *opposite the line affected.* The marks must therefore be quite small so as not to intrude on another line—which may also require a correction.

When 2 or more corrections are made on 1 line, they are written alongside each other and separated by a vertical or diagonal line (*slash*). In extreme cases, some corrections may be written in the left margin and some in the right. When doing this, be sure it is clear where each correction belongs. If you want someone to approve your correction, make a question mark after the slash. If the correction is approved, the question mark is crossed out. If not approved, the entire correction is crossed out.

Corrections that require setting more than about 1 line should be typed on a separate piece of paper and partly taped to the galley. Where the makeup is seriously disarranged, a new layout should be attached. In general, use all means to insure clarity.

The special markings developed for proofreaders should be *learned and used.* As are all such codes, this one is designed to achieve maximum accuracy and efficiency. It is almost universally understood and any departure from it entails the risk of confusion.

PROOFREADERS' MARKS

Marginal sign	*Mark in text*	*Meaning*	*Corrected text*
ℓ	Proofreadings	Delete, take out letter or word	Proofreading
(ℓ)	Legibil/ity is	Delete and close up	Legibility is
first	the‸requirement	Insert marginal addition	the first requirement
⁀‿	of a proof reader's marks.	Close up entirely	of a proofreader's marks.
‿	Symbols should be	Less space	Symbols should be
⊥	made neatly and	Push space down to avoid printing	made neatly and
#	in‸line with	Add space	in line with
eq.#	the text to which	Space evenly	the text to which
¶	they refer. Place	New paragraph	they refer.
	marks carefully.	No new paragraph	Place marks
no ¶	Paragraphs may be		carefully. Paragraphs may be
□	□ indented one em	Indent one em	indented one em
□□	□□ two ems or (rarely)	Indent two ems	two ems or (rarely)
□□□	□□□ three ems. Head-	Indent three ems	three ems.
[	[ings are flush left	Move to the left	Headings are flush left
]	or flush right]	Move to the right	or flush right
] [	] or centered [	Center	or centered
⊔	Marginal marks	Lower to proper position	Marginal marks
⊓	are separated	Raise to proper position	are separated

Marginal sign	Mark in text	Meaning	Corrected text
x	by vertical	Replace defective letter	by vertical
9	lines. The first correction	Invert this letter	lines. The first correction
w.f.	in a line of type	Wrong font; change to proper face	in a line of type
tr.	is beside noted the	Transpose	is noted beside the
?	nearest bend of the line.	Is this correct?	nearest end of the line
Sp.	and the 2nd, next.	Spell out	and the second, next.
	in this way both margins are used	Transfer to position shown by arrow.	both margins are used in this way
b.f.	English Finish	Change to boldface type	**English Finish**
b.f. ital	English Finish	Change to boldface italics	***English Finish***
rom.	*galley* proof	Set in roman type	galley proof
ital.	is laid paper	Set in italics	is *laid* paper
u.c.	Book of type	Set in upper case, or capital	Book of Type
Caps	Book Papers	Set in large capitals	BOOK PAPERS
s.c.	BOOK PAPERS	Change to small capitals	BOOK PAPERS
c.s.c.	Book Papers	Initial large capitals; other letters, small capitals	Book Papers
l.c.	the first Type	Change to lower case or small letter	the first type
x	baseball player	Broken type	baseball player
Stet	to ~~the~~ editors	Retain crossed out word	to the editors
2	Water, HO	Insert inferior figure	Water, H_2O
2	$X^2 \div Y^2 = Z$	Insert superior figure	$X^2 \div Y^2 = Z^2$
≡	printed	Straighten line	printed
‖	The paper The ink The type	Align type	The paper The ink The type
ld	prepare copy and submit it	Insert lead between lines	prepare copy and submit it
hr. #	P/A/P/E/R	Hair space between letters	P A P E R
⊙	to the printer	Insert period	to the printer.
^	the proof but	Insert comma	the proof, but
; or ;/	excellent it is	Insert semicolon	excellent; it is
: or ⊙	to the following	Insert colon	to the following:
'	authors notes	Insert apostrophe	author's notes
"/"	called caps	Insert quotation marks	called "caps"
-/or =	halftone	Insert hyphen	half-tone
1/em	Robert Henderson	Insert em dash	—Robert Henderson
1/en	1939 1940	Insert en dash	1939–1940
?	"Where," she asked.	Insert question mark	"Where?" she asked.
!	"Stop," he cried.	Insert exclamation mark	"Stop!" he cried.
(/)	author see page 2	Insert parentheses	author (see page 2)
[/]	To be continued	Insert brackets	[To be continued]

STYLE

As used here, *style* refers mainly to the optional points of grammatical usage. Normally, this is a concern of the editor, but there are circumstances in which the designer or production person becomes involved and he should be aware of the problems.

Until fairly recently, book printers had a large part of the burden of editorial as well as typographic labor. The printer had his own style, the publisher knew what it was and, if he approved of it, he left the matter in the printer's hands. Even today, many printers and compositors have issued booklets indicating the style they use in the absence of specific instructions. Most large publishers have their own house style and make this known to their printers. Where there is no definite set of rules, the publisher must either (a) give specific instructions with the composition order, (b) permit the compositor to follow a particular stylebook (the most commonly used are those of the University of Chicago and the New York *Times*) or, (c) as is often the case, give *some* specific orders and designate a stylebook to settle the remaining questions.

Obviously, the only reason that "style" exists as a problem is because there is substantial disagreement on certain points. To a large extent, the questions of style divide into two schools, generally designated "British (or English) style" and "American style". While the latter is generally accepted in the United States, many American experts are inclined toward some of the British procedures, which are usually more logical.

In other cases, style questions arise simply from lack of a universally accepted authority. There are several American dictionaries of considerable authority (Funk & Wagnalls' New College Standard, Random House College, New World Webster, etc.), but they are not in general agreement. Until 1962, when the third edition was published, the Merriam-Webster Unabridged dictionary came close to being universally accepted, but many American experts have rejected the new revision on the ground that it is no longer a dictionary so much as a compendium of usage. Its editors have chosen to list common errors and misconceptions as alternate definitions, thus blurring, rather than clarifying, the meanings of words. Many editors prefer to use the excellent second edition, but unfortunately it does not contain the new words and accepted changes in meanings that have come into the language recently. The publishers of *American Heritage* and *Horizon* have prepared a new dictionary which they hope will become the American authority so badly needed.

Following are some of the principal points of style on which a choice must be made. Where the alternative given is British style,

(B) follows. The American style is followed by (A). (A common problem in the U.S. and England is the styling of copy originally set and printed in the other country. If a change of style is required, the changes must usually be made in the copy, as compositors are reluctant to accept blanket instructions to "follow American [or British] style".) Omitted from the following list are questions ordinarily left to the designer, such as the choice between old style or lining figures.

- *Capitalization*—In chapter and subheadings shall all words be capitalized as in book titles, or only the first word and proper nouns? *
- *Division of words*—Shall words at the ends of lines be divided according to pronunciation (A) as in democ-racy, or according to etymological derivation (B) as in demo-cracy?
- *Compound words*—Which words should be hyphenated (as in "week-end") and which combined (as in "everything")?
- *Numbers*—Which should be spelled out and which set as figures?
- *Names*—Which names shall be italicized and which not? (The question arises usually in the case of minor publications, aircraft, television shows, etc.)
- *Punctuation*—When should italic punctuation be used? Shall dashes be 1 em (A) or 2 em (B)? Shall double quotes be used first and single be used for quotes within quoted matter (A) or vice versa (B)? Shall punctuation not belonging to quoted matter be placed inside the quotes (A) or outside (B)?
- *Reference marks*—Shall figures or symbols be used for reference?
- *Spelling*—Presuming that American spelling will be used rather than English ("-or" not "-our", "-er" not "-re", etc.), which dictionary shall be followed in doubtful cases?
- *Continued lines*—In an index and similar copy, when breaking an entry from one page to another, shall the heading be repeated at the top of the new page with the word "continued" after it?

There are many other minor questions involved, as well as variations of those listed above. It is a good idea to have and read one of the better stylebooks, but remember that they differ on many points. See "Read this first" on page vii for a discussion of the style used in this book.

* This question is discussed on page 273, but in any event *all copy* should be typed in lower case with caps only at the beginning of sentences or titles and on proper nouns. When setting type, if the specifications call for all words to be capitalized it is easy to *add* caps, but changing from caps to lower case involves editorial choices and the copy must go back to the editor for marking. Awkward delays can be avoided by proper typing of copy.

6 | Typography

Introduction

This chapter deals with typography in the sense that it is the art of arranging *printed* type. We say "printed" because typography refers also to the physical setting of the type itself (CH.5). Firms that set type are called typographers, as are the designers who arrange printed type.

The term "typography" is often used synonymously with book design, and book designers sometimes are called—and call themselves—typographers. This is a mistake, because typography is only one of several parts of book design, although the most important and obvious part.

TRADITION & CHANGE

The design and use of type is deeply involved with tradition. Some typographers feel that any departure from traditional forms in type design or arrangement is distracting and therefore inefficient. This contention would seem to be supported by the findings of psychologists, who invariably discover that people read most easily the type to which they are accustomed. It is debatable, however, that this truism is a strong enough basis for the retention of old forms.

Mankind is not a single, continuous entity with 1 permanent set of habits. A child born today is no more accustomed to the Roman type forms than was a child of the paleolithic era. A new form would not be strange to children growing up with it. For adults, a change would be a temporary inconvenience, the extent of which would depend on the nature of the change. The traditional view is that no inconvenience to the reader can be tolerated. Most changes in typography have been very gradual, but the pace of development in almost every aspect of life has accelerated far beyond anything considered possible a generation ago, and typography may have to change accordingly. Certainly, we must be receptive rather than resistant to change.

Tradition has enshrined the appearance of the Roman alphabet and the process of printing it, but it is dangerous in our dynamic era to remain committed to this tradition (except in a scholarly sense). Computerized photocomposition, lithographic and electrostatic printing (CH.7) are, in principle, entirely different from letterpress printing with hand-set metal type, so it can no longer be argued that our typographic forms must remain as they are because they relate to the technical process.

The new technology suggests certain changes. Easier character recognition features are needed for scanners; a simpler system of set widths would ease justification problems—abandonment of justification itself would be a boon; typefaces suited to both computer printout and photomechanical reproduction are desirable; and so on. High-speed, automated composition methods using oral as well as written copy would surely benefit from long overdue reform of the Roman alphabet. Today, at least 8 different sounds are given the letter "a" and it has two different printed forms—"a" and "ɑ". Worse yet, the use of the letter is only partly covered by rules. The story of the other vowels is about the same.

The significant point is that type is nothing more or less than a device for communicating thought, and the nub is the thought—not the forms or processes of transmittal. We must be ready to modify these when they no longer serve their purpose efficiently.

With this willingness to change must go a recognition of the possibilities for esthetic improvement. These possibilities become obvious when we look at the abstract design of some other alphabets, such as Arabic, Chinese, Sanskrit, or even Cuneiform. The Roman alphabet can have great beauty in the hands of a fine typographer, but these others seem to look well in any arrangement.

PRACTICAL & ESTHETIC LIMITS

In typography, as in other aspects of bookmaking, it is necessary to reconcile the esthetic and practical demands. Economic danger lies in the fact that it is physically *possible* for a compositor to accomplish almost anything a designer requests—even though the request may be extremely impractical. Many designers go on for years repeating expensive mistakes because compositors seldom (for a number of reasons) bring such matters to the customer's attention. It is most important for a designer to understand the practical limitations of typesetting (CH.5).

Esthetic limitations unfortunately do not exist, except in the form of conventional rules that stop far short of the creative needs of the designer. The only insurance against visual excesses is *taste*, which is basically innate, but which can be trained and sharpened. An effort to develop one's taste is indispensable to the study of typography. Typographical trouble can be avoided by following good models, but creation of excellent work depends on a highly developed perception.

Type classification

Systems of type classification are based generally on relatively insignificant variations of historical rather than visual interest. They classify type according to the time and place of design, even though these factors may have no particular effect on the appearance of the face. Because of the burgeoning of the printing arts during the first 300 years after their invention, much is made of minor changes during this time, and quite dissimilar groups of later faces are either lumped together in catchall classes or ignored entirely. In any case, from a graphic standpoint, the chronological or geographical origins of a typeface are less important than its visual character. In Germany and France there are type classification systems based on visual characteristics, but they are quite complex. True, the variations of type designs *are* very complicated, but it is necessary to make a simple division at first, and go into the complications later.

Ba

Ba

Ba

Ba

Visually, there are 4 broad classes of type (see CH.5 or Glossary-Index for type terminology):

- *Roman*—The classical letter with serifs and graduated thick and thin strokes based on writing with a square-edged tool.
- *Abstract*—Letters based on mechanical drawing, with more or less straight edges and lines of uniform thickness, having no serifs (*sans serif*) or square serifs of the same weight as the letter (*block serifs*).
- *Cursive*—Letters based on slanted writing with a more or less continuous line, including the italic forms of Roman.
- *Decorative*—All the faces that have exaggerated characteristics of the other 3 classes, or distinctive features that place them outside the other classes.

Ultimately, details of type design and subtleties of character are important if first-rate typography is to be produced, but *first* the major characteristics of the typeface must be considered. For broad design purposes, it hardly matters which typeface within each class is used. The graphics of design involve combining lines, forms, and spaces—and the details are less important than the general characteristics.

ROMAN

Variations of Roman type are largely in the shapes of serifs, and to some extent the relative weight of thick and thin strokes. Groups are named for their historical sequence or geographical origin, but it is their visual characteristics that count. The most significant subdivisions are:

▪ *Old Style*—Based on rather freely drawn manuscript writing, there tends to be a flowing passage from thicks to thins and strong brackets on slanted serifs. The types of Jenson, Garamond, and Caslon are typical. This is the style used for the first 3 centuries of printing. A separate category is usually reserved for "Venetian", but this hardly seems warranted. (Much is made of the minor fact that the Venetian lower case "e" has a slanted crossbar.)

Garamond
Caslon

▪ *Transitional*—The types of Baskerville and Bulmer were designed in the middle of the 18th century to be printed on smoother papers. The faces of this group are generally more angular, with sharper contrast between thick and thin strokes. The serifs are straighter, brackets less pronounced.

Baskerville
Bulmer

▪ *Modern*—These faces are a logical development of the Transitional, but are no more "modern" than they, having originated with Bodoni and Didot shortly afterward. They further accentuate the contrast between thick and thin and eliminate entirely the brackets on serifs. Serifs and the other square strokes are perfectly straight, as though mechanically drawn.

Bodoni

▪ *Egyptian*—A 19th century development, this group has particularly heavy serifs with brackets. There is little contrast between thicks and thins, the serifs are usually at least as heavy as the thins and squared off at the ends. Examples are Fortune, Clarendon, and Consort. This group borders on Abstract. The distinctions are discussed in connection with the related group, block-serifed.

Fortune
Consort

▪ *Miscellaneous*—In the ever-expanding catalogue of type faces, there are some that do not fall exactly into one of the above groups. Examples of these will be given in the discussions of both text and display types.

ABSTRACT

The main subdivisions of Abstract faces are (a) serifed and (b) nonserifed. The serifs in this class are simply short strokes of about the same thickness as the main parts of the face and have no brackets at all, or only a slight rounding at the junctures. If the bracket becomes pronounced, and a variation of thickness occurs within the curved lines, the face is better classed Roman (Egyptian) than Abstract.

▪ *Sans-serif*—These may have strokes of uniform or varying thickness. The strokes may have perfectly straight edges, as in Futura, or be slightly curved, usually with a slight swelling at the ends of straight strokes and the middle of curved ones. Examples of these are Lydian and Optima. Almost all of the sans-serif faces have various weights—some varying from a spidery fineness to a heavy black.

Futura Light
Futura Medium
Futura Bold
Futura Ex Bold

Lydian
Optima

▪ *Block-serifed*—The variations in this group are somewhat smaller than within the sans-serif. Typical are Beton, Karnak, Cairo, and Memphis. Each has numerous weights. This is the group that

Beton
Memphis
Karnak

borders on Egyptian, and is considered Egyptian (note the names) in most systems. However, there is an important distinction visually between the faces of almost purely mechanical design (Abstract) and those that are strongly modified in the direction of Roman. So, although there are borderline cases, the extremes are far enough apart to justify the distinction, as the examples show.

CURSIVE

Garamond Italic
Bulmer Italic
Bodoni Italic

Typo Script
Kaufmann Script
Brush Script

The primary graphic features of these faces are the slanted letter with a generally continuous feeling. They vary mostly in the character of their line, usually indicating the kind of tool used.

- *Italics*—A slanted form of Roman faces, based on the handwritten books of Italy at the beginning of printing. Early types designed by Aldus Manutius were italic and resembled a slanted writing done with a narrow, square-tipped pen. Almost all the italics are variations of this Aldine type.
- *Scripts*—These are faces drawn to look as though they were handwritten, and have no serifs or other resemblance to Roman type. They vary from very formal pointed-pen scripts based on 18th century models (Typo Script or Bank Script), through round-pointed pencil or pen scripts (Kaufman Script or Mistral), to the most informal brushwriting, such as Brush Script.

Some faces based on free lettering are vertical in feeling and cannot be classed as Cursive. These belong in the next group.

DECORATIVE

PROFIL
Ornata
RUSTIC
Old English

There is no way to subdivide these faces as they are usually exaggerated or embellished forms of the other classes. Some, such as Rustic or Astur, are so bizarre as to be unique, but even the others can be treated as individual graphic elements of a special character without reference to their antecedents. Examples are Ornata, Profil, Saphir, etc.

One Decorative group that deserves special mention is *Text, Black Letter*, or *"Old English"*. Now obsolete, this group of faces was the common form of writing in Northern Europe well past the Middle Ages, and persisted in German printing into the 20th century. Today, it is used only to imitate or suggest antiquity (or Germany), mainly on newspaper titles, churches, and schools.

Type characteristics

Text types are those used for the body of the book and are generally considered to be no larger than 18 pt. Display types are any size of any type that is designed for use in headings, titles, initials, etc. These may be made in sizes from 12 or 14 pt. up to 72 pt., 86 pt., or occasionally larger. In photocomposition, of course, the sizes may be modified.

Theoretically, the only difference between text types and display types of the same name is size. In practice, it is often true that the name is all they have in common. The two are usually made by different manufacturers, of different materials, by different processes, and created by different designers. It seems logical that they should be studied separately.

TEXT TYPE

Text types are still made by foundries, but the use of these in books is confined to relatively undeveloped areas of the world where type-casting machinery is not available, and an occasional private press book. In most cases, text type is produced by Linotype, Intertype, and Monotype machines in the composing room. For visual purposes, text type may be said to be produced by photocomposing machines also (CH.5).

The problems of *copyfitting* (CH.17) tend to divide text faces into groups according to width (characters per pica—see CH.5). Some are exceptionally thin for their height (Linotype Granjon, Electra, Times Roman, Bodoni Book; Intertype Garamond and Weiss), some are normal in width (Linotype Baskerville, Caledonia, Caslon, Janson), and some are particularly wide (Intertype Waverly, Linotype Primer). The difference in width of individual characters is minute, but multiplied by a half-million or so this difference will seriously affect the length of a book. For example, in a book of 500,000 characters, with an average page size, a shift from 11 pt. Caledonia to 11 pt. Granjon will save 24 pages. Remember, however, that the *appearance* of 2 faces of the same body size can differ greatly (CH.5).

Bookmaking
Bookmaking
Bookmaking

top to bottom, *14 pt. Granjon, Caledonia, Waverley*

Text types vary in general character just as much as display types, but the differences are not as noticeable, because of the smaller size. While the reader may not consciously perceive the distinctive nature of a text face, he is affected by it and the face must be chosen for its harmony with the text.

One of the most discernible differences in types is in their degree of masculinity or femininity. Some are definitely strong and rugged, some are definitely light and delicate, some are, of course, in between. Here, as in other areas of classification by character, there will be differences of opinion due to varying subjective reactions. It is reasonably safe to say that almost everyone would find Caledonia, Times Roman, and Monticello masculine; Granjon, Weiss, and Bodoni Book feminine; but even with these, and certainly with the borderline faces, a certain amount of the feeling conveyed depends on the way the type is used.

Times Roman
Weiss Roman

Type faces—like people's faces—have distinctive features indicating aspects of character. Some features are quite pronounced, some are very subtle and subject to individual interpretation. Here are some text faces with capsule character analyses.

Baskerville—Classical and elegant
Janson—Round and warm
Granjon—Round, warm, and graceful

Baskerville
Janson
Granjon

Caledonia
Times Roman
Electra
Fairfield
Bodoni
Waverley

Caledonia—Clean, firm, businesslike
Times Roman—Stiff, cold, formal
Electra—Light, cool, efficient
Fairfield—Fussy
Bodoni—Dramatic
Waverley—Round and cool

In choosing type it is better to consider these characteristics than to follow historical or conventional rules. After all, it is the type's character, not its history, that affects the reader.

No primarily cursive faces are in regular use for book texts. The British Monotype Company cut an italic face called Blado, which is rarely used except as the italic of a roman face called Poliphilus, and a face called Arrighi, which is used as the italic of Centaur.

There is a general reluctance to use italics for large amounts of text. It is said that they are harder to read than romans, but this is true (if at all) only in the sense that people are less accustomed to reading italic. As with most statements concerning readability of type, this will never be proved. The only valid study would be one that neutralizes the factor of experience, and this would require a controlled experiment with subjects who had *always* been exposed to italic and roman in reverse of the present proportion—a most unlikely occurrence.

Electra Italic
[Oblique]
Electra Cursive

An attempt to overcome the problem of reading italic was made by W. A. Dwiggins in 1935 when the Mergenthaler Linotype Company introduced Electra with an italic that is actually a slanted roman, lacking the cursive feeling of other italics. Probably because it makes too little contrast with the roman, Electra Italic (or "Oblique", as it is generally called) was not accepted as an italic, and Electra Cursive was issued later. However, "Oblique" is useful where large amounts of type must be set in a style distinct from, yet similar to, the main text.

Janson *Janson*
Baskerville *Baskerville*
Caslon *Caslon*
Granjon *Granjon*

Among the other text faces, the italics vary somewhat in their cursiveness and style, the most distinctive being Linotype Janson. Some italics, such as Linotype Baskerville, Caslon, and Granjon, contrast with the roman particularly well. This is a factor in choosing type for books in which italic is much used for emphasis.

Spartan
Metro
Erbar Light Condensed
Optima
News Gothic
Vogue
Gothic Condensed No. 2
GOTHIC NO. 31

Memphis
Cairo

There are about a dozen Abstract text types in general use. Among sans-serifs are Linotype Spartan, Metro, Erbar, Optima; Intertype News Gothic and Vogue. A number of the older text "gothics" are little used now because the mats fell into disrepair when these faces lost popularity in the '30s. However, fashions in type run in cycles and there is renewed interest in the old gothics. In block-serifed faces there are Linotype Memphis and Intertype Cairo.

Each of the Abstract faces has variations of weight in both roman and italic. The italics of these types are actually obliques, having no cursive feeling. They do not contrast well with the romans.

Spartan Heavy

Spartan Heavy Italic

The block-serifed faces are quite similar to each other, but the sans-serifs vary considerably. The contrast between Roman and Abstract type is so striking that people tend to ignore the differences among individual sans-serif faces (the way that people tend to think that those of another race "all look alike"). Yet, there is at least as much difference among sans-serif types as among Romans. In general, Spartan, Metro, and Vogue are more uniform of thickness and straight of line than the others. Optima in particular has characteristics that make it almost a serifless Roman rather than an Abstract.

DISPLAY TYPE

There is a much larger variety of *display types* than of text types, but relatively few are frequently used in books. Some of the others are used occasionally, and some hardly at all.

The rarely used faces tend to be in the Decorative class. Such faces are generally foundry type and are relatively expensive to use (CH.5) for letterpress printing. Also, most of the more decorative faces are produced for advertising typography and are slow in getting accepted for books. There is some justification for this disdain in that advertising display types are designed to attract attention, which is not the purpose of book typography (except on jackets). However, many of these faces are well designed and can be effectively utilized where they are suitable.

A skilled designer can use such types in a way that exploits their special qualities yet avoids a blaring effect. The general idea is to use them as an *accent* to the rest of the page rather than as the dominant element. Their impact can be diminished by reduction in size, by letterspacing, and by counterbalancing with contrasting blocks of space or type. Even where a decorative type is the only element on the page—on a part-title, for example—it can be restrained in its relationships to the space around it.

It is almost impossible to achieve a successful page using a poorly designed display face, even though the type is appropriate and is skillfully used. One poor element in a design tends to spoil the whole as the rotten apple spoils the whole barrel.

In the Roman display types, Monotype Janson, ATF Baskerville, and ATF Caslon 471 are fairly close in design to the Linotype faces of the same name—but Monotype Garamont, Bodoni 175, and Caslon 337 are quite different from their Linotype namesakes.

Not all of the text faces have display types of their name, but there are display faces of sympathetic character for any of them. For example:

Caledonia—Scotch, Bulmer
Electra—Corvinus, Bodoni Book
Fairfield—Garamond, Deepdene
Granjon—Garamond
Waverley—Scotch

Baskerville
(Monotype)

Baskerville
(ATF)

Garamont
(Monotype)

Garamond
(ATF)

Some confusion is caused by the practice of naming typefaces after the designers of earlier models. There may be several versions of 1 face produced by the same foundry, as the numerous Caslons offered by ATF, or the various Monotype Bodonis. In other cases, different companies have made their own cuttings of 1 early design, such as the quite dissimilar Baskervilles of ATF and Monotype, the Garamond of ATF and the Garamont of Monotype, and the many variations of Bodoni and Caslon by American, English, and European foundries. Thus, in using display faces named after early designers, consider each face on its own merits. For example, Caslon 540 (ATF) is one of the most beautiful of the Roman types, while New Caslon (ATF) is a crude affair. Bauer's Bodoni sings, Monotype's Bodoni 275 is a simple oaf.

There are a number of Roman display faces that have names unlike any of the composing-machine text types. Among these are:

- *Old Style*—Elizabeth, Orpheus, De Roos, Trajanus
- *Transitional*—Columbia, Horizon, Mademoiselle
- *Modern*—Corvinus, Normande, Modern 20, Torino
- *Egyptian*—Egizio, Consort, Fortune

Besides the italics of the Roman faces, the Cursive display types most used in books are those based on Spencerian script (Typo Script, Bank Script, Royal Script, Excelsior Script, etc.). In general, the other Cursive types are too informal for most books. However, not all books are serious works of classical stature, so even the least formal letter may find an appropriate use. Below is a selection of miscellaneous Cursive display types:

Stationers Semiscript
Slogan
Constanze
Commercial Script
Legend
Excelsior Script
Mistral

Maxime
Scritta a Lapis
Lydian
Charme
Bernhard Tango
Reiner Script
Murray Hill

Stradivarius
Salto
Virtuosa No 1. and 2
Ondine
Champion
Gavotte
Royal Script

Of Abstract display faces there are large numbers and a great variety. The variations of weight and style are about the same as for text types, *plus* open, shadowed, extended, and condensed forms.

Sans-serif faces range from the relatively hand-lettered feeling of Lydian or Post Title to the mechanically drawn regularity of the numerous Gothics—Franklin, Airport, News, Alternate, etc.—and the more recent Futura, Venus, Standard, and Microgramma series.

Some of the sans-serif faces have been copied by competing founders, so that 2 identical faces will have different names. Monotype's Twentieth Century and Baltimore's Airport Gothic are the same as ATF's Futura; Baltimore's Noontime is like ATF's Venus; etc. The cutting of the imitations is usually, though not always, somewhat inferior to the original.

The block-serifed faces are less numerous and range less widely in style, as they tend to run into the Egyptian group once they form brackets. Below are some examples:

OUTLINE

LINED

SHADOW

Extra Condensed

Extended

Memphis Medium

Stymie Medium Condensed

BETON OPEN

Tower

Girder

BOLDFACES

The desire for contrast in type color, to make distinctions in style, or to create graphic interest, has led to a demand for "boldfaces". With rare exceptions, bold forms of Roman faces are unsuccessful designs and are best avoided. The reason is that they are not new faces at all, but simply thickened versions of the regular face. The overall dimensions of the type are altered hardly at all, but the relationships of weight, form, and line—so carefully balanced in the original design—are distorted far from the ideal in order to achieve the desired "color". If no attempt were made to retain the appearance of the regular weight, it would be possible to produce a boldface of good design, but the need to combine the new proportions and the old characteristics dooms Roman boldfaces to ugliness.

Garamond

Garamond Bo

The Abstract faces seem to withstand fattening much better. Some of them range from wire thin to heavy black—with each weight as successful as any other. This is due in part to the absence of distinctive details, such as brackets, serifs, etc., to be retained as the weight of the face changes. Also, where the Roman faces have a special character related to their origin in writing, and cannot be

Venus Light Extende

Venus Medium Exter

Venus Bold Exten

Venus Extrabolc

Bodoni

Bodoni Bold

oni, Ultra

modified too far before they lose that character, the Abstract faces are original constructions that can be modified almost indefinitely with success—provided each variation is individually designed.

The modern "fat faces" (Ultra Bodoni, etc.) succeed because the original design is based on a sharp contrast in weight between thicks and thins, so the extreme contrast creates a different and interesting form while retaining the basic features of the regular design. On the other hand, Bodoni Bold simply disturbs the happy proportions of the regular face and fails to create a valid new design.

All of the faces named so far are metal types. In photocomposition there are a large number of faces with names and characteristics identical to the metal types and others very similar (see Part D "Typeface widths"). It is relatively easy to produce faces for photo machines and there will no doubt be many additions both familiar and completely new during the coming years. However, the foregoing discussion and classifications will still be valid because they are based on visual principles.

Typographic design

While it is true that the vast majority of readers are neither aware of nor informed about typefaces, it is wrong to assume that they will fail to respond to good typography—even in its more refined state. Their reactions are subconscious, but are no less definite for being so. Indeed, as Sir Cyril Burt shows in his *A Psychological Study of Typography,* the conscious choices of the layman frequently differ from his responses as revealed by psychological tests. This casts some doubt on the importance of habit in typography and suggests that the designer should strive for maximum excellence by visual standards and make the minimum compromise with "popular taste".

COMBINING TYPE

In combining type it is better to use very close *harmony* or definite *contrast* than to mix faces that are only slightly dissimilar. The near-miss relationship creates a sense of uneasiness, even among those who are not familiar with type. They sense a difference and get a feeling that something is wrong because they are not consciously aware of the difference. As an example, the use of a Roman Old Style face like Janson with a Transitional like Baskerville in text sizes would usually create this effect.

Baskerville
Janson

The use of an Abstract face with a Roman, or any other combination of types of different classifications, provides a contrast that has a settling effect because it leaves no doubt as to the designer's intentions.

Univers
Janson

The surest and safest procedure is to use the same face throughout, but it is possible to mix faces of the same category without disturbance if they are *close enough* in appearance (Granjon with Garamond, Bulmer with Baskerville, etc.).

Garamond
Granjon

Bulmer
Baskerville

A judicious use of both contrast and harmony is usually the best solution. The cardinal sin in design is to be equivocal and vague. Relationships may be subtle, but there must never be any doubt that the relationship was intended. Design *is* intention, the deliberate creation of order.

Variety is essential in design, but not necessarily in large amounts. As indicated above, an entire book can be printed in 1 typeface—or even 1 size of 1 face—with great success. On the other hand, it is possible to make a mess using many different faces, or using too many variations with few faces. There is no one "right" way to use variety. The degree of activity or restraint that is proper depends on 2 factors: the nature of the book's content (CH.15) and the visual requirements of the design. In both cases, the only guides are intelligence and intuition.

EMPHASIS

To establish a relative order of importance, or to lead attention to an element of copy, it is necessary to give type various degrees of emphasis. There are many ways to do it, because type has so many aspects. Emphasis can be achieved by the choice of:

- *Typeface*—A decorated or cursive face will take more attention than another, all other things being equal.
- *Type weight*—A boldface is more prominent than a lighter one. A strong face will dominate a thin, weak one.
- *Type size*—Large size is, of course, more important than small.
- *Italics*—In most cases, italics imply emphasis.
- *Capitals*—Size for size, capitals have more importance than lower case.
- *Position*—This is a difficult point about which to generalize, but there are a few broad principles. Emphasis may be achieved by isolating an element, placing it at the top of the page, placing it adjacent to the most important element or in any unique situation —at right angles to the rest of the type, on a slant, upside-down, etc.
- *Color*—The ability of certain colors to advance may be utilized (CH.15).
- *Spacing*—Letterspacing is used in Europe sometimes to emphasize proper names. A block of copy can be emphasized by increasing or decreasing leading.

The attention-getting power of *contrast* is a key factor in establishing emphasis. Any element will become conspicuous (and therefore emphasized) if it is unlike any other. A word in 8 pt. type can be made most important in a page of 30 pt. A line of lower case will stand out if every other line is in caps. Roman stands out among italics. Even a gray blue will outshine bright red if it is unique.

KINDS OF ARRANGEMENT

No general style of typographic layout is better than another. The only criterion is success, and it is just as possible to do a bad job with a centered arrangement as with an asymmetrical one.

However, symmetrical arrangements are relatively simple, and the centered style has the fewest problems. The moment that dependable central axis is left behind, the designer finds himslf in an unmarked expanse, without guidelines or conventions. It is the difference between traveling on roads and navigating the open sea.

Thomas Jefferson's
Farm Book
WITH COMMENTARY
AND RELEVANT EXTRACTS FROM
OTHER WRITINGS
EDITED BY EDWIN MORRIS BETTS
PUBLISHED FOR
THE AMERICAN PHILOSOPHICAL SOCIETY
BY PRINCETON UNIVERSITY PRESS
1953

symmetrical

The asymmetrical arrangement permits a far greater range of expression, but it also requires much more skill. The problem is not only to make a visually pleasing and effective arrangement of type and space, but to achieve a solid structure with unequal balance. With a central fulcrum you know that each side must have the same weight. When you move the fulcrum off center, you must be able to determine how much weight is needed on each end to prevent collapse. In graphics there is no way of computing this. Everything depends on the designer's sense of balance. The difficulty of creating such a structure with complex copy is not to be taken lightly.

While the centered arrangement is easier because a structural framework or skeleton is present, the use of this style by no means guarantees success. The *worst* disasters (common in asymmetrical layout) will be avoided, but the achievement of an excellent page still depends on a superior choice and disposition of the various elements of design.

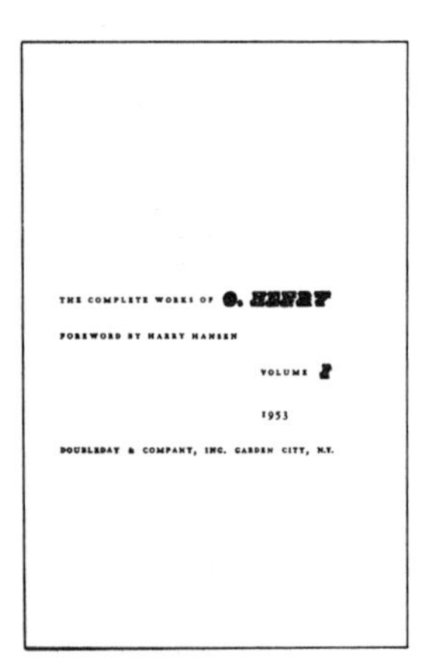

THE COMPLETE WORKS OF O. HENRY
FOREWORD BY HARRY HANSEN
VOLUME [illegible]
1953
DOUBLEDAY & COMPANY, INC. GARDEN CITY, N.Y.

asymmetrical

It is *possible* for a combination of symmetrical and asymmetrical elements to be used successfully in a book, but this requires such mastery of design that it is extremely improbable. Since there is rarely any need to have such a combination, there is really no reason to attempt it. This is not a "rule" (there is only 1 rule in design: *If it works, it's good*), it is a logical conclusion. As soon as an unsymmetrical element is introduced into a symmetrical arrangement, the design ceases to be symmetrical. A centered element in an asymmetrical layout does not of itself make the design symmetrical, but it does introduce an ambivalence that is just as unsettling and out of character. A single centered line in an asymmetrical layout is usually absorbed by the overall plan and doesn't seem to be centered at all. When there are 2 or more centered lines together, they create a sense of conflict that is death to design. This is true even if the centered lines appear on a separate page.

A formal arrangement may be centered, but it may also be aligned to one side or the other. "Formal" implies a certain *regularity* of arrangement, rather than any particular one.

An informal style results from the placement of elements according to caprice rather than a rigid structure, and from the use of elements that suggest a topical approach rather than an effort to court eternity. This includes typefaces and illustrations that have a light, fresh touch—even a bit of eccentricity—as opposed to classical forms.

formal

THE STONES OF
FLORENCE
BY MARY McCARTHY
PHOTOGRAPHS BY EVELYN HOFER AND OTHERS
NEW YORK ✤ HARCOURT, BRACE AND COMPANY

ITALIAN
FABLES

The Orion Press
New York

by ITALO CALVINO
translated from the Italian
by Louis Brigante
illustrated
by Michael Train

informal

There are many ways to convey dynamism in graphic design. Strong contrast is dynamic, and so is strong movement. Sharp curves are more dynamic than gradual ones, diagonals are generally more dynamic than horizontals, short lines more than long ones, and an informal arrangement is more dynamic than a formal one. The converse of these axioms are applicable to placidity. The choice of elements is not as significant in this respect as their interaction—the result of their combination and arrangement.

The masculine and feminine characteristics do not need to be described, but it is worth pointing out that any kind of design—symmetrical or asymmetrical, formal or informal, dynamic or placid, etc.—can be either masculine or feminine in feeling. Certainly, there are both men and women with any given combination of attributes who are, nevertheless, masculine or feminine respectively.

CHANGES

The elements of typographic design are numerous, and their interaction complex. No element can be introduced, deleted, or changed without affecting all the others. The successful design is a perfectly balanced construction of type—with its many variations of style, size, weight, and category—illustration (if any), and space. In some cases, a change can be countered with a corresponding modification in another part of the design, but in a simple and delicately balanced composition any change may require a new start. (One of the designer's worst frustrations is to have a sketch come back with the notation "O.K. as corrected", when a subtitle or an author's middle name has been added or deleted.)

THE SHAPES OF WORDS

One of the least understood principles of typography is that the visual form of the copy is a vital factor. For example, many designers, particularly beginners, are fond of making a vertical arrangement of the words in a title. This has been done with great success and will be again, but only when the words *in the particular title* lend themselves to such a scheme. The words must be of such length as to form an interesting pattern when disposed vertically—either aligned to one side or centered on each other. (They may sometimes be staggered with satisfactory results.) Also, if a large size of lower case display type is used, a great deal depends on what the words are, as the occurrence of ascenders or descenders in the wrong place can be ruinous.

Any combination of words and letters can be beautifully and effectively arranged, but they must be arranged to suit their own form—not squeezed into a designer's arbitrary scheme. The decision to use caps or upper and lower case, the choice of size, placement, or style of type must be based *first* on the nature of the copy,

HOLIDAYS
IN
THE
SUN

awkward

THE
OLD
LIDO
SUN

less awkward

IN
SUNNY
SOUTHERN
ITALY

pleasant

Thy
Only
Myth
of
Logic
Holy

awkward

Thy Only Myth of
Logic Holy

less awkward

THY
ONLY MYTH
OF LOGIC
HOLY

better

as this is an unchangeable element. It is not a bad idea to begin by simply sketching out the display words in *both* caps and ulc. Often, the words will take a shape that suggests the most natural arrangement.

USING SPACE

The design of any flat surface consists of 2 parts—the covered and the uncovered areas. In a sense, one is no more important than the other. When we print a word in black ink on a rectangle of white paper, we are creating a composition in black and white. While the type's primary value is in its symbolic and graphic (black) pattern, it is also delineating areas of space around and within itself. In a well-designed page, the white areas are effective elements interacting with the black—the page is alive. In poor typography, the type seems printed *on top of* a white background—the page is dead.

ITALIAN
MANUSCRIPTS
IN THE
PIERPONT MORGAN
LIBRARY

Descriptive Survey of the principal Illuminated Manuscripts of the Sixth to Sixteenth Centuries, with a selection of important Letters and Documents. Catalogue compiled by Meta Harrsen and George K. Boyce. With an Introduction by Bernard Berenson.

THE PIERPONT MORGAN LIBRARY
NEW YORK · 1953

live page

GUNS of ARIZONA

Originally published as
BREED OF THE CHAPARRAL

NELSON C. NYE

KLEY PUBLISHING CO
• New York

dead page

LETTERSPACING

Both capital and lower case letters in our alphabet vary so much in shape that a nasty visual problem can arise from an unlucky sequence. The occurrence of capital IN together creates an entirely different pattern of space than the combination LAT. Yet these combinations make one word—LATIN—which is by nature uneven in "color". It is impossible to reduce the space between LAT, but we can add space between I N to make an evenly spaced LAT I N. This word is an extreme example, but a problem arises to some degree in any line of caps (or small caps). If the amount of copy is small and the size of type large, spacing between letters can be adjusted as shown. Where optically adjusted letterspacing is impractical (for example, in Linotype cap or small cap subheads and running heads [CH. 18]), some uniform spacing should be added, and as much as possible. The addition of 10 pt. letterspace to L A T I N doesn't eliminate the irregularity of space, but the latter becomes proportionately less significant.

LATIN

LAT I N

The problem is even more acute in the lower case alphabet and grows with the size of type. The word "billowy" in 60 pt. is almost hopeless, but can be saved with considerable letterspacing.

billowy billowy

There is a prejudice in America against letterspacing lower case, although the stricture wouldn't be applied against selective spacing as shown above. It is really directed against the practice of using letterspacing as a means of filling out a line of text. This is a common procedure in newspapers, where the narrow column often creates awkward problems. If a line starts with 2 long words and the next one is an unbreakable word such as "through" that doesn't quite fit on the line, the alternatives are: (a) leave a giant space between the 2 words or (b) letterspace them. Of the 2, letterspacing is probably the less objectionable solution. The *best* procedure is to reset a few previous lines to get a better break. (In photocomposition it is possible to distort the type to make a line fit.) Repeated occurrence of lines with excessive word space results in unpleasantly loose composition and noticeable *rivers* [jagged vertical white lines caused by a series of wide spaces in about the same place on successive lines].

enlarged word spaces

seemed so irrelevant at the time, had been eliminated! Unquestionably, Germany would then have conquered all Europe, and would still have been ruling it today. From the

letterspaced

seemed so irrelevant at the time, had been eliminated Unquestionably, Germany would then have conquered all Europe, and would still have been ruling it today. From the

reset

seemed so irrelevant at the time, had been eliminated! Unquestionably, Germany would then have conquered all Europe, and would still have been ruling it today. From the Atlan-

ALLUSION

The relationship of typography to content in books is discussed in CH.15. In principle, it is best to avoid the kind of allusive typography that is nothing more than imitation of the style of another period or place. There is nothing wrong with *suggesting* another time or place, but imitation is neither honest (which should rule it out) nor effective. Typographic imitation becomes more unsettling the better it is done. One begins to wonder whether it is an imitation or the real thing. The best practice is to express the *spirit* of the period or subject, rather than to make an imitation of its typography.

Readability

Readability and legibility are sometimes considered synonyms; actually, they are not. There is a tendency (hastened by a recently published "dictionary") for the distinctions among words of similar meaning to blur and disappear, but in an increasingly technological society we need all the precision of language possible. The terms readability and legibility are needed to describe 2 quite distinct qualities.

Legibility is the quality of type (or writing) that makes it *possible* to read. Readability is the characteristic of a body of type that makes it *comfortable* to read. Both are relative terms. For example, 4 pt. type used for a credit line under an illustration may be legible because it *can* be read at the normal reading distance for a book. For reading on a billboard atop a building, the smallest legible size of letter may be 6″ high. Similarly, 8 pt. type with no leading may be readable for an encyclopedia in which the text for each item is only a paragraph or two, but it would not be readable for a 320-page novel, although it would be legible in both cases.

Both readability and legibility are so fundamental to the design of books that there is no more need to praise them here than to praise structural strength in discussing architecture. The desire for these qualities may be taken for granted. Our concern with them is not *should* they, but *how* are they to be achieved. In this, we may assume that legibility has been achieved when readability has been.

There has been a considerable amount of research in readability, but the problem has too many subtleties to ever yield to rational study alone. Nevertheless, where many tests are in agreement with each other *and* with the observations of experienced designers, it is fair to assume that some truth has been found. Thus, the opinions expressed in this section, while those of the author, relate to the scientific data available.

The readability of a page is affected by no less than 9 factors:
(a) typeface,
(b) size of type,
(c) length of line,
(d) leading,
(e) page pattern (which includes "margins"),
(f) contrast of type and paper (which includes color),
(g) texture of paper,
(h) typographic relationships (heads, folios, etc.), and
(i) suitability to content.

Some factors are more significant than others, but it is their combined effect that gives the page its character, and it is only when all are in perfect balance that a truly readable page results.

Paper is covered in CH.8, typographic relationships are discussed elsewhere in this chapter and in CH.18. Suitability to content is referred to in CH.15 and elsewhere throughout the book. The following discussion deals with the remaining factors of readability.

TYPEFACE

We have seen that typefaces—even text types—have individual characteristics that can be matched with corresponding characteristics of the text. The choice of typeface should be made initially on this basis. If it becomes apparent that the face chosen cannot produce the required number of characters per page (CH.17), a compromise may be necessary. As always, begin with that which seems best and give up only what you must.

SIZE OF TYPE

It is the apparent, or visual, size of type with which we are concerned first. The actual type size will affect the book's length, but it is the appearance of the face that affects readability (CH.5).

Readability is relative to the reading ability of the book's user. Within the limits of normal book use—that is, with a general audience of adult readers—minor differences in type size are not significant. When the potential readers are either very old or very young, type size becomes an important factor.

It is generally recognized that larger sizes are desirable for children who are learning to read, but most children's book editors in America favor extremely large type in comparison to the sizes ordinarily used in England and other countries. In the lowest age group—say 5 to 7—the 18 pt. faces in use are probably not excessive, as the children are still having some difficulty recognizing letters. From 7 or 8 up to about 10 there is probably no need for anything larger than an average 12 pt. face, although 14 pt. is often used. Between 10 and 12, a good reader needs no more than a large 11 pt. and over 12 years old an average child does not have any difficulty reading the 11 pt. faces commonly used for adult books, as long as the other elements of the text page are selected for particularly good readability. Some editors and teachers feel, however, that larger sizes are necessary to make reading seem easier.

The use of large type for children is based more on psychological than optical reasons, and these are somewhat debatable. With elderly readers, larger sizes may be needed because failing sight requires them. Yet, little attention is given to this consideration. (It is true that proper eyeglasses would eliminate the problem, but the book designer's function is to accomodate the reader [and the author and publisher], not to drive him to the oculist or optometrist.)

In books intended primarily for people over 60, the text type should not be smaller than a large 11 pt. Where space permits, 12 pt. is preferable. The other elements of the page should be chosen, as they are for small children, for maximum readability.

For adults whose sight can be presumed to be normal, the larger 10 pt. faces are adequate, if the other elements of readability are favorable. Most hardcover books are set in 11 pt., although paperbacks have enjoyed a tremendous public with 10 and 9 pt. text types.

Readability is relative also to the *kind* of reading. Normal sizes of type are needed for sustained texts such as novels, etc., while brief texts, as in encyclopedias, can be set smaller without impairing readability.

LENGTH OF LINE

There are few aspects of readability that are truly measurable, but length of line is one. In view of this, it is insupportable that the most frequent destroyer of readability is excessive length of line. The reason is quite obvious. Long lines of type, especially when well leaded, look graceful—just as tall, slender models do. But the models are too skinny for anything but modeling, and long lines of type are not efficient for reading.

rooms (when the normal day ending at 10 p.m. would be much prolonged) girls have asserted . . . that they enjoy the excitement of such nights, unless too often repeated; the furious haste with which the work is pushed on, the speculation as to whether it will be finished in time, and the additional refreshments provided on such occasions,

Tests have shown many disadvantages in long lines: (a) the eye must blink at intervals during reading. After each blink, an optical adjustment and refocus of vision takes place. The longer the line, the more frequently blinks occur within, rather than at the end of lines. (b) There is the time and visual effort lost in traveling back to the beginning of the next line. (c) When the measure is too wide, there is momentary difficulty in determining which *is* the next line (sometimes the wrong one is selected). Each interruption —the blink, the trip back, and the search for the right line—causes loss of reading efficiency, or poor readability.

Another optical factor that affects reading comfort is the span of vision. Without moving your eyes or head you can see clearly straight ahead and about 2° to each side. Naturally, the less movement necessary, the less fatigue. (A very small amount of movement is desirable, but more becomes tiring.) Consequently, there is a maximum comfortable measure for each distance from eye to object, the ideal width becoming greater as the distance increases. At normal book-reading distance (about 16″) the maximum comfortable measure is about 5″. At billboard-reading distance, a line of 20 feet in length can be read with no more muscular effort than required by a 5″ line in a book.

All the factors of visual comfort tend to suggest a *maximum* of about 70 characters per line in a page of average size. Fewer characters is better—down to about 50, where it becomes difficult to set justified lines without excessive hyphenation of words and irregular word-spacing, both of which reduce readability. The ideal is probably between 55 and 60 characters per line, at a length of about 4″ (24 picas) for justified text. For unjustified lines, 45 characters is about optimum. It may be necessary to vary from the ideal for economic reasons, but then it is better to make a radical change in the basic decisions than to exceed by very much the maximum and minimum limits. However, the limits depend on the reading capabilities of each audience. For children, the elderly, and the visually or mentally handicapped, the lower limits are applicable. For the experienced reader and the mentally gifted, the upper limits may be used.

LEADING

Neither size of type nor length of line can be selected independently of leading. The larger the type the more leading is needed to avoid confusion. If the space between lines is not sufficient in relation to the space between words, the horizontal movement of the eye is disturbed. The longer the line, the more leading is needed to distinguish the lines and facilitate finding the beginning of the next one.

every page at full width

Up to a point, the more leading the better. Beyond this point, additional leading may detract from readability. The optimum amount depends on the typeface, its size, and the measure. Where word spacing is unusually large, as in books for young children, the amount of leading should be in proportion. With so many variables involved, the choice of leading is more a matter of visual judgment than mathematics.

In general, average 10 pt. and 11 pt. faces on measures up to 22 picas can do with 1 pt. of leading; from 22 to 25 picas with 2 pts.; over 25 with 3. Types of 12 and 14 pt. generally need a minimum of 2 pts., require 3 when set wider than 25 picas, and read better with 4 pts. on 28 picas or over. Small sizes, such as 8 and 9 pt., need proportionately more leading than the larger sizes, to compensate for their lower readability. When set in narrow measures, this need diminishes. For example, 8 pt. set 12 picas wide can be read quite comfortably with 1 pt. (or no) leading. On a 20-pica measure it might need 2 pts., on 23 picas, 3 pts. Remember, however, that the x height of each face greatly affects the leading desirable. For this reason, a table indicating the proper leading for each size and measure would not be practical.

When I wrote the following pages, or rather the bulk of them, I lived alone, in the woods, a mile from any neighbor, in a house which I had built myself, on

8/9 x 12

When I wrote the following pages, or rather the bulk of them, I lived alone, in the woods, a mile from any neighbor, in a house which I had built myself, on the shore of Walden Pond, in Concord, Massachusetts, and earned my living by the labor of my

8/10 x 20

When I wrote the following pages, or rather the bulk of them, I lived alone, in the woods, a mile from any neighbor, in a house which I had built myself, on the shore of Walden Pond, in Concord, Massachusetts, and earned my living by the labor of my hands only. I lived there two

8/11 x 23

When there is too much space between lines, there is a loss of efficiency (readability) because the reader expects to find the next line at the customary distance. His eye goes first to this point and then makes an adjustment. When the adjustment is small, the loss of efficiency is probably not significant. Where the leading is very large—say, 8 pts.—the disturbance is probably considerable and may persist throughout the reading of the book.

In this matter, as in other aspects of readability, habit and experience are larger factors than is generally conceded. Most psychological testers of reading acknowledge these elements to some degree but, in the end, they usually draw conclusions from the performance of their subjects without giving much weight to the influence of training. Since peoples of other cultures learn to read easily in alphabets very different from our own, it is reasonable to assume that we would respond very differently to reading tests if we had been otherwise trained. Thus, the testers' conclusions are not empirical facts so much as observations of conditioned behavior. For example, if it is a fact that more than 3 or 4 pts. of leading hampers reading—as many psychologists claim—why do typesetters prefer double-spaced typescript having about 12 pts. of leading? Even allowing for the large size of typewriter type and the usually wide measure of typescript, double spacing is proportionately the equivalent of about 9 pts. of leading in a page of 11 pt. type set 24 picas wide.

PAGE PATTERN

The term "*page pattern*" may seem unfamiliar in this context, but it is used deliberately to avoid the word "*margins*". The concept of a page as a block of type surrounded by a frame of "margins" is a vestige of hand-press days. Then the page was indeed a rectangular block of metal arranged on the page so as to leave enough paper on each side to meet the printing and binding requirements of the time. The proportions of these margins were determined largely by the need to minimize the size of the 4-page forms generally used in the early days of printing. This meant reducing the head and inside margins to get the pages as close together as possible, so that a good impression could be obtained with a minimum of effort. This left plenty of paper on the outside and bottom edges of the printed page. The practical necessity soon became an esthetic dogma and the conventional margin proportions have been taught to apprentice printers ever since.

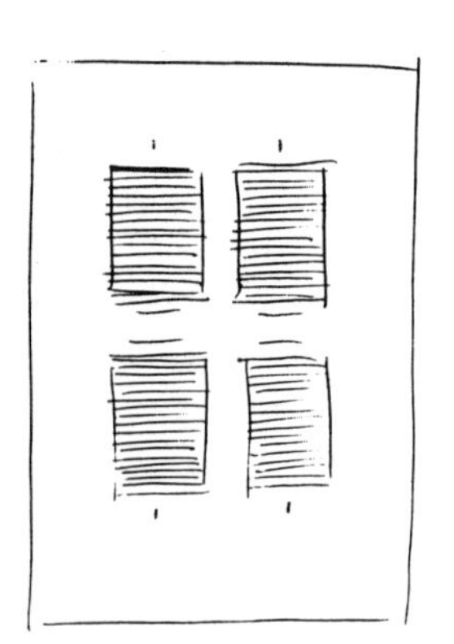

To see what bookmakers would do without the mechanical restraints of printing, look at the early manuscripts. In these, the pages were regarded as areas to be filled in the most beautiful and effective way with words, pictures, and space arranged over the entire *spread*, rather than the individual page. The manuscript

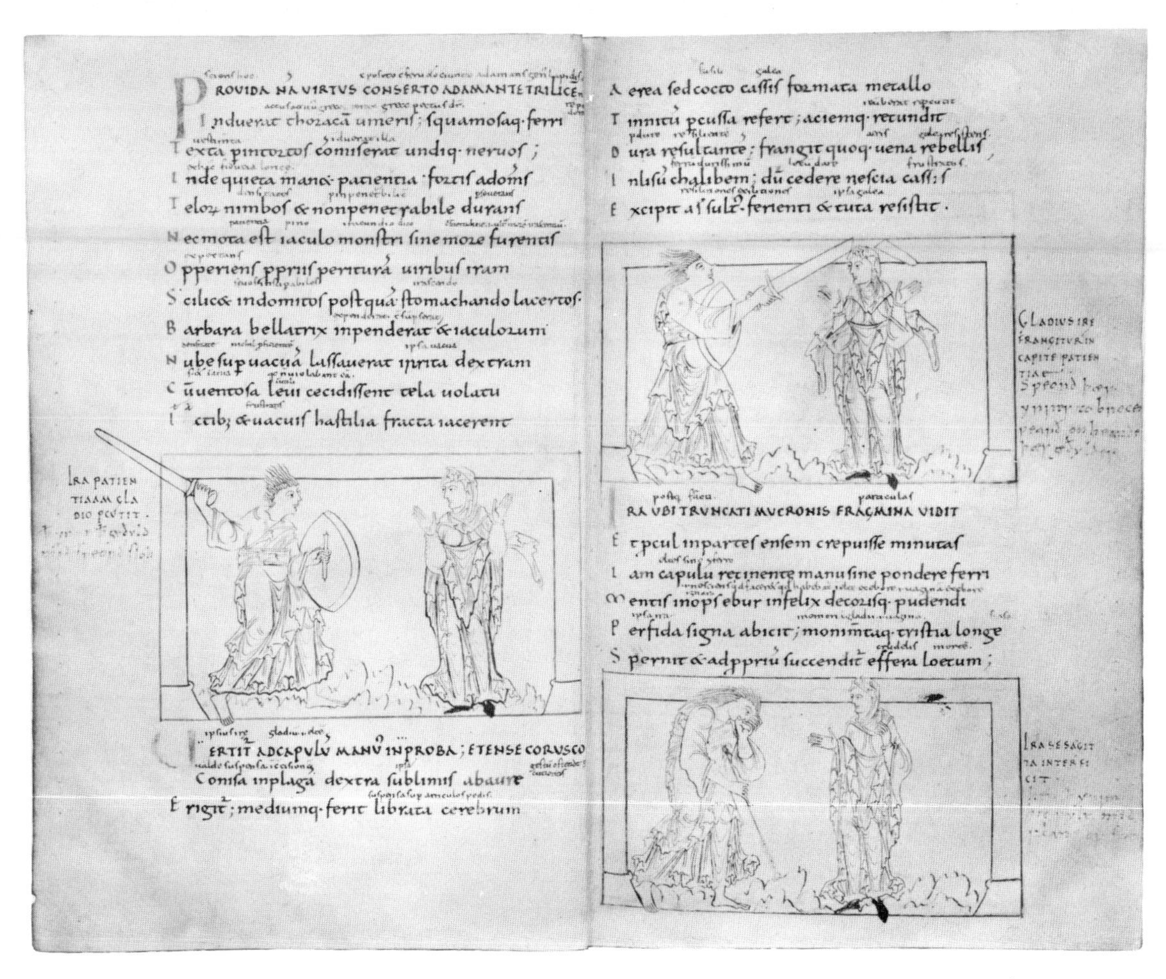

8th century manuscript.

maker's criteria were visual and functional, not conventional and mechanical—at least in the beginning.

The graphic freedom of the manuscript books is available again. In any method of printing in which photomechanical plates are used—and they are used in all—the mechanical limitations of the hand-press no longer apply. There *are*, sometimes, extra costs involved in nonconventional page layouts, but there is no significant reason—esthetic, practical, or economic—to remain bound by the obsolete conventions of "margins".

It has been suggested that the type page should not come too close to the outside edge in children's books because young readers have a tendency to swing off the page at the end of a line. Whatever the merits of that claim, there is certainly no such consideration in adult books. Millions of paperbacks are sold and read with outside margins of minimal size. In defense of the conventional arrangement it has even been claimed that a large foot margin is necessary to provide room for the reader's thumb! Aside from the obvious fact that anyone able to read would have sense enough to move his thumb if it happened to cover the next word, no one is likely to hold a book at the bottom unless he is reading while walking—an uncommon and risky practice.

This is not to say that a conventional page pattern is bad. It may very well be the best. The point is that the size, shape, and position of the type areas and other elements on the page should be determined by the visual, practical, and economic requirements of the individual problem, not by the application of a rigid formula. If the problem is well analyzed and solved, any arrangement is fully justified.

Conclusion

A truly personal style in typography takes many years—decades—to develop. There are some who feel that in book typography the designer's personality should be completely submerged. It is doubtful, however, that the personality of a designer, as it is revealed in a well-done book, is any more detrimental to the content than the personality of an actor is to a play or that of a conductor to a symphony. As long as the interpreter's personality does not *dominate* or *alter* the work, it can enliven and enrich it.

The heights attainable in typography are limited by talent and experience. In the beginning, simplicity is best because it is necessary for success. Later, it becomes an essential part of the designer's outlook. In between, experiment has its place.

This chapter has dealt with typography in general—later chapters discuss typography in relation to particular phases of bookmaking.

7 | Plates & printing

General

Successful bookmaking requires a knowledge of both the principles of printing and the equipment. A design must be matched to the press available or a press must be found that is suited to the design. An eighth of an inch more in a book's page size could add much more to the cost of printing—planning a book for rotary instead of cylinder presses might mean a saving of 20% in printing, paper, and binding cost. A printer is not likely to let you put a job on an unsuitable press, but it is best to know enough about printing yourself to insure against a costly mistake.

Unless printing is done directly from metal type or slugs, it involves plates of some kind. The plates being merely an adjunct of the presses, albeit the most important one, each kind will be discussed within the section devoted to the printing process in which it is used. The basic processes of printing and platemaking are explained below.

PLATEMAKING PROCESSES

There are many kinds of plates, but they divide into 2 basic categories: (a) duplicate plates molded from type and (b) photomechanical plates.

- *Molded plates*—The page of metal type is covered with a substance which forms itself into a negative (female) *mold*. The mold is then filled with the plate material. When this material hardens, the mold is stripped away, leaving a positive (male) duplicate of the printing surface.
- *Photomechanical plates*—A film negative or positive is made by some means: (a) by a photocomposition machine, (b) by photographing black and white copy (repros, photoprints, artwork, etc.), (c) by photographing the surface of metal type after blackening the nonprinting areas and then burnishing the face (the *Brightype* process), (d) by making a *Scotchprint* [a proof made on

translucent plastic, which may be used as a film positive], (e) by taking an impression of type on a special film which is then treated to opaque the non-image areas (the *Cronapress* process), or (f) by printing (or drawing) an opaque image on any transparent or translucent sheet. The film is placed against a photosensitized plate and exposed to light. The plate is then treated with chemicals that affect the exposed parts differently from the rest. This results in a distinction between the printing and nonprinting parts that makes printing possible.

There is another method of making a plate, by *xerography*, but this is more a method of printing than platemaking so it is explained under printing processes. The use of xerography in platemaking is merely a substitute for a *part* of the photomechanical process, whereby the copy image is transferred to the plate by static electricity rather than through the use of a photosensitive coating.

PRINTING PROCESSES

There are numerous variations of the basic printing techniques, and more are announced almost daily. The fundamental principles of the 3 dominant methods are:

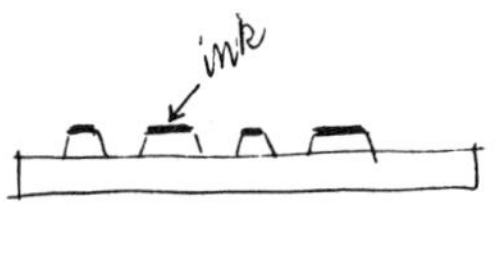

- *Relief printing* (*Letterpress*)—The printing parts are raised on the plate and are inked. The ink is transferred to the paper by pressure.

- *Planographic printing* (*Lithography*)—The printing parts are virtually level with the rest of the plate, but they are treated to accept a greasy ink, which the nonprinting parts repel. The process is based on the antipathy of grease and water. The ink is transferred by contact.

- *Intaglio printing* (*Gravure*)—The printing parts are etched into the plate and are lower than the rest. They are filled with ink, which is transferred to paper by pressure and suction.

Two other principles are of interest. Although they are not (at present) used in printing the text of books, they are used in some bookmaking operations:

- *Screen printing* (*Silk screen*)—A fine mesh screen is stretched taut and the nonprinting areas are blocked out. The screen is placed over the paper and ink is squeezed through the open parts.
- *Electrostatic printing* (*Xerography*)—The printing image is photo-projected onto the paper where it is electrostatically charged. The ink is oppositely charged and is thus attracted to the image.

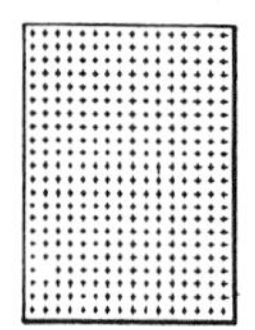
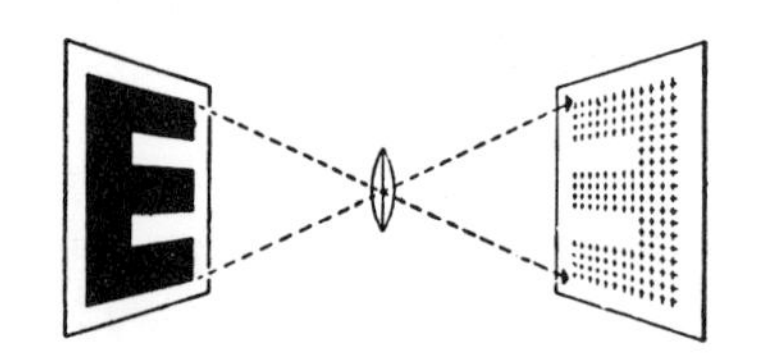
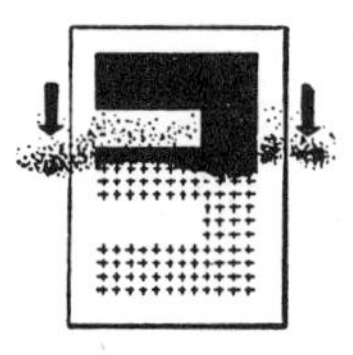

1. The paper is given a positive charge. 2. The image is projected onto the paper. Where there is no image, light strikes the paper and removes positive charge. 3. Negatively charged powdered ink is applied to paper, sticks only where there is positive charge.

One variation of the basic printing methods is very significant—*offset*. Generally associated only with lithography (offset lithography is often referred to as "offset"), the offset method can be applied to any printing process and is now used widely with letterpress (*letterset* or *dry offset*) and gravure. In this method, the plate transfers its ink not to the paper but to a rubber-covered cylinder which in turn "offsets" the ink to the paper.

IMPOSITION

Regardless of the method of composition, platemaking, or printing used, a certain number of pages will be printed at one time. This number is determined partly by press size and binding requirements (CH.10). A large page—say 8½ x 11″—may be printed with only 8 pages on each side of the sheet; with an average page—say 5½ x 8¼″—there may be 64 on each side. (One factor is printing quality, which is easier to control on a small sheet.) While any number of pages can be printed in 1 form, binding requires a multiple of 4—and preferably 8. Most books are printed in forms of 16, 32, or 64 pages.

Imposition is the arrangement of the pages in a form so that they will be in correct order when folded. The plan is determined by the binder according to the folding equipment to be used. The imposition also involves placing the pages so that the margins will be correct.

The designer should have an imposition diagram (CH.10) in hand while making illustration page layouts (CH.21). In cylinder press printing, one edge of the sheet is held to the cylinder by *grippers* requiring about ½″ space, so there can be no *bleeds* [illustrations running off the edge of the page] on the gripper edge. If bleeds are essential there, a larger sheet must be provided.

work-and-turn

sheetwise

Sometimes, 2 small forms are printed together on one side of a sheet and kept on the press while the pile of sheets is turned over lengthwise and the other side is printed. Thus, form 1 backs up 2 on one end of the sheet, and 2 backs 1 on the other, so that 2 complete units are printed with the number of impressions required for 1, with only 1 form to make ready instead of 2. This is called a *work and turn* imposition. A normal imposition, in which a single form is backed by another is called *sheetwise*.

When small units, such as endpapers, are printed in large quantities, they may be imposed with 4, 8, 12, or more units in 1 form (*4 up*, *8 up*, *12 up*, etc.), provided the reduced number of impressions required justifies the increased plate cost and the larger press.

Making photomechanical plates with multiple-unit impositions means making as many negatives as there are copies wanted, combining them in position, and then exposing them as in making a single plate. Even where only 1 color is involved, the several negatives (and there may be 20 or more) must be accurately positioned so that when the printed sheet is cut apart, all copies will be square and have correct margins. When the copy has several colors, the problem of positioning becomes formidable because of the importance of *registering* each color (see "Color printing"). Most printers and engravers now use high-precision *step-and-repeat* machines to achieve the positioning required, at much greater speed and with more accuracy than by hand.

Sometimes, books are imposed for printing 2 up in order to facilitate 2 up binding. This is a very economical practice, provided that large quantities are involved.

Letterpress

This is the oldest method of printing and it remained remarkably unchanged for hundreds of years before the advent of power presses. Until a generation ago, it was unchallenged as the leading method of printing books. Today it shares the spotlight with offset lithography although, with recent developments in photomechanical platemaking, letterpress printing is no longer dependent on metal-type composition and some of the former distinctions between it and offset lithography are disappearing.

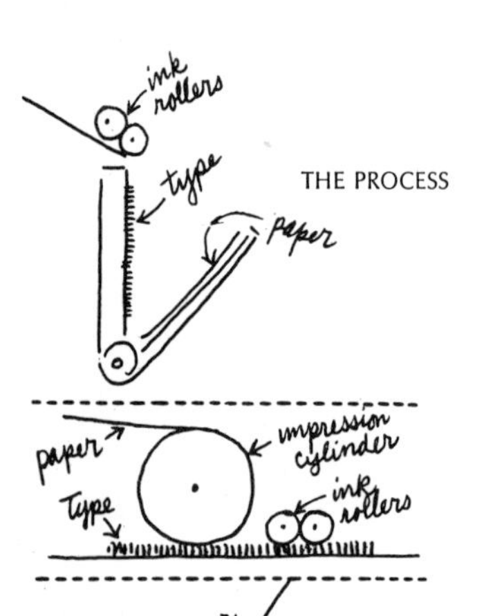

THE PROCESS

There are 3 different techniques of letterpress printing.

- *Platen*—the type form is held vertically and the paper is fed onto a metal plate that is hinged below the form and swings against it, much as a clam shell would close. Ink is applied to the form by rollers which pass alternately over it and a flat ink plate above it.
- *Cylinder*—the type or plates are held on a horizontal or vertical plane (*bed*), while ink rollers and sheets of paper (carried by a cylinder) alternately pass over it.
- *Rotary*—curved plates are clamped to a cylinder which revolves against a revolving cylinder on which the paper is carried. Ink rollers revolve against the plate cylinder on another side. The paper may be fed in sheets or from a roll. When a roll (*web*) of paper is used the process is called *web-fed rotary*.

In general, rotary is faster than cylinder, which is faster than platen. Web-fed rotary produces more impressions per hour than any other process.

By adding cylinders, rotary and cylinder presses can print 2 or more colors with 1 run through the press, or may print both sides of the paper in 1 run. Presses equipped for the latter are called *perfectors*, and are actually 2 presses in 1.

Makeready is the preliminary process of adjustment to compensate for irregularities of the press and the type or plates. This involves placing sheets and pieces of paper on the bed and/or cylinders of the press at the low points, to make the impression equal all over. The quality of letterpress printing depends more on makeready than any other single factor.

Makeready is also a very expensive part of letterpress printing (nothing is being produced during this time) and much effort has been spent on finding ways to reduce it. The most successful product is the 3M Makeready Sheet. This is placed on the impression cylinder to receive an impression of the form. After a heat processing, the sheet is put back on the cylinder to compensate for the irregularities. The process is economical only when *halftones* are involved (see "Photoengraving").

PLATES

Linotype slug metal is hard enough to print the number of copies in the first printing of an average book, but then begins to show signs of wear, depending on paper used, the typeface, and the presswork. A publisher who believes that a book will have more than 1 printing usually orders a set of plates—particularly if later printings are likely to have corrections, as the newly set lines will look distinctly sharper than the original type. This is true also of Monotype to a lesser extent.

Plates provide security against loss or delay if the type is damaged during printing or shipment. With a mold or negative available, a plate can be produced in a matter of hours or minutes. The alternative—resetting type, reading proofs, makeup, etc.,—is a far more costly and time-consuming operation.

The cost of making plates is partly balanced by the fact that it costs less to print from plates than from type. This is due to the relative ease of handling plates in the pressroom and shipment. Storage is also less expensive, as plates take much less space than type. It is possible to obtain some of the benefits of plates, without all the cost, by making only molds and holding them against the possibility of needing plates later. The kind of plates available are described below.

▪ *Molded plates*—The most expensive of the molded plates is the *electrotype* (or *electro*). A mold is made of one of 4 or 5 materials, depending on the quality required. The cheapest is wax, the best is lead, in between are various plastics. A thin layer of copper is deposited on the inside of the mold by electrolysis. Lead is poured into this shell until the proper thickness is attained. The back of the plate is shaved to make it level, and the face may be coated electrolytically with nickel or chromium to give it more resistance to wear. (A nickel- or chrome-plated electro is called *steel-faced.*) The edges are beveled to facilitate the use of catches to hold them on press. Electros are superior in their ability to hold fine lines or dots and they are easier to correct than other duplicate plates. Curved electros can be made for use on rotary presses.

Plastic plates are made by pouring a *thermosetting* plastic powder [it softens when heated, but once cold will not soften again] into a plastic mold. These plates are quite satisfactory for type and fairly simple line illustrations and have almost entirely replaced the much more expensive (about 100% more) electro for ordinary book printing. Plastic plates *can* be used for fine-line engravings and halftones, but they are not always satisfactory. Another drawback is the difficulty of correcting them. On the plus side is their light weight—a factor in shipping. The better kind will last almost as long as electros.

Rubber plates are made in the same way as plastics and provide even less quality of reproduction. In durability they are much superior to electros, however, and they require less care in printing than any other kind of plate. Rubber plates are ideal for printing large runs in which quality is not expected. For that kind of work they are often made curved to run on rotary presses. These hard rubber plates used for book printing should not be confused with the soft, hand-cut, "rubber stamp" kind used for printing cartons and rough-surfaced materials.

A newer plate, the *Chemotype*, combines the surface hardness of plastic and the resiliency of rubber. It can hold fine lines and yet will accommodate itself to the unevenness of paper and type, so considerable makeready time is saved. Chemotype plates wear much longer than plastics. The unique properties of this plate are the result of a 3-layer construction. Into a plastic mold is sprayed a compound that forms the hard outer surface. The second layer is the resilient core material and the third is a hard plastic backing.

The cost of Chemotype plates compares favorably with plastics under certain conditions, although it is initially somewhat higher. A reduction of time on press results from adhering the plates for an entire form in position on a sheet of tough plastic in advance, and then mounting the whole unit on the press. Other plates are usually attached individually to the press by catches. When reruns are made, the saving in press time plus the shorter makeready becomes significant.

Lightness and flexibility are important qualities in plates if they are to be used for rotary printing. By mounting the plates for a form on a single carrier and using them on a web-fed rotary press, letterpress can compete with offset lithography in high-speed, long-run work. There is a great deal of experimentation to develop the ideal "*wraparound*" plate for this purpose. Among the molded plates competing are the "*College electro*", the *Daxene,* the *FLXO Type,* and the "*Thomas*" *plate.* Most are multilayer plates, and vary mainly in the filler material.

▪ *Photomechanical plates*—Much hope has been invested in *magnesium* as a plate material because of its special properties and relatively low cost (it is made from sea water). Magnesium is lighter than aluminum, is easily etched by an automatic process, and is not only long-wearing but is said to *harden* with repeated pounding. Letterpress printing can compete with offset lithography by making magnesium plates from photocomposition products. The procedure is about the same as for making lithographic plates, except that exposure of the sensitized coating makes the printing areas resistant to an acid which eats away the nonprinting areas to a depth necessary for relief printing. The main drawback is magnesium's tendency toward pitting in storage. Also, the material is so fine-grained that the edges are sharp and tend to cut the paper. The cost of these plates is almost 3 times that of molded plastics.

Even more promising than magnesium plates are those made of photosensitive plastic (*photopolymer*). Here, the entire thickness of the material is affected by exposure to light, not merely a coating. This enables the etching to go down as deeply as desired and almost at right angles to the surface. In other etching processes there is a tendency for the acid to etch sideways as well as down, which results in either undercutting the printing area or *stepping* [terracing] on its sides. In photopolymer plates the developing process does the etching, so a major step is eliminated. These plates are made in about 20 minutes in contrast to the 1½ hours required for making an etched metal plate. The photopolymer process was developed by DuPont under the trade name *Dycril*. Several versions of this plate are made for rotary presses. While the cost of Dycril plates has come down considerably as their use increases, they are still more than triple the price of molded plastics.

Other etched plates developed for this use are the *Kodak Relief Plate* and *Techniplate*.

The relative costs of plates as given in this discussion refer to prices per square inch. However, evaluation of the ultimate economy of a particular kind of plate must take into account the factors involved in its *use*. Wearing qualities, makeready economies, storage and shipping problems, etc., have as much significance as initial cost.

PHOTOENGRAVING

Photoengraving is the name applied to a branch of photomechanical platemaking concerned with making metal relief plates for letterpress printing. These plates are used mostly for reproducing illustrations and are referred to as *cuts*. There are basically 2 kinds: *line cuts* and *halftone cuts*.

▪ *Line cuts*—These are made by photographing black and white copy, exposing the negative on a zinc plate and then etching. Very detailed copy may be etched on copper, which holds fine lines and dots better than zinc. Magnesium is sometimes used, and many engravers now use a special alloy (*Micrometal*) in place of zinc.

▪ *Halftone cuts*—These are made from copy with continuous tones (photographs, wash drawings, etc.) and are almost always made on copper. The copy is photographed through a glass plate containing a grid of very fine lines. This breaks up the subject into thousands of tiny black squares, each one varying in size according to the amount of light reflected by the subject at that point. Theoretically, black reflects no light, so the squares will be full size; white reflects the maximum light, so no square will appear at all (they usually appear in very small size); a middle tone of gray will produce a square of half size, and so on. The effect of light rounds off the corners of the squares so that they look like round dots to the naked eye. The overall impression conveyed by these thousands of tiny dots of varying size is an illusion of the tones of the subject. The finer the grid (*screen*) the better the illusion. Halftone screens range from about 50 lines to the inch up to 150. The sizes generally available are: 50, 60, 65, 85, 100, 110, 120, 133, 150.

Below, *a 133 screen halftone and a detail enlarged to show dot pattern.*

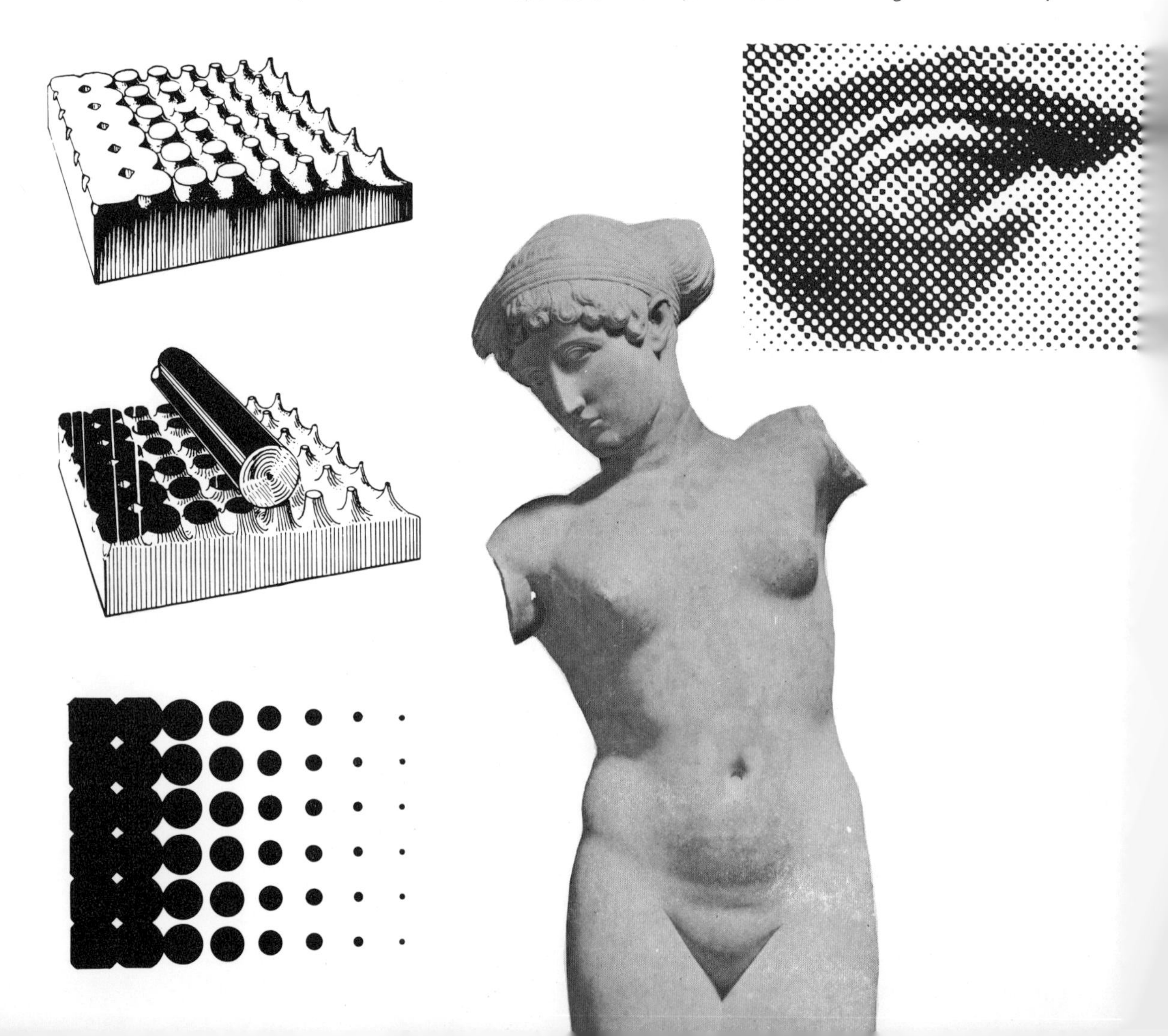

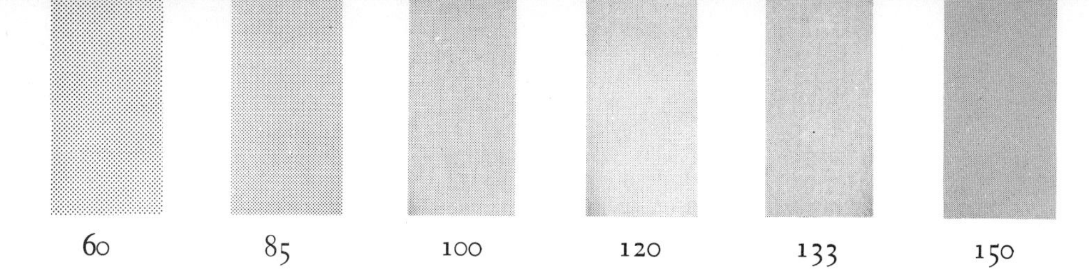

Etching of line plates is now done almost entirely by machine (*powderless etch*) but it was a tedious hand process until recently, done in several stages or *bites*. Where light was admitted through the negative, the plate's coating resisted the acid, but after the initial acid bath had eaten into the nonprinting parts of the plate, the *sides* of the dots, lines, or areas were exposed and unprotected. The plate was then brushed with a resinous powder called *dragon's blood*, which, when heated, protected the sides from etching away (*undercutting*). This was repeated at least 4 times. A similar process takes place in the machine, but it is simpler and faster.

Halftones are exposed and etched much as line cuts, the screened negative being only a finer combination of black and white. However, after a preliminary shallow etch, halftone plates are etched to full depth in 1 bite. Then they are painted with an acid-resist where the etching is satisfactory and given another acid bath to reduce the dots in the other areas. This (*staging*) is repeated as necessary. Further correction is accomplished by *re-etching* [applying acid in a localized area to reduce the dots there], *burnishing* [rubbing the dots hard enough to spread them], or *tooling*, which involves handwork with engravers' tools. These are highly skilled operations. Halftones can be etched by machine also, but there is a loss of control.

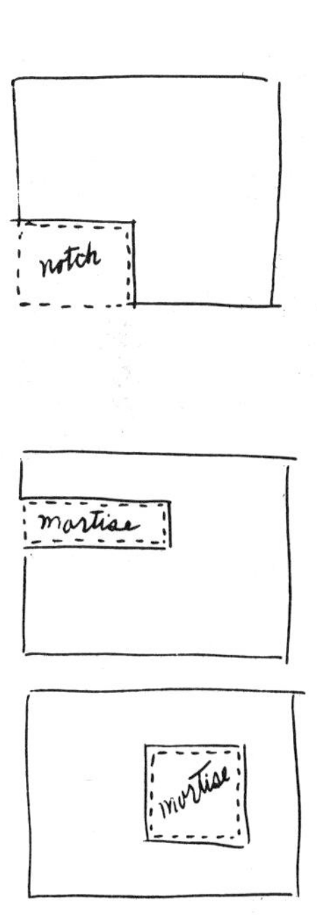

On all plates, after etching, the larger open areas (*dead metal*) are routed to prevent them from printing. The plates are usually mounted on wooden blocks to make them type-high. They may be nailed, but most are held with adhesive (*flush blocking*). (On a cut with no open areas inside, the nails must be placed along the edge, creating a shoulder which prevents any type or other cuts from coming closer than about ⅛″. Nailing is used now only for special cases.) Both line and halftone cuts may be mortised or notched.

There are several variations possible in making photoengravings. A halftone can be combined with a line cut (*combination plate*); the background can be eliminated in a halftone, leaving only a figure or object (*silhouette*); the background can be made to fade away (*vignette*); or the screen can be dropped out of areas in which pure white is desired (*highlight halftone*) to accentuate contrast; screen patterns (*bendays*) can be added to line cuts; halftones can be made with straight, wavy, or circular line screens instead of dots.

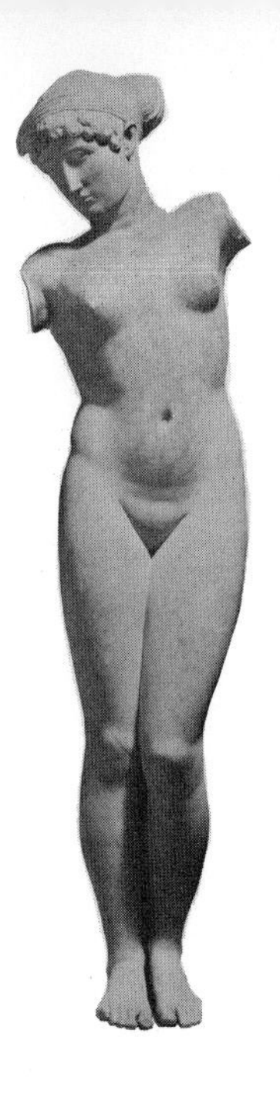

silhouette

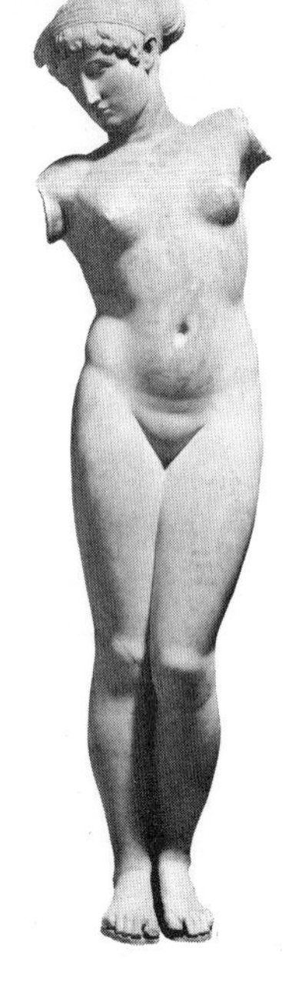

dropout

vignette

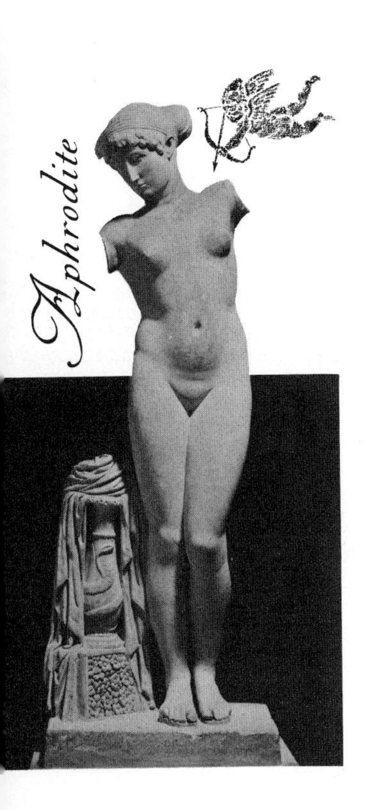

combination

circular screen

benday

Tone screens are measured according to their size (as halftone screens) and their degree of darkness (*tint*). The tint is determined by the size of the dots or lines and is usually specified in percentages of solid black. Thus, a request for a benday tone must include both screen size and tint (for example, 120 screen, 70% tint, etc.). Tints are also designated by letters from A (about 10%) to H (about 90%), but it is probably safer to use the percentage method.

tints, 120 screen

A

B

C

D

E

F

G

H

These effects, variations and combinations of them, are available at somewhat higher rates than simple line or halftone cuts.

Most of the special effects are achieved by skilled craftsmen working with the negatives on a translucent glass table lighted from underneath. The negatives are assembled on a paper, glass, or plastic sheet (called a *flat*) to be stripped-in. Silhouetting, highlighting, and other effects in which the screen is eliminated are accomplished by painting the negative on the affected areas to make them opaque or by *masking* areas to reduce the light admitted. This is expensive work, and some of it can be done on the copy by an artist or retoucher at less cost and with more control over the results. For further discussion of ordering photoengraving see CHS. 11 and 20. Photoengraving for color is covered later in this chapter under "Color printing".

The proofs of photoengraving plates are pulled on very smooth paper and are called *engraver's proofs*. They are carefully made and presumably represent the best printed result possible from the plate.

PRESSES

Speed is an important consideration in choosing presses, but size is paramount. Size in a press means the maximum size sheet it can take. For large orders, paper can be made in special sizes, but in most cases it is best to use one of the standard sizes carried in stock (CH.8). When a stock size of paper is used, there will probably be a press to fit it, and this is almost certainly the press to use. A smaller press would require cutting the paper and printing a smaller form —which means more forms and more impressions—and a larger press means paying a higher rate than necessary because the hourly cost of running a press increases with its size.

The cost of presswork is the charge for use of a press for a period of time, so the running speed is not as significant as the amount of work the press can perform per hour. Press A may not run any faster than Press B, but it may be printing 4 colors, or both sides of the sheet in 1 color, while B is printing only 1 color on 1 side, and it may deliver folded sheets while B delivers them flat.

It does not necessarily follow that Press A is the one to use, because the more a press can do the higher the cost of using it. Not only is it a more expensive piece of equipment but being more complex it requires more time to make ready and may require more help to run. Multicolor presses will usually do a multicolor job much more cheaply than a single color machine, but only if the run is long enough to warrant the longer time needed to set up.

In all cases, the speed at which the press is run will depend to some extent on the kind or quality of work it is performing. Halftones on coated paper or very detailed illustrations on any paper will be run more slowly than type on regular book stock. In general, the higher the quality desired, the more slowly the job is run. In letterpress, quality printing requires frequent examination of sheets to see when adjustments, type cleaning, etc. are needed.

Small work, such as jackets, endpapers, illustrations, etc., is generally printed on cylinder presses which handle sheets of about 17½ x 22½″ or 19 x 25″. Unless the run is very short, say under 10,000, a duplicate set of plates will be made and the work will probably be printed 2 up. For example, the sizes mentioned will accommodate 2 jackets for average-sized books. If the run is very long, say 25,000, 3 extra sets of plates may be made and the job will be run on a 22½ x 35″ or 25 x 38″ sheet. Presses of these sizes normally run at speeds of 2 to 4000 impressions per hour.

The text is most likely to be imposed in 32- or 64-page forms, and be printed on a cylinder press ranging from 38 x 50″ (32 pages 6⅛ x 9¼″) to 50 x 76″ (64 pages 6⅛ x 9¼″). The commonly used sizes are discussed in CHS. 8 and 16.

On all presses there is a maximum printing area which is somewhat smaller than the maximum sheet size. This is due to the space required for guides, grippers, and other mechanical features of the machine.

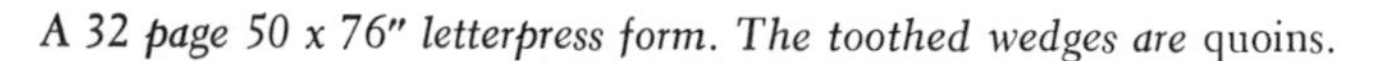

A 32 page 50 x 76″ letterpress form. The toothed wedges are quoins.

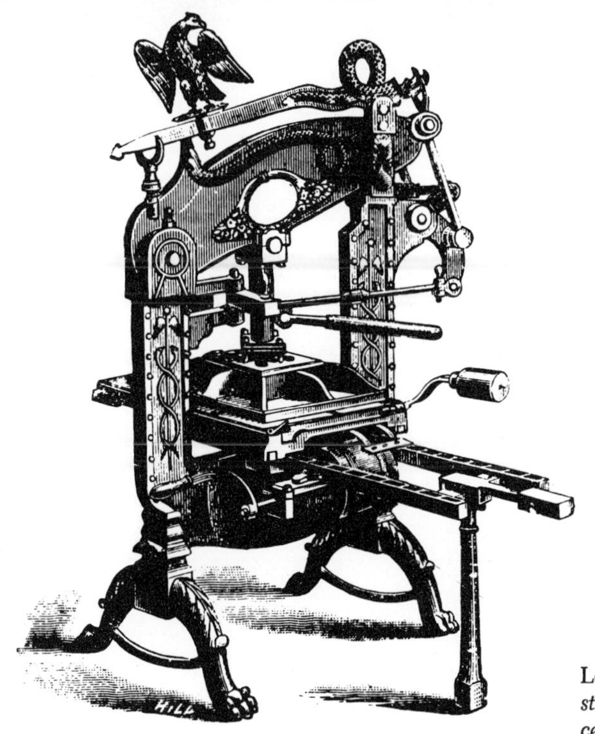

Left, a Columbian hand press. These were still widely used at the beginning of the 20th century.

Below, a 2-color, sheet-fed rotary press.

The development of flexible "wraparound" plates and press improvements are enlarging the use of rotary presses, but they are still practical only for fairly long runs. There is some difference of opinion as to the point at which letterpress rotaries become feasible, but the range is between 15 and 25,000 impressions. Two-color and perfector presses are used on runs of 10,000, but 4-color presses are not economical for quantities under 50,000 sheets.

Modern rotary presses usually have folders and slitters built in. This means that a sheet can be printed with 64-page forms on both sides and delivered as 4 completely folded 32-page *signatures* ready for the next bindery operation (CH.10). The maximum efficiency is achieved with web-fed rotary delivering folded sheets. One difficulty here is the limitation on *cut-off* [the length of sheets cut from the roll], which is determined by the size of the impression cylinder and in turn determines the final *trim-size* [page size].

Lithography

While lithography has been used in some form since 1798 when it was invented by Senefelder in Bavaria, its application to mass production is comparatively recent. The necessary techniques were developed in the early part of this century, but it was not until the 1920s that any considerable commercial printing was done by this method, and it was not until after World War II that it became a major book printing industry.

The primary economic merit of lithography is its ability to print type and illustrations with virtually no more trouble or cost than type alone. The method would have had more use in its early days had it been able to deliver a better result, but the skills were not well enough advanced to avoid the gray, flat quality that marked lithography as a "cheap" process. Good lithography depends on achieving a perfect balance of water and ink, and even today some printing done by this method is inferior to letterpress. However, given good copy, plates, and presses, with the proper paper and ink, a good printer can turn out a first-class job for any purpose. Some of the finest halftone and color process printing being produced today is done by lithography.

With the advent of photographic typesetting, lithography was given a major boost. Since the lithographic plate is photomechanically produced, the product of photocomposing machines can be applied directly to the plate—thus bypassing the repro proof and camera steps. This not only reduces the cost of lithography, it improves its quality. Indeed, the combination of phototypesetting and lithography would probably result in the complete submergence of letterpress were it not for the development of photomechanical letterpress plates described earlier in this chapter.

If no illustrations are involved and type must be set, there is usually no advantage in using lithography. Where metal type is used, the cost of producing litho plates is about the same as making duplicate plates from the type, and the cost of presswork is likely to be fairly even. (For directories and other books that are partially revised between printings, litho plates are used to avoid the contrast between new and worn metal type.) The use of photocomposition tends to change the picture, but only where the typesetting itself is more economical by photography. It is not possible to be more definite about comparative costs because the advantage can be thrown to either side by variables such as the kind of copy, the length of run, or the standards of quality involved. There is no satisfactory alternative to comparing detailed cost estimates for each method on a specific job.

As more illustrations are added, the cost factor swings in favor of lithography, particularly where the pictures are large. A large line negative for a lithographic plate may cost $5, where a zinc line cut might cost $15 and a copper cut $30. For a book with many illustrations, the advantage of offset is overwhelming.

Special factors may affect the cost picture significantly. A reprint of a printed book (for which the original type is not available) can be done much more cheaply by lithography if the printed text is used for camera copy. The quality of the printing cannot be any better than that of the original edition, but the saved cost of typesetting is substantial. On the other hand, an illustrated book can be done more cheaply by letterpress if cuts or electros from another edition (or a magazine) are available. Again, comparative estimates are the best course.

THE PROCESS

Lithography means "stone-writing" in Greek, and it is originally a method of printing by (1) processing the surface of a flat, smooth stone into grease-receptive (printing) and water-receptive (nonprinting) areas, (2) wetting the stone with water (*dampening*) so that the nonprinting areas would repel a greasy ink which (3) was spread over it, and (4) pressing paper to the stone to transfer the ink from the printing areas.

Stones were used until the end of the 19th century. By that time, lithography was a popular medium for artists because it was much easier then engraving in wood or metal and permitted a wider range of graphic techniques and effects. Many lithographed posters and magazine illustrations were produced by leading artists. The stone is still used (on flat bed presses) by artists but for commercial printing it has been replaced by metal sheets treated to duplicate the stone grain.

Another important change in the technique of lithographic printing is the use of the rotary offset method. Several advantages are gained by printing on a rubber blanket first instead of directly on paper: (a) the plates last longer, (b) less water comes in contact with the paper (c) the resilient rubber cylinder permits printing finer copy on rougher paper, and (d) speed is increased. All of these are essential to the commercial success of lithography, which has come to be known as *offset lithography*.

In offset lithography, 5 kinds of cylinders or rollers are involved:

(a) *the plate cylinder* around which the plate is wrapped,

(b) *the blanket (offset) cylinder* around which the rubber blanket is attached,

(c) *the impression cylinder* which carries the paper,

(d) *ink rollers,* and

(e) *water rollers.*

As the plate revolves, it comes in contact first with the water rollers, then the ink rollers, then the blanket cylinder. The impression cylinder presses the paper against the blanket from which the inked image is offset (printed). On commercial-size presses there are several water and ink rollers for better distribution and control.

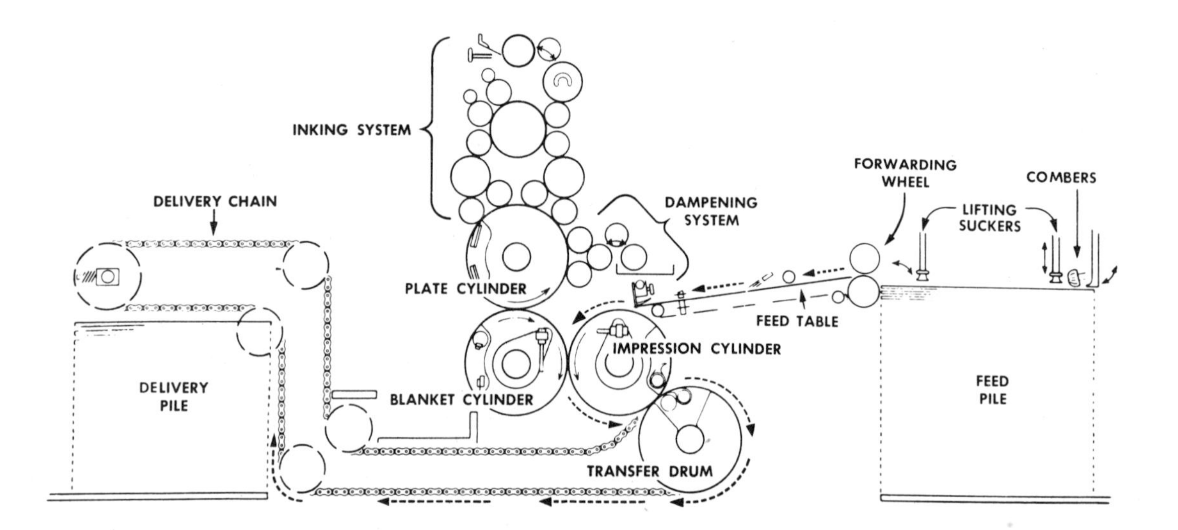

Diagram of an offset lithography press used for printing large sheets.

Since the paper is printed by the rubber blanket rather than the plate itself, there is virtually no makeready done in offset lithography. Quality of plate and correct adjustment of inking, dampening, and press are the main factors in the result.

Two factors that affect quality and *can* be controlled are halftone screen size and paper. Because of the light impression (*kiss impression*) of the rubber blanket, 133 and 150 screens can be printed on papers too rough-surfaced for any but the coarsest screens to be printed by letterpress and, on smoother papers, up to 300-line screens can be used where 133 would be the limit in letterpress. Provided that choice of paper and printer are right, a finer screen will produce better results.

Paper will be discussed in CH.8, but it should be noted here that paper characteristics tend to affect lithographic printing quality very strongly, due to the fact that less ink is deposited than in letterpress, and to the use of water in the process. The moisture that enters the paper may gray the ink, and it may cause a certain amount of paper distortion—with resultant problems in register. Another relevant factor is the tendency toward *picking* [pulling fibers or pieces of coating from the paper surface], due to the tacky inks used.

PLATES

The lithographic stone was a thick and heavy fixture immobilized on the flat bed of a press. A modern offset lithography plate is a thin sheet of lightweight metal wrapped around a rapidly turning cylinder. There are many variations in these plates, but they are the same in principle—the printing areas accept ink, the others repel it. The only essential difference is in the materials used to form the printing and nonprinting areas.

The platemaking process is similar to photoengraving in many respects. The preliminary techniques of camera work, film (negative or positive) stripping, masking, opaquing, etc., are virtually the same.

However, where the photoengraver produces individual cuts or pages, the lithographer strips-in all the pages of a form on a single plate. It is this feature which gives lithography some of its economic advantage and its interest for the designer (CH.16).

An offset lithography plate room. In foreground: light table and tools for stripping film. At far corner: film being exposed onto plate in vacuum frame.

There are a great many kinds of lithographic plates, with improvements and variations being developed constantly. However, these divide roughly into 3 groups: (a) surface plates, (b) deep etch plates, and (c) multimetal plates.

▪ *Surface plates*—A metal sheet is coated with a light-sensitive, ink-receptive substance. When this is exposed to light through a negative film, the coating hardens in the (printing) areas where the light hits it and remains soft in the other (nonprinting) parts. The soft parts are then washed out and a coating of water-receptive material is applied. This adheres only to the bare metal, so that the plate is divided into ink-receptive (printing) parts and water-receptive (nonprinting) parts. Surface plates differ in materials and, to some extent, processes. The main varieties are *albumens, presensitized,* and *wipe-on.* These are used for most printing purposes.

▪ *Deep-etch plates*—Where surface plates leave the printing areas on the surface, and thus subject to wear, deep-etch plates are made in reverse with film *positives,* leaving the printing areas slightly *below* the nonprinting areas (somewhat like an intaglio plate). These plates are used for longer runs and for especially fine work such as color-process printing. Their cost is somewhat higher.

▪ *Multimetal plates*—For even longer runs and better quality, there are *bimetal* plates. These have a light-sensitive protective coating on an ink-receptive metal base. After exposure, development removes the coating from the nonprinting parts, which then receive a plating of water-receptive metal in an electrolytic bath. Another bath washes away the remaining coating, exposing the ink-receptive base metal in the printing areas. On some plates, the metals are reversed, i.e. the plating is ink-receptive while the base is water-receptive. Bimetal plates are rarely used for runs under 100,000 because of their high cost.

On *trimetal* plates, the base metal is given a plating also. Such plates appear to be virtually indestructible.

Small offset lithography machines (such as the Multilith) can print with plates made by typing or drawing on a specially treated paper. The ink used will stick to the carbon image produced by the typewriter, while the paper repels the ink. Only a few hundred copies can be obtained in this way. *Paper plates* can also be made photographically in the same way as metal ones. Some of these are capable of quite long runs. Another method of making paper plates is by xerography. A grease-receptive, negatively charged powder is applied electrostatically to the printing areas on a positively charged, water-receptive paper. In general, paper plates are used for office duplicating work rather than commercial printing.

A sheet-fed offset lithography press. This size is generally used for printing jackets and other work on small sheets.

PRESSES

An offset press is actually a rotary press, with all the potential advantages of one—speed, multiple-color printing, and web-feed. It is not surprising that the search for these properties has pointed in the direction of offset lithography.

Substantial savings are possible with high-speed, web-fed, rotary presses, provided the job is suited to the equipment. Mainly, this means long runs. Unfortunately, the bulk of book printing consists of runs too short to effectively utilize these presses, which can turn out 25,000 impressions of a 64-page form in 1 hour. A first printing of 5000 copies (very common for tradebooks) would thus be completed in 12 minutes of running time—and the time needed to make the press ready would be 15 times as long. Paper spoilage might go as high as 30%. However, runs as short as 7000 can be feasible if the number of forms is large enough to effectively utilize the roll of paper.

Unlike letterpress, offset lithography presses are basically the same, whether large or small. Except for the difference between web- and sheet-feed, the essential distinction between the smallest office machine, such as the Multilith, and the largest litho press (about 55 x 78″) is the control mechanism. The same 5 kinds of rollers and cylinders are used in all, although the larger presses will have more of each to increase efficiency and control. In lithography there are also perfector presses, both sheet- and web-fed. Small presses that print jackets run at 5 to 7000 impressions per hour, the larger sheet-fed machines at 4 to 6000.

Collotype

This is a little-used process, but it is capable of extremely fine reproduction of illustrations under limited conditions. No screen is involved, the tones result from varying amounts of ink. The printed surface, which has a barely perceptible grain, gives an effect of continuous tone. While these tones can be very delicate, and fine detail can be held, the process does not permit strong contrast or a wide range of values. The ink is transparent and type tends to look weak.

The process is similar to lithography in that it is based on the antipathy of grease and water, but in collotype the entire plate accepts ink in varying degrees, rather than being divided between ink-accepting and ink-repelling areas. The surface of the plate is a sheet of photosensitive gelatin which becomes impervious to water to the degree that it is exposed to light through a film negative. Before printing, the plate is soaked in water. The darker tones hold more ink because they accept less water, while the lighter tones hold more water and less ink.

Printing by collotype is a precarious matter, in which room temperature and humidity are critical. The plates get damaged easily —usually after a few hundred impressions.

This process is expensive for long runs because of very slow press speeds, but the plate cost is low and runs of 100 to 1000 copies are the most economical. Rotary collotype runs faster and is practical for somewhat larger quantities. Collotype is sometimes called *photogelatin.*

Gravure

Printing from an engraved plate is an ancient process, perhaps older than letterpress. Engraving in wood and metal was a highly developed art thousands of years ago, but it was not until the application of photography that gravure became feasible for commercial printing, although many book illustrations were printed from engraved copper and steel plates in the 18th and 19th centuries.

The gravure process is the most difficult and complicated of the 3 major printing methods and is consequently the most expensive. This is particularly true in the United States, where comparatively little quality gravure work is done in bookmaking. Skill and time are larger factors in gravure platemaking than in most other kinds, and these elements are becoming relatively more costly.

Like offset lithography, gravure is by nature a rotary process readily adapted to web-feed. Web-fed gravure, letterpress, and lithography cost less per impression than sheet-fed when runs are long enough to justify their use. In gravure, however, the high cost of platemaking accentuates the difference to the point where sheet-fed printing in moderate quantities (say 6 to 10,000) is possible for only expensive illustrated books, while web-fed gravure in the long runs of magazine printing (say 200,000 and over) is no more expensive than any other method.

Gravure is at its best in reproducing continuous-tone copy, particularly photographs. Its attraction for newpapers and magazines is its ability to print pictures well on relatively cheap paper. For fine-quality picture reproduction in books, gravure appeals to those who prefer not to use coated paper. Until recently, the choice for such work was entirely between gravure and letterpress, but now lithography is beginning to compete. In any case, sheet-fed gravure is a superior method of printing where richness of tone and fidelity of detail are required.

The weakness of gravure is that it must print type with a screen. Gravure screens are very fine, ranging from 150 to 300 lines, and the black tone is solid, but there is always a fuzziness on the edges of type due to the sawtooth pattern of the diagonal screen. For fine books, it is best to print the text in letterpress or lithography, even if the illustrations are printed by gravure.

THE PROCESS

The entire area of the gravure plate is covered by a grid similar to a halftone screen. The lines are level with the surface and the square spaces between the lines are etched to varying depths. The darker the tone, the deeper the square is etched and, consequently, the more ink it holds. The squares—which appear on the paper like dots—are all the same size, but they vary in tone according to the amount of ink deposited, i.e. they vary in opacity. Thus, gravure is a true halftone process, whereas letterpress and lithography only simulate tones by optical illusion. The only flaw in gravure reproduction of tone is the grid of white lines, but this is virtually invisible due to the fine screens used. In the darker tones, so much ink is deposited that the dots run together and eliminate the white line altogether.

There is a process (*News-Dultgen*) in which a combination of the gravure and letterpress halftone screens is used. The wells between the lines vary not only in depth but in size.

Gravure printing is mechanically very much like rotary letterpress. A plate cylinder revolves against an ink roller and then against the paper which passes between it and an impression cylinder. The one important difference is due to the nature of the gravure plate. After the plate is inked, a flat bar, called a *doctor blade,* wipes the ink off the surface, leaving it in the recesses only.

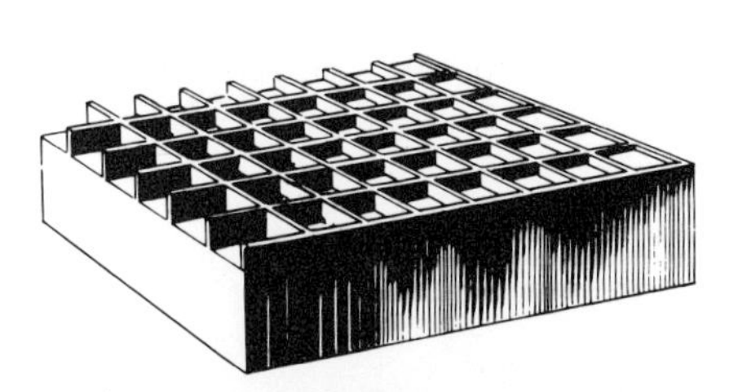

Because of the need to wipe the ink cleanly off the plate surface on each impression, a thin, fast-drying ink is used. This ink tends to spread on the paper and helps close the spaces between the dots. The ink must be thin also because it acts as a transparent wash—letting the paper show through in varying degrees according to the amount deposited.

The offset method is used in gravure as well as in lithography and letterpress, but mainly for printing on plastics and other specialty materials.

PLATES Although gravure plates have a screen, it is not used when photographing the copy. A continuous tone negative is made and, because a gravure plate is the opposite of relief plates in that the *printing* areas are etched, a film positive is made from the negative.

The screen (not the lines but the black squares between) is printed on a sheet of tissue which backs a sheet of photosensitive gelatin. The gelatin (called a *resist*) is exposed to light through the screen, then it is turned over and exposed through the film positive. The gelatin is soluble in water, but becomes less so as it is exposed to light. So, when full light strikes it (as through the lines of the screen) it will not dissolve at all; it remains soluble in varying degrees according to the tones in the film positive. After exposure, a warm water bath washes away the gelatin in proportion to the amount of light it received in each square.

The sheet is then laid on the copper plate or cylinder, the printed tissue is peeled away, and an acid etch bites into the metal according to the thickness of the gelatin. This leaves the screen lines as walls around millions of tiny square wells of varying depth.

Gravure plates are made up in complete forms from flats of stripped-in film in the same way as for lithography.

PRESSES Sheet-fed gravure presses range in size from 12 x 18″ to about 30 x 44″. Their speed is slightly slower than that of comparable offset and cylinder presses. They tend to be slowed by the need for strong pressure against the plate to enable the paper to draw all ink from the wells. However, on smoother papers less pressure is needed.

Web-fed gravure (known as *rotogravure*) is very advanced in equipment due to its use by newspapers and magazines. Very large presses are available for single color and multicolor printing, and most have built-in folding machines. The plates for rotogravure presses are copper cylinders (rather than copper sheets wrapped around cylinders). Rotogravure runs at very high speed.

Silk screen

Until quite recently, silk screen was a process for producing rather simple designs in small quantities. It was essentially a handcraft used to make posters in runs of a few hundred or less. With the introduction of machinery capable of relatively high-speed production, silk screen became feasible for long-run commercial work.

Even now, silk screen is much more expensive than other methods of printing, but it has certain unique advantages which make it worth the price when its special qualities are needed. Two features are outstanding: (a) any kind of surface—including rough cloth—can be printed and (b) the ink may be completely opaque "paint" which can be built up to a thickness comparable to embossing. These attributes are obviously of interest in relation to covers, and will be discussed further in CH.26, but there is also use for them in printing endpapers, jackets, and illustrations.

There are many silk screen printers, but few are equipped with machinery to do book work, and prices may vary considerably. It is worth some investigation to find a printer suited to the work needed.

THE PROCESS

The nonprinting parts of the screen may be blocked out by application of a liquid filler, but the most common method is to use a sheet *mask* or *stencil*. Simple masks can be cut by hand, but for most work, film is used and the image is cut photomechanically. Although the process is best suited to printing fairly large areas of flat color, it is possible to reproduce small type, and even halftones, provided conditions are suitable.

The mask is applied to a very fine screen (it may be silk or metal mesh) which is stretched tightly on a frame. This is then mounted horizontally on a press and the paper is fed underneath, where it receives ink squeezed through the screen by a *squeegee* [a rubber-edged bar]. A separate mask is made for each color, although it is possible to print more than 1 color at a time if the design is properly prepared. Inks may be bright metallics or rich, flat finishes. They may be applied very thin or thick enough to cast a shadow.

Xerography

Static electricity is not new to printing, but it existed only as a nuisance until recently. Letterpress printers have to contend with sheets sticking together and the attraction of unwanted particles because of the tendency of oppositely charged matter to draw together. This phenomenon has now been turned to our advantage. An entirely new printing process (xerography) has been based on the principles of electrostatic action.

The idea was first put forward as a practical possibility about 1948. Within a few years, the process was commercially available as a means of making copies of letters and other documents in small quantities, and for making inexpensive master plates for small offset duplicators. The quality of reproduction was good when the machines were perfectly adjusted, but they required frequent attention. The *Xerox* Copyflow machine produces copies at high speed on a continuous roll and can reduce or enlarge. In 1964, the Xerox Company announced a machine capable of printing 2400 sheets per hour. This puts the process in competition with the other printing methods, but it remains to be seen whether the quality and cost of copies made on such machines will also be competitive.

THE PROCESS

A specially coated paper is given a positive charge of static electricity. The printing image is projected onto the paper through a lens. Where the image strikes the paper the positive charge remains, but the light reflected from the nonprinting areas removes the charge. The paper is then covered with a negatively charged black powder (ink) that adheres to the positively charged printing area only. Heat then fuses the powder, which hardens when cool.

Some machines use the offset principle. The ink first adheres to the image on a selenium drum and then offsets to the paper. The advantage here is that an untreated paper may be printed. Xerox uses this method. The direct method is used by Bruning, American Photocopy, and others.

Color printing

There are 2 kinds of color printing: simple and process.

- *Simple color*—This includes: (a) *flat* or *line color* for printing type, rules, borders, solid or benday areas in illustrations, and illustrations themselves (including where several colors are used, and even where colors are produced by *overprinting* [printing one color over another]) and (b) *halftone color* for printing halftones in a single color. Essentially, each simple color plate is an individual line cut or halftone no different from any other, except in the ink used to print it.
- *Color process*—This is the reproduction of full-color subjects such as paintings and color photographs (see front endpapers), and is much more complex and far more expensive than simple color. It can be used with any printing method. Costs vary considerably, but a set of 4-color process plates may cost about 20 times as much as a *monochrome* [single color] plate of the same subject.

COPY

For any photomechanically made simple color plate, the copy should be black and white. (If the copy is a color, it should be dark enough to photograph as black.) If more than 1 color is involved but none overlaps, the copy may be pasted into position on 1 board. If the colors overlap, separate black and white copy is prepared for each. The most important color (usually black) is pasted on a board as the *key plate* and the other colors are pasted on transparent overlays. (See CH.11 for discussion of preparing camera copy.) It is possible to make flat color plates from copy which is not separated for color, but the cost is almost as high as for color process, since the first part of the procedure (color separation) is the same.

There are 2 kinds of copy for color process: (a) opaque (reflection) copy (drawings, color photographs, and original paintings or prints) and (b) transparent copy, i.e. the *transparency* [color slide] obtained from some color film (*Kodachrome, Ektachrome,* etc.). The original subject (paintings, etc.) is the best copy, the next best is a transparency or a color photoprint. Transparencies do require more work, so the cost of plates made from them is somewhat higher.

PLATES

Making photomechanical plates for simple color printing, regardless of the kind, is exactly the same process as making plates for printing in black. Provided the copy is separated so that each color is an individual black and white subject, the platemaker or engraver proceeds without regard for the color at all. If the colors do not overlap and are on the same board, the entire copy is photographed once for each color and the negatives are *opaqued* [portions not wanted are painted out] so that each is left with the copy for only 1 color. Then the individual plates are made as otherwise. When simple color is being printed by letterpress from duplicate plates and the colors overlap, the type is first separated so that everything that prints in each color is made up as a separate page (*color breakup*). Then plates are made of each color, just as for ordinary black printing pages. If the colors do not overlap, the page is locked up with *all* the type, a plate is made for each color, and each plate is routed to leave 1 color only.

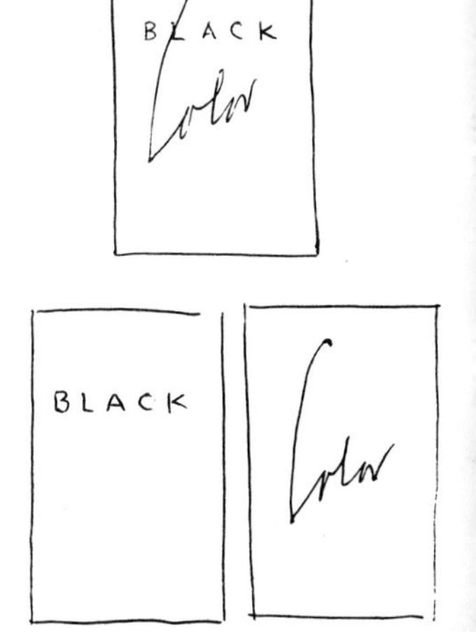

Above, *page printed in 2 colors.* Below, *the separated copy.*

Color process plates involve 3 distinct operations—each of which must be performed well or the result will be poor. Full-color reproduction is at best a compromise, so there is not much room for failure.

- *Color separation*—The copy is photographed 4 times, once with a special lens to get black, the other 3 times with colored filters that exclude all but blue, yellow, and red, respectively. Sometimes the black shot is omitted. Theoretically the 3 primary colors will combine to produce all others, but in practice the addition of black is needed to add depth and brilliance.
- *Color correction*—It is practically impossible to obtain a satisfactory reproduction with color-separation photography alone, so it is necessary to modify the negatives by hand. This is a highly skilled operation requiring considerable time. Many printers and engravers send their color separation and correction work to specialized companies, rather than keep such expensive help on the payroll.

There are now *color-scanning* machines that electronically separate the colors and balance them, thus eliminating the need for hand correction of negatives. Used on a very large scale, such machines produce important savings, but they are too expensive for small operations at this time. Another aid to color correction is the film *mask*. A set of separation negatives made with special filters is combined with the primary set to control the density of each film. The Kodak *Tri-Mask* film accomplishes this with 1 shot.

■ *Platemaking*—The corrected separation negatives are exposed against a sensitized film to make positive films, and these are exposed against another film with a halftone screen in the middle. The result is a set of screened halftone negatives which are used to make plates in the manner usual for the printing process involved. The halftone screens are placed at different angles for each color, so that the colored dots will print alongside, rather than on top of each other. Reduction or enlarging may be done during any of the film stages.

PRINTING

In simple color printing, the only extra cost is the ink *washup*. The previous color must be completely washed out of the press before the new color is used. On short runs there may be a small charge if a color is specially mixed. Otherwise, the presswork is about the same as printing black. Thus a 2-color job costs about twice as much as 1 color, 3 colors cost 3 times as much as 1, etc., provided, of course, that the printing problems in each color are otherwise equal, and each color is run separately.

On any press run, more care is required when halftones or very fine line copy are involved, but printing with 2 or more colors brings in the problem of *register* [placing each plate in correct position relative to the other(s)]. The register may be very simple or extremely fine. Assuming that the copy and plates were properly aligned, there are still several obstacles to perfect register. Poor feeding, faulty plate mounting, irregular trimming of paper are causes of trouble, but the most difficult problem is distortion of the sheets due to moisture. This may result from excess water in lithographic printing or from a change in general humidity between impressions. Because the paper is likely to expand or shrink more in 1 direction than the other, a serious problem in register may occur, especially in large sheets. Preventive measures include sizing paper to resist moisture (CH.8) and pressroom air-conditioning, but these are sometimes not enough. Moisture causes least trouble when all colors are printed in 1 run through the press on multicolor presses. Then there is no time for distortion to take place.

There are 2 methods by which colors may be used at less than the usual cost. One is *split fountain*. On cylinder and rotary presses, ink is picked up by the roller from a trough called a *fountain*. The fountain can be divided into sections of any width and a different color ink put in each section. The roller is then inked with the different colors along its length and transfers the colored inks to the corresponding parts of the plates or type. Thus, if the fountain were divided into 3 parts, with black on the left, red in the middle, and blue on the right, everything on the left side of the sheet would be printed black, everything in the middle red, and the right blue.

If a printing job is designed to take advantage of this arrangement, a quite spectacular multicolor effect may be obtained at very little more than the cost of 1 color. Theoretically, there is no limit to the number of colors possible with split fountain, but there are some practical limitations. Unless the ink roller is actually cut into sections so that the colors cannot meet, there is bound to be some mixing of color where the inks come together. The vibrating of the ink rollers normally spreads the mixed area to about 2½″, although it is possible to reduce the vibration to much less. The mixed color can be avoided entirely if no printing appears in the border areas. This may cause the designer some difficulty, but the cost of cutting a roller is quite high, unless a long run is involved.

A second means of printing color at lower rates is the use of multicolor presses. A 2-color or 4-color press prints that many colors with a single run-through of the paper. These presses are more expensive than single color machines, and the presswork is more complicated, so the cost is higher than printing 1 color, but it is not nearly as high as doing each color in a separate run. For 2-color presses, a minimum of about 10,000 copies is needed for economy. At least 25,000 copies are necessary to warrant the use of a 4-color press.

Color process printing is not simply a matter of making as many runs through the press as there are colors. The problem of register is acute because each dot pattern must be perfectly related to the others, and the inks must be perfectly chosen and applied or the color will not be true. However, the main problem is correction of the plates, and if this is done well there should be little trouble in the presswork. It is possible to compensate for some inadequacies in the plates by makeready, by using modified inks, by using specially selected paper, or by changing the usual order of printing the colors (yellow, red, blue, black), but the scope of such measures is limited and they cannot fully overcome the handicap of poor plates.

PROOFS

Simple color proofs, pulled on the same paper as the actual job, are used to check register, color (particularly the effects of overprinting), and plate quality. For the latter, black and white engraver's proofs are essential, but it is best to have color proofs also, as the plate may be adequate for printing in black and white but not in color.

Proofs of color process plates are shown singly and in combination in the "process inks"—a more or less standard yellow, a violet-red (*magenta*), and a green-blue (*cyan*). These *progressive proofs* are usually presented in the order of printing—first the yellow plate alone, then red alone, then yellow plus red, blue alone, yellow and red plus blue, black alone, all 4 together (see front endpaper). Where more than 4 colors are used, the same procedure is followed.

In checking color process proofs, compare the copy with the final proof to see if the balance of color is correct. Defects in color may be corrected in 2 ways—by modifying the plate itself or by modifying the color of ink. If there is an excess of 1 color—say red—in 1 area, the trouble may be corrected by thinning down the dots in that part of the red plate; if the whole subject is too red, it may be possible to correct by changing to a different red ink. Unless you are quite expert in such matters, it is best to simply complain to the engraver or printer about what seems wrong and leave the choice of remedy to him.

The main purpose of progressive proofs is to enable the printer to check results as he runs each color, rather than wait until all is finished. If the bookmaker wants to have control of the result, there is no practical alternative to checking press proofs against progressive proofs at the pressroom (it is rarely feasible to let a press stand idle while press sheets are sent out for approval) as *each color* is made ready. To decide that the red is too strong after the job is done is useless, unless the sheets are to be thrown out and a new printing made. On a 4-color press, the problem is much simpler because the results are apparent immediately.

There is one means of checking an intermediate stage of color process—the *3M Color Key proofs*. These are separate film positives in color of each color separation negative. The colors obtained by placing these films over each other are not a true indication of the final effect, but the proofs are useful for checking size, blemishes, etc., and they are very good for making presentations.

8 | Paper

From the time it was invented (probably in China in the 2nd century A.D.) until the introduction of machinery in the early 1800s, the varieties of paper were comparatively few. The technique of making paper of rags by hand determined its character, and there was so little paper produced that it barely met the needs of bookmaking. There was then neither the demand nor supply of this precious commodity for the fantastic variety of its uses today, from fish wrapping to computer printout. The subject of paper is tremendous, but even the book uses alone are too numerous to be covered here. Of these, many items (such as shipping cartons) are purchased as finished products, and others—proof papers, the printer's tympan paper (for makeready), the paper used to reinforce bindings, etc.—are purchased by suppliers according to their needs. This chapter will deal with only the book uses of paper in which the bookmaker exercises a choice.

A knowledge of paper is important for 2 reasons: (a) paper has properties that affect the success or failure of a design and (b) a large part (usually about 20%) of the production cost of a book is in its paper.

With a few exceptions, printing paper is bought from distributors rather than from manufacturers. The distributor takes a small profit in return for providing service—stocking and delivering the paper, giving advice, and supplying samples as needed. The paper merchant's advice should be sought, not only because it is being paid for but to take advantage of his special knowledge.

The process

Each kind of paper is made a little differently, but the basic process of papermaking is common to all. Variations are more in the ingredients and finishing than the method of manufacture. The essentials of this method are described below.

INGREDIENTS

The chief ingredient of most papers is wood. The better papers contain cotton fiber and the best are made entirely of cotton. The character of a paper depends to a large extent on the kind of wood used, but the major distinction is between the long-fibered woods used for strength (*kraft* paper) and the shorter-fibered woods used in quality printing papers. The cotton fibers used are taken from waste in fabric manufacture and discarded fabric articles such as mail bags, uniforms, work clothes, etc.

Water is the other main ingredient. Dyes and pigments for coloring, rosin and alum for sizing to resist penetration of ink and water, titanium and clay *fillers* for opacity and surface improvement, and a few other chemicals are added as required.

PREPARING THE STOCK

Stock is the term for fiber when it is processed. The wood pulp and/or the rags are chopped up, soaked, cooked, bleached, beaten, and mixed with the appropriate chemical ingredients until they are a slushy mass. In this process, the fibers have been reduced to the proper size and shape for the kind of paper being made. Cheaper papers are made with finely ground, uncooked wood pulp. These fibers deteriorate more rapidly. A paper free of groundwood is called a *free sheet*.

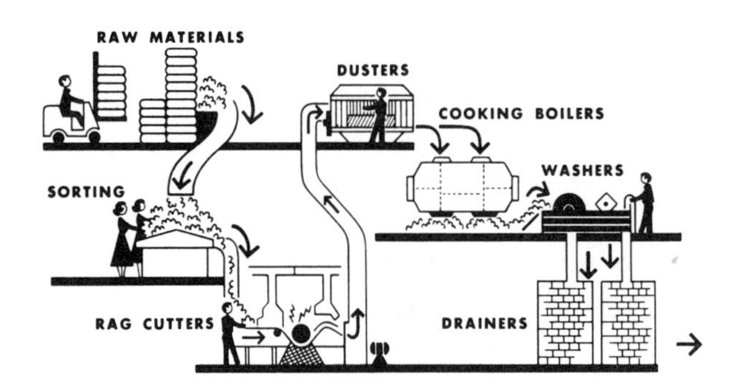

1. Processing the raw materials.

THE PAPER MACHINE

Around 1800, the Fourdrinier brothers in England produced a papermaking machine, the principles of which are still in use. The stock (or *furnish*, as it is called when all ingredients have been added) is introduced at the *wet end* where it is poured onto a wide (6—25′) endless belt of fine wire screen. The *wire* carries it over a long (sometimes 50′) distance, constantly vibrating so that the pulp fibers mesh and the water drains away. Despite the vibration, the fibres tend to lie in the direction of flow, and this is the way the *grain* of the paper runs. The top side of the paper is laid down by the *dandy roll*, a cylinder of finely woven wire cloth, which revolves over the wire and affects the surface characteristics. By the time the end of the wire is reached, the stock has dried enough to become a sheet of very soggy paper. The sheet then passes over a felt blanket onto a series of rollers that squeeze out a large part of the water, then over heated drums that reduce the moisture content to the proper level. The paper then goes through a *calender*, where it is pressed between a series of steel rollers to give it the desired degree of smoothness. The side of the paper that ran over the wire (*wire side*) is usually a bit rougher than the other, or *felt side*. Considering that the furnish is 99% water and the paper that comes off the machine has only 5% water, it is apparent that the machine is basically a moisture-removing device.

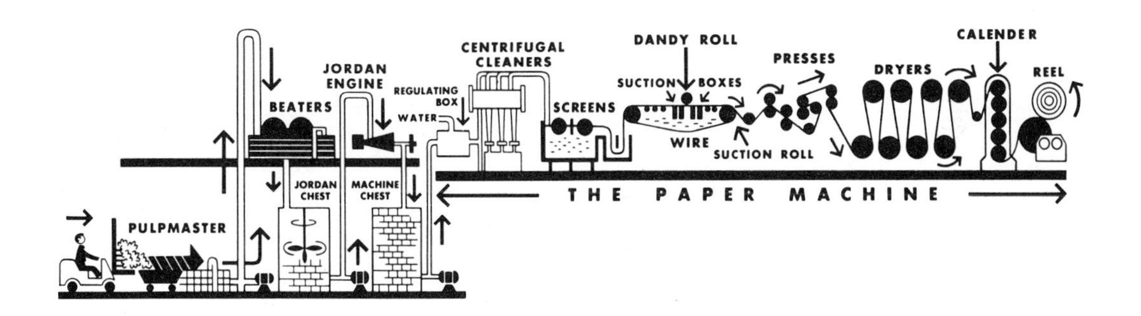

2. *Preparing the stock.*

3. *Making the paper.*

FINISHING

Some finishes are applied during the process of manufacture, either by pressure from a dandy roll or by the texture of felt blankets on which the paper is pressed. Other finishes are applied by separate machines after the paper is made. Textures are made by pressing the paper between special rollers, coatings are generally flowed on. Surface sizing is applied by running the paper through a vat of sizing material.

Papers intended to be used on web-fed machines are, of course, shipped in rolls, but other paper is cut into sheets. Large orders are

4. *Finishing and packing.*

shipped on *skids* [wooden platforms] containing about 3000 lbs. Most printing paper is stocked in *cartons* of about 150 lbs., and some of the better papers are wrapped in *packages* of 250, 500, or more sheets, depending on their weight and size.

Some papers are stocked with a *deckle* edge [the feathery, untrimmed edge] on 2 sides.

Kinds of paper

The varieties and finishes, qualities, weights, etc., of papers are almost unlimited, but there are 4 main kinds of manufacture, of which all others are variations.

ANTIQUE

These are the soft-finish, "toothy" papers used for most letterpress printing. They are generally cheaper than other varieties because they have no extra ingredients or finishes. In the antique category, *eggshell* is a fine-textured finish and *vellum* is even smoother. Some antique papers have a *laid* finish, which is a pattern of close parallel lines crossed by a series of widely spaced lines pressed into the paper by the dandy roll. Paper without laid marks is called *wove* finish.

MACHINE FINISH

Most papers are made more compact by calendering on the paper machine. Some are given a little extra calendering to achieve a smoother surface. This is called *machine finish.* A still smoother surface is *English Finish.* Stocks intended for this finish have very short fibers and a heavy mineral content, which produce a rather shiny smoothness when calendered. The smoothest uncoated paper is *supercalendered* (*super*), which is run through a special calender with heated rollers separate from the paper machine.

COATED

Finishes of still greater smoothness require coating with fine clays which are flowed onto the surface of the paper with adhesives and then supercalendered with extremely smooth rollers. Some coated stock is made with clays that finish dull and are less calendered. These are called *dull coated,* the other, *gloss coated.* Some papers are coated on 1 side only, others on both sides. A relatively new group of papers called *pigmented* papers have generally replaced supercalendered sheets. They are actually lightly coated papers—very smooth, but less expensive than fully coated.

SURFACE-SIZED

Sizing is applied to papers in 2 ways. It may be mixed with the stock (*internal sizing*), in which case it becomes part of the paper itself, or it may be applied to the surface. Most papers have some sizing in them to retard penetration of ink and water. Lithographic papers are *surface-sized* to prevent penetration of water and to increase surface strength. Most antique papers are now given enough surface sizing to enable them to be printed by lithography as well as by letterpress.

USE CLASSIFICATIONS

Since the same kind of paper may be used for different purposes—for example, coated paper may be used for the illustrations in a book *or* the cover of a paperback—the sale and distribution of paper is organized according to use rather than kind, although with some exceptions. Thus, the papers commonly used for the pages of books are classified as *book papers*. The more expensive book papers are often made in colors (for use in promotion pieces, pamphlets, etc.) and are designated *text papers*. A category of thicker papers of all kinds and finishes called *cover paper* is used for the covers of pamphlets and paperbacks. Some papers are made with the characteristics required for *endpapers*. These and others are sometimes stocked in rolls and are designated *binding papers*. Some surface-sized papers are classified as *offset* or *litho papers* (although this designation is being dropped because most sheets are now litho-sized). Any of these categories can be and are used for purposes other than the one named, but this is how they are generally listed in catalogues and price lists, and this is the basis for some of the standards used in paper distribution.

Weight, bulk, size, & grain

WEIGHT

The term "weight" is sometimes used to refer to thickness of paper, but this is misleading, because paper is sold (mostly) by its actual weight in pounds and this does not always correspond to its thickness. Obviously, a supercalendered paper will be much thinner than an antique eggshell weighing the same amount. Pick up a book of coated paper and notice how heavy it feels in contrast to a book of the same thickness with antique stock.

The weight of paper is determined and specified by a system that seems complicated but is really quite simple. It is usually possible to leave the matter entirely in the hands of the paper merchant, but anyone who buys paper should understand the weight system himself, in order to make his own calculations.

When a paper is called "60 lb." (*substance* 60), it means that 500 sheets (a *ream*) of it in a certain size (*basic size*) weigh 60 lbs. (*basis weight*). (The basic size of book papers is 25 x 38″, but for cover papers it is 20 x 26″.) Since paper is not always sold in its basic size, it is sometimes necessary to know the *actual* weight of the paper being used or shipped. If the latter were 38 x 50″ (*finished size*), 60 lb. basis weight, the actual (*finished*) *weight* per ream would be 120 lbs.—that is, twice the basis weight because the finished size (in area) is twice the basic size (area). Thus, basis weight to basic area equals finished weight to finished area ($W:A = W':A'$).

The billing and shipment of book paper refers to reams, but

prices are based on weight, usually using 1000 sheets as the unit. The weight of 1000 sheets is referred to as *M weight.* To find this, use the above formula and multiply the ream weight by 2. In the example, M weight (finished size) would be 240 lbs. (240M). With the formula, one can always find basis or ream weight if M weight is known, and vice versa.

The weight of a particular paper may be expressed in terms of its basis weight—44 x 66″, sub. 50—or its M weight—44 x 66″, 306M —or both—44 x 66″, 306M, sub 50. (The term "*basis*" is used generally for weight and "*basic*" is used with size, but sometimes the words are interchanged.)

BULK

The proper term for thickness in paper is *caliper*, but the term used in book publishing is "*bulk*", although the word has come to suggest an artificial, blown-up character. (Whereas paper is improved in printing qualities by being compressed to a harder, smoother sheet, many book papers are sold in the least compressed state possible, to satisfy the publishers' demand for fatter books [CH.16].)

Bulk depends on fibers as well as manufacture, so the more fiber there is, the thicker the paper, given the same manufacture. More fiber may mean bulkier or additional fibers. The latter results in heavier paper (100 lb. paper has about twice as much fiber as 50 lb. of the same grade) while bulky fiber may add thickness without weight. This is because the fillers are heavier for their mass than the fibers.

Paper manufacturers and distributors print bulk tables showing the number of pages to the inch of each weight and finish in almost all grades of paper. Obviously, the more calendered sheets will have less bulk than others of the same weight, but there is also considerable variation among different makes of paper in each category. The table shows the approximate range in the most common grades and weights.

GRADE	50 lb.	55 lb.	60 lb.	65 lb.	70 lb.	75 lb.	80 lb.
Antique	350—380	310—350	290—310	270—290	250—270	230—250	210—230
Eggshell antique	420—470	390—420	350—390	330—360	310—330	290—310	260—290
Machine finish	520—580	480—520	440—480	410—440	380—410	360—380	330—360
English finish	620—660	570—620	520—570	480—520	450—480	420—450	390—420
Litho	530—600	480—550	440—510	400—470	380—440	350—400	330—380
Pigmented	660—800	600—730	550—670	510—620	470—570	440—520	410—490
Coated	800—850	730—780	670—710	620—660	570—610	530—570	500—530

SIZE

The paper merchant keeps hundreds of items in stock—different brands, kinds, qualities, finishes, colors, weights, and sizes. Obviously, he wants to reduce this number to the fewest possible. The printer has presses of various sizes, but the number is limited. Presuming that publishers want to utilize the full size of the presses, they need mainly the paper sizes that fit the presses available. Consequently, paper is made in a few standard sizes and any others must be made to order (*making-order*). Each paper mill has its own minimum quantity requirements for making special sizes in each grade of paper, but the average for book papers is 5000 lbs., and for text and cover papers 2000 lbs. These minimums may often be cut in half but may require payment of a 10% penalty.

In book papers, the stock sizes and the page size (trim-size) to which they fold are:

35 x 45″ — 5½ x 8½″
38 x 50″ — 6⅛ x 9¼″
41 x 61″ — 5 x 7⅜″
44 x 66″ — 5⅜ x 8″
45 x 68″ — 5½ x 8¼″
46 x 69″ — 5⅝ x 8⅜″

The first 2 would take 32-page forms, the others, 64s (CH.7). The line under 1 number in each size indicates that the grain runs in that dimension.

Text and cover papers are stocked in generally smaller sizes:

23 x 35″
25 x 38″
26 x 40″

and sometimes in

35 x 45″
38 x 50″

The stock sizes given here are American. Other sizes are used elsewhere.

GRAIN

When paper is folded against the grain, the fibers break, the surface cracks, the fold is ragged, and the pages won't lie properly. These effects are more pronounced in some papers than others, but it is always desirable to fold with the grain. For this reason it is important to know how the sheet is to be folded when ordering paper.

Book papers are frequently stocked with a choice of grain directions, while the more expensive text papers are usually available only 1 way. In making-orders, it is usually possible to get the grain in either direction.

Ordering paper

Choice of paper should be made in consultation with both paper supplier and printer, because many judgments are involved and the specialists can be of great help. In *ordering* paper, a knowledge of the system should be sufficient, but it is such a complex system that it pays to check your calculations with the paper salesman, even if you think you have the answer.

Papermaking is no longer the art it was when done by hand, but neither is the manufacture so precise that it can be depended upon for perfect uniformity. Some variations of color, finish, weight, etc. may occur and cause trouble. To a certain extent this is to be expected, but when the acceptable limits are exceeded, a complaint is in order. At such times (and many others), it is good to be dealing with a reliable merchant. And bear in mind that difficulties with the paper may be due to faults in the pressroom as well as in the mill.

CALCULATING QUANTITIES

When buying paper in sheets for the pages of books, determine how many pages will *cut out* of [divide into] each sheet (twice the number in each form) and divide this into the total number of pages in the book to get the number of sheets needed per book. Multiply this figure by the number of books to be printed and add a certain percentage of the total for *spoilage*. This percentage varies according to the number of colors, difficulties of printing, and length of run. Most of the spoilage occurs during makeready, when trial and error is the rule. On short runs (3 to 5000), this may be 5 to 7% per color, on long runs perhaps 3 to 5%, depending on the printing problem. The amount of extra paper provided should allow for some spoilage in binding too, usually about 3%. The printer and binder should be asked what they require for spoilage in each case.

Example: An edition of 5000 copies of a 256-page book with a trim-size of 5⅜ x 8″ being printed in 64-page forms, with 2 colors on each form.

(1) To print 64-page forms of 5⅜ x 8″ requires sheet size 44 x 66″

(2) 64 pages on each side of sheet = 128 pages per sheet

(3) 128 pages per sheet requires 2 sheets for a 256-page book

(4) 2 sheets per book x 5000 books = 10,000 sheets

(5) 5% printer's spoilage per color x 2 colors = 10%. Binder's spoilage of 3% makes total of 13%

(6) 10,000 sheets plus 13% (1300) = 11,300 sheets to be ordered

The same principle applies when ordering paper for jackets or for any other purpose. The size of the sheet required is always decided with the printer, partly because it must fit on one of his presses and partly because he may be printing 2 or more up and will need a correspondingly larger sheet.

Ordering paper in rolls for web-fed printing or binding machines is not very different in procedure. From the size of each page or unit the size of the form is determined, and this decides the width of the roll—although either dimension may be used for the width, depending on the way the grain is to run (the grain of the paper will always run with the roll, never across it). The other dimension is multiplied by the number of impressions involved and this figure is multiplied by *half* the number of forms to be printed (the other half back up). To this amount is added spoilage.

Thus, if the book used in the preceding example were being printed on a web-fed rotary in a quantity of 50,000 copies:

(1) To fold properly, the grain must be the long way of the page, so the width of the roll will be 44″

(2) Every 66″ of length will contain 64 pages. 50,000 x 66 = 3,300,000

(3) There will be 4 forms of 64 pages, of which 2 will back the other 2, so 3,300,000 is multiplied x 2 for 6,600,000″, or 550,000′

(4) Spoilage of 15% (web spoilage runs higher) makes a total of 632,500′.

Actually, such a book would probably be printed with 2 webs running together, each with a 32-page form on both sides. The rolls would then be 22″ wide, and each would be 632,500′ long. Except for lightweight papers, it is more common to order rolls of paper by weight rather than length. To calculate the weight needed, simply find the sheet size and figure as though ordering sheets (but add the extra web spoilage).

When paper is ordered from stock, the exact amount required will be delivered. When the paper is made to order, it is not possible to be sure of the quantity because the paper machine runs so fast it cannot always be stopped at precisely the point desired, and spoilage in the various papermaking operations are indefinite. The smaller the amount made, the larger will be the percentage of variation. Paper trade customs provide that the customer must accept and pay for a certain percentage more or less than the amount ordered, or elect to specify "not more than" or "not less than" a certain quantity. In the latter case, the variation in one direction that he must accept is considerably larger in percentage than otherwise. In large quantities, the percentage of variation (*overrun* or *underrun*) is not likely to be serious—perhaps 1 or 2%. On small orders, say 1000 lbs., the amount delivered may be as much as 20% off. (Only a few mills will even make orders so small.)

It is easy to make a drastic arithmetical error in calculating paper quantities, and even the most experienced people get a trifle nervous about ordering large amounts. Although the paper salesman checks your figures, he may make the same mistake you made, so use this simple practical test: Take a book of about the same size and kind as yours will be and weigh it. If it weighs 1 lb. and you are making 5000 books, you know that you should be ordering about 5000 lbs. of paper. (The cover on the book you weighed will account for spoilage and then some. A more accurate result can be obtained by using a paperback.) This won't show up a minor mistake, but you will certainly know that you shouldn't be ordering 500 or 50,000 lbs., nor 2500 or 10,000 lbs.

CALCULATING COST

The price of book and cover paper is based on weight. For each brand and grade of paper there is a sliding scale of prices per pound according to the amount ordered, with the lowest prices for the largest quantities. The range is considerable, the highest prices being 2 or 3 times as much as the lowest, so it is vital to know the exact amount of paper needed. A small difference in quantity may shift the price into another bracket and make a difference of 15% or more. Because of this, it is quite possible for a larger amount of paper to cost less than a smaller amount.

The price brackets vary somewhat from paper to paper, but the most commonly used are: 1 carton, 4 cartons (1 *case*), 16 cartons (4 cases). 5M lbs., 10M lbs. Both smaller and larger brackets exist but are less often used. The amount of paper in a carton varies according to the size and weight of the sheet, but it is usually about 150 lbs. Large quantities may be bought on skids or may be packed in cartons at a slightly higher price. (M = 1000)

A price list will give prices for each bracket and show the M weight and number of sheets per carton for each size of sheet in stock. Thus, if we are buying paper for the book used in the previous example, the table will show that there are 2000 sheets per case for the 44 x 66″, 306M, sub. 50 item. We are ordering 11,300 sheets, which is 5+ cases. This puts us in the 4-case bracket (anything from 4 cases to 5000 lbs.). Let us say the price per lb. is $.2360 (the price is usually given per 100 lbs., but it is easy to move the decimal point). Now it is necessary to know how many pounds are needed. If 1000 sheets weigh 306 lbs., then 11,300 will weigh 11.3 x 306 or 3458 lbs. Multiply this by $.2360, the cost per lb., and you have the total cost of the paper, $816.09. If a making-order were involved, there could be additional charges for special size, finish, grain, or color, or a variation due to an under- or overrun. (Very lightweight papers also carry a price penalty because of the extra fillers needed for opacity.)

While the base price of paper made to order is no higher than stock paper (if the quantity is sufficient), the color or finish may not come out exactly as hoped for, there may be an overrun to pay for, or the delivery time may be a problem. Worse yet, a strike or accident may make it impossible to deliver the order at all. Also, bear in mind the problem that might arise if a reprint is needed in a quantity too small to warrant a making-order. If there is a stock size larger than the sheet required, there is only the cost of extra paper, but the problem could be serious if no larger size is made.

Against these considerations may be weighed the advantage of having a special color or finish, and the money saved when a special size prevents a waste that would occur if the stock sheet were used. For example, if the page size of a book is 5¾ x 9¼″, there would be an unused strip 3″ wide and 38″ long on a standard 38 x 50″ sheet. Thus, 8% of the paper cost is wasted. It can be saved by having the paper made 35 x 50″.

Selecting paper

It might seem more logical to put "selecting paper" ahead of "ordering paper," but it is necessary to know the problems of paper buying in order to make practical selections. Unless a making-order is feasible, availability may have as much effect on paper choice as price and preference. Where price is a consideration (and it usually is), it is much easier to choose between a half dozen possibilities if you can roughly calculate the prices yourself.

The selection of paper involves esthetic factors in the choice of color, texture, etc. (CHS.15,16), but the first consideration must be suitability to the technical requirements. This is discussed in terms of the printing processes.

■ *Letterpress*—Any paper can be printed by letterpress, although those sized or coated solely for lithography cause some difficulties. For printing type and average line cuts, any of the antique papers are suitable. Very fine line cuts and coarse screen halftones (up to 100) will work on vellum or machine finishes but only under proper conditions (CH.16). Halftone screens of 100 and 110 lines require an English Finish or super. Pigmented papers can be used for 120 screen, but a coated stock is more satisfactory. Anything finer than 120 should be printed on coated. Dull-coated will work with any screen, but the results will be a little inferior to those possible on gloss-coated.

Books are printed usually on 50 to 70 lb. paper. Most common is 55 or 60 lb. antique, with 50 lb. (and occasionally 45 lb.) used for books with very many pages, and 70 lb. (and occasionally 80 lb.) for those with few. In general, publishers like as thick a book as feasible (CH.16) up to the point where there is no longer much sales advantage and it becomes desirable to keep the paper cost down. However, if the use of bulky paper fails to produce the thickness wanted, it is necessary to increase the weight. In books of very many pages, the lighter weights of paper are used, but it is best to use a more calendered finish to reduce bulk rather than extremely light weights. The latter are not only expensive, but they cause difficulty in printing, especially in large sheets. Most printers charge a penalty for handling paper below 40 lb. substance.

Opacity is related to weight and is usually affected by bulk. Bulking antiques have good opacity, because the light is scattered by the loose construction, and heavier weights have better opacity due to more fiber and/or filler, although a heavily calendered 60 lb. stock may be less opaque than a bulky 50 lb. Two sheets of the same weight and finish may vary in opacity if their ingredients differ. Papers coated on both sides are very opaque because of the density of the 2 layers of clay. Coated-one-side, which is usually used over an opaque surface (labels, jackets, etc.), tends to poor opacity because the base stock needs, and has, very little. Opacity is important in books with halftones or with pages of irregular layout in which type or illustrations back up areas of open space.

▪ *Lithography*—Paper used for offset lithography is surface-sized to resist moisture and picking (CH.7). The proper sizing can be applied to almost any kind of paper, although strong, long-fibered sheets are best. Also, the amount needed tends to spoil the soft appearance of antique stock. (The paper on which this book is printed is a good compromise between lithographic printing suitability and antique appearance.)

Sheets made for color process reproduction by lithography are either litho-coated or litho-sized. For color process or monochrome halftone printing in any process it is best to have maximum contrast between the color of paper and ink. Since most litho papers are made with halftone printing in mind, they tend to be hard of surface and bright white. In some lines, fluorescent dyes are used to increase the brightness. For books in which the halftones need not dazzle, there are off-white, relatively unsized papers available (such as this one).

Because of their sizing, litho papers tend to stiffness, and are comparable in this respect to unsized papers 10 lbs. or more heavier in substance. On the other hand, litho papers tend to bulk less than antique letterpress sheets of the same weight.

Any litho-sized paper will take 133 screen, and the fully sized sheets are able to handle 150 very well. For 175- and 200-line screens a supercalendered stock is best. Screens over 200 should have a coated stock, but they can be printed on a smooth uncoated. Perfectly good halftones—and even color process—can be printed on papers with embossed textures.

Surface-sizing adds a small amount per pound to the price of paper.

▪ *Gravure*—There is no connection between screen size and paper in gravure printing, as the finest screens can be printed on any kind of paper. Indeed, since the only bar to reproduction of continuous tone is the grid of white lines separating the dots, it is desirable to have the ink spread over the lines. Formerly, this was accomplished by printing on dampened antique paper with heavy pressure. However, the tendency of the antique stock to absorb the ink produced a relatively soft effect, which is not always desirable. Today, much gravure printing is done with lighter impression on coated or pigmented sheets—on which the ink spreads more by surface flow than absorption. The results are more brilliant.

Dull-coated paper is generally preferred over gloss, particularly since there is a tendency for the coating to be damaged by the relatively heavy pressure of gravure printing. Some, but not all, litho-sized papers can be used. Almost any other kind of paper is usable, including the cheapest groundwood sheets (witness the rotogravure sections in some Sunday newspapers). However, although it is possible to get quite good results on almost any surface (including acetate) by this process, the results do vary, so it is best to check with the printer before selecting.

The color of the paper is particularly important in gravure because the ink is transparent. A darker shade will give a softer effect, but as long as the color is clear and bright the result is good. For the most brilliant results, a white paper is best, although the fluorescent whites cause trouble. Avoid light weights of uncoated paper (under 60 lb.) as there is a possibility of the thin gravure ink bleeding through.

- *Collotype*—As in lithography, water is used and there is also danger of picking due to very tacky ink, so the paper requirements are similar. There are 2 main differences: (a) collotype has no screen, so a difference of surface is not so significant and (b) the ink coverage is even less than in lithography, so clarity of paper color is very important. Sharp contrast is impossible in collotype, so whiteness is not necessary. The soft, luminous effect is best achieved with a sheet having the characteristics of gravure paper.
- *Xerography*—In the offset method, any paper with characteristics suited to the printing machine can be used. The direct method requires that the paper be coated with a zinc oxide compound. Any paper (and virtually any other material) can be used for this purpose.
- *Silk screen*—Any paper can be printed.

9 | Illustration

Relation to design

Far from simply "laying out" pictures supplied with the Ms, the designer may initiate the idea of illustrations and suggest their character. Few authors think in graphic terms—and fewer still are well acquainted with the techniques of visual expression. The book designer operates as a graphic engineer, utilizing the science and art of visual presentation to achieve optimum communication, so it is appropriate for him to advise on this aspect of the book. Therefore, the conception, inclusion, and selection of illustrations—as well as their placement and reproduction—are parts of book design. Properly, these matters are discussed by author, editor, designer, and production manager jointly—with a view to producing the best book possible.

The use of illustration is considered less often than it should be, due to the impression that it necessarily involves great expense. This is not so, as will be shown.

Kinds of illustration

There is a wide range of visual material included in "illustration". This becomes clear when the kinds of illustration are divided by function. There are 4 kinds: (a) Informative, (b) Suggestive, (c) Decorative, and (d) Representative.

▪ *Informative*—Those whose purpose is to explain or depict facts, circumstances, characters, things, or places. Included here are the realistic drawings commonly used in teenage fiction, the photographs, drawings, diagrams, etc. found in many technical and other nonfiction books.

▪ *Suggestive*—These include all graphic elements designed to establish or enhance mood or atmosphere.

▪ *Decorative*—These are graphic elements whose purpose is simply to ornament the page.

▪ *Representative*—These are pictures being shown as works of art, for the purpose of producing an approximation of the pleasure of seeing the original. This includes the reproductions and prints in art books.

Some illustrations fall into more than 1 category, but a dominant purpose is usually definable. Realistic illustrations may have such evocative power as to place them in the suggestive category. If they are more valuable for the moods they induce than for the facts they impart, they may be used accordingly. Some decorative material may be particularly allusive and find its way into the suggestive group. Hardly anything less abstract than type rules and some stock ornaments can fail to suggest subject matter, although the medieval and renaissance illuminators used floral decoration with no subject relationship to the text on the page.

One picture may be used for different purposes and thus fall into a different category in each case. The distinction is in the intent. The distinction is important because it will determine how the illustration is used and reproduced. For example, suppose you had a particularly fine photograph of Wall Street. Used in a guidebook to show what Wall Street looks like, the picture would be informative. In a book of poems about city life the same picture might be used to create an urban atmosphere (suggestive). In a book of photographs, this one might be reproduced to give the reader the pleasure of seeing an excellent shot of tall buildings or, it might even be inserted as a print. In either case it would be in the representative class.

Ways of introducing illustration

INFORMATIVE

It is sometimes desirable to use a map or diagram to clarify a point in fiction or narrative nonfiction. The simplest sketch can do the trick. It need be no more elaborate than the kind you would make to show someone the way to your house. Drawn directly and simply, such a sketch can be very effective. Another possibility is to use antique maps.

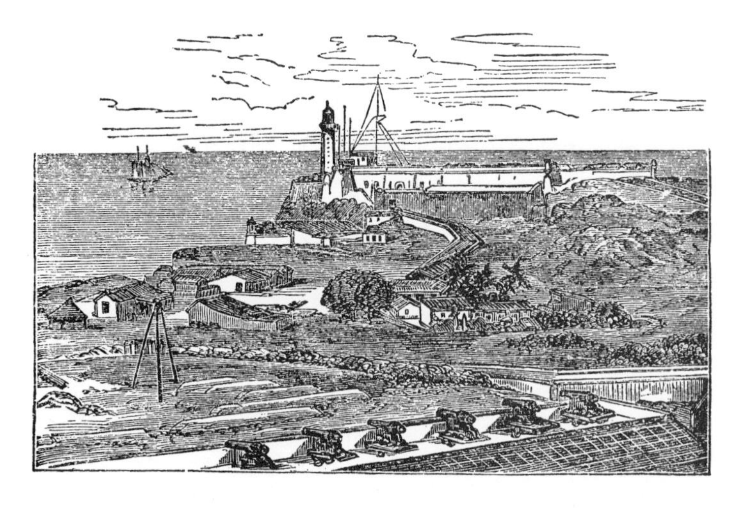

Illustrations of objects, characters, and places can be useful and interesting. These too can be rough sketches by the designer (or the author) or they can be taken from existing pictorial material. For example, some charming and accurate engravings of carpenter's tools were taken from an old hardware catalogue and used in a new book on finishing cellars and attics. Many travel books of the 19th century had pen-and-ink drawings of various places. These could be used in travel books, biographies, fiction, etc.

SUGGESTIVE

Here the opportunity for illustration is truly unlimited. The whole range of symbolism, from literal to abstract, is at the designer's disposal.

Of literal symbols there are all the insignia, emblems, and devices of organizations, nations, families, societies, companies, etc. A book about submarines can use the submarine officer's insigne, a book with England as its subject can have a British lion or even a royal coat of arms, and so on. Other symbols can be created from type ornaments and rules. Anything that establishes or enhances a mood or atmosphere can be used. The most abstract device can have suggestive power. A classic example is the black border that effectively creates a funereal mood.

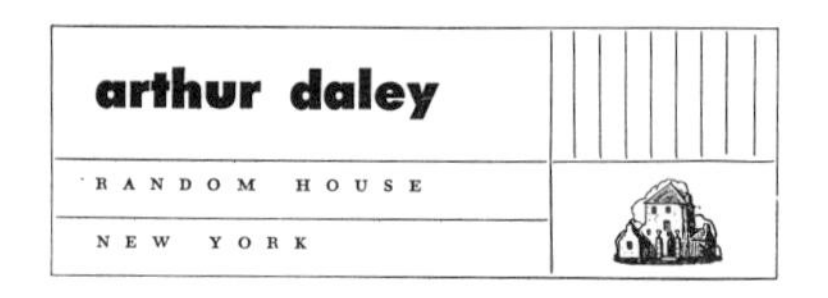

Pictures can be used to enhance atmosphere. Among the thousands of works by artists over the centuries there are some expressing virtually every state of feeling. Gay, sad, tragic, bucolic, orgiastic, tender, terrible, pictures abound—many by great masters. These can be your background music. Old Chinese drawings of bare trees were used to create a wintry feeling, bacchanalian scenes from Greek pottery have been used to set a gay mood. Countless wood engravings and other pictures have been used to provide the flavor of a particular period characterized by a style of illustration. The possibilities are endless.

DECORATIVE

An excess of decoration in the late 19th century led to a severe functional attitude in the second quarter of the 20th. It can be argued that pure decoration, without informative or suggestive value, is meaningless and therefore superfluous. Yet, the total absence of decoration in architecture has brought a new demand for decorated surfaces. The now-familiar pierced pattern walls of Edward Stone are being copied widely—and will eventually bring their own revolt—but they have demonstrated that decoration need not be at odds with function. (Louis Sullivan, one of the prophets of the "form follows function" school of architecture, used decoration extensively—as did his follower Frank Lloyd Wright.) It is, however, quite difficult to use decoration functionally—and very easy to use it as pointless gaud. In any case, it must not be allowed to take precedence over other aspects of the book.

Where decoration is used to suggest the style of a period related to the text, it ceases to be decorative illustration and becomes suggestive. Any decoration using elements of a distinctly allusive nature is suggestive. It hardly seems worth using decoration that has no suggestive value, but it can be done. There is a great deal of typographic ornament available (although it is decreasing because of disuse), ranging from purely abstract rules, dots, squares, etc. to the most elaborate florets. These may be combined in infinite ways to create a pattern on a whole page—one of the more interesting uses of decoration—or a spot on a chapter opening or title page.

REPRESENTATIVE

For the most part, this kind of illustration is an integral part of art and photography books. However, a reproduction of a picture can enhance the beauty (and value) of almost any kind of book—poetry, biography, history, etc.

When a picture is used whose subject is related to the text, the illustration has suggestive value, but if its main purpose is representative, it must be so treated. An abstract or nonobjective picture presents no such problem.

A single reproduction may be used as part of the frontmatter or several may be scattered through the book, either at random or at specific places, such as part-titles (CH.22).

Sources of illustration

There is a huge store of graphic material available to the designer who has the imagination and knowledge to use it. Illustration can be obtained in 4 ways: (a) by commissioning an illustrator, (b) by paying for reproduction rights to existing pictures, (c) by using graphic material in the public domain or available without charge, and (d) by doing it yourself.

ILLUSTRATORS

It is desirable to keep a file of the names of artists who do a variety of work. A folder for each, with some photostats of his or her work is worth the trouble and space. Such a file can be developed by interviewing artists and by clipping interesting illustrations from magazines and newspapers or making photocopies of illustrations from books. A useful source of artists is the *Illustrator's Annual,* a catalogue of the yearly exhibitions sponsored by the Society of Illustrators. Also, there are agents who specialize in representing illustrators.

In general, younger artists charge lower prices and sometimes do work that is fresher and less commercial looking than that of the more experienced illustrators. It is possible to get attractive work (at even lower prices) from art school students. The disadvantage here is in the comparative uncertainty of the results. It takes long experience to develop a reliable technique and a sure approach. It is not enough to have the *ability* to do an excellent job, one must be able to deliver a good job in a very high percentage of tries, under the pressures of time and stringent requirements. This comes with years of practice.

Book illustration is an artistically attractive assignment, and many first-rate artists prefer this (at least occasionally) to advertising or magazine work. Consequently, they can sometimes be persuaded to accept little or no more than what a mediocre professional illustrator would be paid. This seems like an exploitive attitude, but it is not, when one considers that the economics of (most) book publishing will not permit the kind of fees paid in advertising and magazines. The choice is not between high and low fees, it is between small payment (in comparison with advertising) and no illustration.

It is good to support and encourage living artists, and a lot more could be done in this respect than is being done, but sometimes this is not possible. Then it becomes necessary to look to other, less costly means of finding illustration.

REPRODUCTION RIGHTS

If the illustration needs of the book can be met with pictures that already exist (thus eliminating the uncertainties of made-to-order illustrations), the rights to use such material can be obtained for much less than it would cost to commission the work initially. Presumably, the artist or photographer has already been compensated for producing the work, so that whatever he (or the owner of the picture) receives for reproduction rights is extra money. How much the fee will amount to is a matter to be settled in each case. It can be very little or the artist/photographer/owner may ask for a lot. If the price is too high there is no need to accept the terms. The price is based to some extent on the use. A larger fee is requested, usually, for advertising than for book use.

There are 2 kinds of material for which reproduction fees are paid:

▪ *Copyrighted material*—This includes most works published in the United States during the previous 56 years. The present U. S. Copyright law (which is liable to be revised at any time now) provides protection for 28 years with renewal possible for an equal period. Illustrations in a copyrighted publication are protected by that copyright, or may be separately protected. A work copyrighted more than 28 years ago may or may not be in the public domain—depending on whether or not its copyright was renewed.

Unpublished works (including pictures) are protected by common (unwritten) law indefinitely. Some unpublished works (including pictures other than *prints* [multiple copies of a picture printed from a plate made by the artist] and reproductions) may be registered for copyright for the usual 2 terms, but they lose their protection if published—unless a proper copyright notice is added. Under certain circumstances, exhibition of a picture may be considered publication.

Note that it is *the fact of publication* (making available to the public) *with a proper copyright notice* that establishes copyright. Registration with the Copyright Office is merely a *claim* of copyright—although it is probably indispensable to any successful legal action. If there is no notice on a published work, it may be assumed that there is no copyright.

It is not always clear who has the right to authorize reproduction of an unpublished picture. If the terms of sale specifically transfer that right from the creator to the new owner, the matter is clear enough. But where no such assignment is made, some doubt exists. Many artists have claimed that sale of a picture involves possession of the physical object but no other rights. If the picture is by a long deceased artist (who never assigned reproduction rights) it is very doubtful that the owner has any legal rights in the matter. However, the owner has possession and therefore has the power, if not necessarily the right, to authorize reproduction. Museums do, in practice, exercise these powers and it is best to respect their requirements—or risk being denied access to their collections thereafter.

To the complexities of domestic copyright law must be added the international problem. Under the Berne Convention (1886), works protected in 1 contracting nation are protected in each, according to its own laws. Most Western countries belong to this agreement, but the United States does not. However, its terms are generally respected by American publishers—who expect similar treatment in the other countries. Under the UNESCO Universal Copyright Convention (1955), of which we *are* a signatory, protection in all participating nations is obtained by publication in any one, provided the proper notice is used (a c in a circle ©, the year, and the name of the copyright owner) in the proper place. Again, the protection given in each country is the same as given to works published under that country's laws.

Copyright law—both domestic and international—is not only often imprecise, it is riddled with exceptions and special conditions. The foregoing outline is meant to provide a general view of the subject, not a legal definition. It is a good idea to become familiar with current copyright requirements and to check whenever in doubt.

The copyright owner has a right to demand a fee for reproduction or to refuse permission altogether—and violation of copyright is punishable by law. Sometimes there is genuine doubt about the copyright status of a particular work. In such cases, inquiries should be made on the assumption that there *is* protection.

▪ *Non-copyright material in private ownership*—A vast amount of graphic material published more than 56 years ago, and other material not protected by copyright, is yours to use—if you can get it. There are several kinds of agencies that collect such material for the purpose of charging reproduction fees. These include picture agencies, photographers and photographic agencies, some private museums, libraries, etc. Most of these will search their files for pictures you request, and then charge a fee for supplying them for reproduction. Your payment is almost always under an agreement that it is for 1 use only. Fees generally start at about $25 for 1 picture and go up from there according to the difficulty of finding the material, the reputation of the photographer, the use, etc. It is the owner's picture, and he can charge whatever he wants.

This can be a relatively expensive way to illustrate a book, but it usually costs less than hiring an illustrator, and sometimes the material is unobtainable otherwise. The larger picture agencies, such as Culver, Bettman Archive, Acme, P.I.P., etc., have excellent facilities. There are dozens of sources of picture material, some quite specialized.

It is possible, also, to obtain printing plates of illustration material under certain circumstances. Museums, art galleries, book and magazine publishers have plates of pictures which they have used, and they will usually provide duplicates or reproduction proofs of these at cost plus a fee that varies according to the owner. At most, the fees are a fraction of the cost of making a new set of color plates. The matter of reproduction permission and fees is not affected by such arrangements. If plates are obtained from someone other than the owner of the picture, the latter still should be approached for permission.

Some museums reserve the right to deny permission if the quality of reproduction fails to meet their standards. Again, there may be no legal right involved, but it is unwise to cross a great museum whose facilities may be denied in the future.

FREE MATERIAL

By far the greatest quantity of picture material in existence is available without charge. Man has been creating pictures for thousands of years, and much of this output is of excellent quality. There is no reason why it should be dormant when it can be effectively used. The problem is simply to find it. One publisher, Dover Publications, has made a business of selling, in book form, reprints of old pictures. Their quality is excellent, and the pictures are available for reproduction to anyone. However, Dover has merely scratched the surface—and could never reprint more than a handful from the oceans of picture material extant.

There are 2 kinds of free graphic material: (a) that in the public domain and (b) material in private ownership.

▪ *Material in the public domain*—This includes all uncopyrighted material obtainable without charge and without permission. Again, be careful about determining what is in the public domain. (For example, nonmechanical (handmade) *reproductions* of works in public domain may be protected by copyright.)

The primary sources of free illustration are old books. The great libraries are treasure houses of such material, but you need a special key. Except for some specialized collections, the books are catalogued according to their literary content and a great deal of searching is required to discover pictures among them—unless you know in advance of specific titles containing the pictures you want. Librarians can be very helpful in this respect, but most are not trained to think in terms of illustration, and their time is limited. It is best to go first to a specialized source or to someone familiar with the subject.

The print collections of libraries, historical societies, and museums are excellent sources of free pictures. (In almost all cases, a charge of between $1 and $6 is collected for photostats or photoprints supplied, but this is so small compared to the value of the pictures that they may be considered free.) The curators are usually able to guide you to material by subject, although most collections are catalogued by artist, title, number, etc. Some very old and rare prints and books may be unavailable for reproduction because of their condition.

There are several general picture collections that arrange material by subject and lend pictures for reproduction or similar use at no charge. The best of these are at the Main Building of the New York Public Library and the Library of Congress in Washington. The latter combines the features of a print collection and a picture collection, while the former confines itself mainly to clippings, movie stills, and some magazines. There is a good collection at the Philadelphia Free Library and others of varying size elsewhere. The use of pictures from these collections requires no fee to the lender, but the borrower is responsible for getting permission from copyright owners where necessary.

Old books, magazines, catalogues, prints, etc. can be bought in secondhand bookstores cheaply, if you count the value of the pictures they contain. With luck—and time—you can pick up good picture material at country auctions. A few cents will sometimes buy a boxful of old publications of no value to anyone but a picture user.

- *Privately owned material*—Thanks to the desire of many business and other organizations to publicize themselves, there is a tremendous amount of free picture material available to anyone who can provide a credit line. Almost any medium-sized or large company will gladly supply pictures of their products, and some of the largest corporations maintain picture libraries of considerable scope. (A notable one is that of Standard Oil Company of New Jersey in the RCA building at Rockefeller Center, New York.) The public relations department is the place to ask. Another good source is the promotion department of a country, state, or resort anxious for publicity to attract visitors.

Movie stills can be purchased for small amounts (rare ones are not cheap) at shops in the larger cities or directly from the movie companies. Usually, permissions but no fees are required, although the companies like to get credit lines. Used imaginatively, movie stills are a rich source of illustration. Their possibilities are practically unlimited and are, so far, almost unexplored.

It is worth repeating that the real problem in getting illustration material is finding it. No one who has not done picture research himself has any idea how much time it can consume. To make the use of existing pictures feasible, you must be able to go to the proper source without too much trial and error. Study the history and development of illustration to become familiar with general and specific sources. When looking for pictures, keep in mind the possibility of future use. Some excellent material may be discovered in the course of a search for something else. It is a good idea to build up a picture collection of your own. Save old magazines, catalogues, etc. and cut out usable or unusually interesting graphic material. File your pictures by subject and you will sometime save yourself a trip and some money. Always remember that the picture you want to use may be someone else's property and that the copyright laws are to be observed.

DO-IT-YOURSELF

A certain amount of illustration may properly be considered part of the design. If the designer introduces a minor decorative element into a title page he should, under most circumstances, execute the drawing as part of his function. If the illustration is at all extensive, and the designer is capable of producing it himself, he should be considered as an illustrator and paid accordingly.

Even those who are not trained or experienced in illustration can execute simple drawings and diagrams. There is a minimum of talent required, however, if the work is not to sink below the general level of the book. If you are in doubt, get some competent outside opinion before you include your own drawing in a book.

Treatment of illustrations

Illustrations must be treated according to their nature and purpose and to the considerations arising from their physical relationship to the text. The factors involved are:

(a) Editorial requirements of position (CH.16).
(b) Methods of binding (CH.10).
(c) The processes of platemaking and printing (CH.7).
(d) The paper (CH.8).
(e) Layout (CH.21).
(f) Preparing the illustrations for camera (CH.11).

How these factors are taken into account is discussed in CH.16.

10 | Binding

Binding is a complex process. Hardcover binding involves about 18 different operations and uses a dozen materials, most of which are chosen individually for each book. This multiplicity provides many possibilities for variation—with both esthetic and economic significance. Such possibilities are discussed in CH.26—this chapter describes the mechanics and materials themselves.

There has been little radical innovation in binding compared to composition, platemaking, and printing. Since the hand operations were first converted to mechanical processes in the 19th century, there have been very few changes in the principles by which they are performed.

The main area of improvement today is in reduction of handling between steps. Machines are being built to perform several operations, and new plant layouts have a continuous line of machines, with the product of one feeding automatically into the next.

Electronics and computer technology are improving the efficiency of binding machinery and will make possible a considerable degree of automation, but there is nothing in sight comparable to the revolutionary effects of photography on composition and printing.

The term "binding" without further qualification is taken to mean conventional (hardcover) book binding, and it is to this that the foregoing comments generally refer, but there are some fairly radical departures in technology when other kinds of binding are considered.

Kinds of binding

There are basically 3 kinds of binding: (a) *case* (or *hard binding*, or *hardcover*), (b) *paper* (or *paperback*, or *softcover*), and (c) *mechanical* (including "spiral" binding, etc.), with many variations of each kind. The distinctions will be discussed later in this chapter. Up to a point, however, the binding process is the same for all kinds. This is the basic operation described below.

The basic operation

FOLDING

For each job, the method of folding printed sheets is determined before the pages are imposed for printing (CH.7). There are many methods, each one based on (a) the number of pages on the sheet, (b) the arrangement of signatures desired, and (c) the characteristics of the paper. An imposition is selected by the binder with the concurrence of the printer, so that all their requirements, as well as the conditions listed above, are met.

The fewer signatures there are in a book, the less its cost. This would suggest making signatures with as many pages as possible, but the number is limited by the bulk and flexibility of the paper. Too many pages in a signature cause wrinkling, buckling, and a tendency to spring open. Generally, antique stock up to 70 lb. is folded in 32-page signatures, from 70 through 80 lb. in 16s, and over 80 lb. in 8s. These limits should be lowered as more sizing, filling, and calendering are present. Very lightweight papers may be folded in 64s, up to about 30 lb.

Given a certain number of pages per signature, the sheet may be folded in different ways. The more pages on the sheet, the more variations possible. Successive folds may be parallel or at right angles to each other, the sheet may be cut into 2, 4, or 8 sections on the folding machine, the sections may each be folded in a variety of ways, and, finally, the sections may be inserted into others to become parts of larger signatures, or may become complete signatures themselves.

The chief reason for choosing one imposition over another is binding efficiency, but the choice may also be a means of distributing color throughout the book more effectively. For example, if a second color is printed on only some forms, the imposition can be arranged so that the pages with color will be in different parts of the book rather than all together, or they may be imposed to fall consecutively in some places rather than alternately. Considerable flexibility is possible, but any deviation from the simplest imposition usually adds to the cost of binding.

Too much space would be needed to describe all the standard impositions, and there are innumerable special impositions used in unusual circumstances. A simple 16-page example is described below to illustrate the principle.

To make a 16-page signature from a sheet with 8 pages on each side, using 3 right-angle folds, each form would have 2 rows of 4 pages each printed head to head, i.e. 1 row would be upside-down. The arrangement of pages would be:

front

5	12	9	8
4	13	16	1

back

7	10	11	6
2	15	14	3

Take a sheet of paper and mark it this way. It will be seen that 1 backs 2, 3 backs 4, and so on. Fold the sheet in half, then again in half at right angles to the first fold, then again at right angles to the previous one, and you will have a signature in which the 16 pages are in consecutive order.

Folding machines vary according to the kind of folding done, the size of sheet handled, and the principle of operation. Most book folding is done by the *tape-and-knife* method. The sheet is carried on a set of narrow endless belts or *tapes* until it is in position for a dull blade to drive it between rollers, which press the fold to a sharp crease. This operation is repeated until the sheet is finished. The machine slits or perforates certain folds to prevent *gussets* and wrinkles and to allow the trapped air to escape. On the larger machines, a sheet can be cut into sections, each of which is folded separately but simultaneously. Thus, a 128-page sheet may come out of the folder as eight 16-page signatures, four 32s, etc. The machine may deliver a 32-page signature folded from a single sheet (*straight* 32), it may consist of two 16s, one inserted in the other (*double* 16 *insert*), or the two 16s may be in consecutive order (*double* 16 *straight*).

tape-and-knife fold

Small units, such as endpapers and inserts, are folded on a *buckle* or *loop folder*. The sheet is passed between 2 plates until it hits a stop which causes it to buckle in the proper place. Two rollers grab the buckle and press it to a sharp fold.

buckle fold

Most rotary presses have coordinated folders built in so that the printing of the sheet (both sides) and its folding are virtually simultaneous. This means folding at a speed of about 25,000 sheets per hour instead of the usual 3 to 4000. The tape-and-knife method cannot work fast enough, so a different principle is used. It is too complex to be explained here, but it is based on high precision manipulation of the sheets by grippers and reduction of the number of right-angle folds needed, by cutting the sheet into small units.

TIPPING, & WRAPPING, & INSERTING

The signatures delivered by a folding machine are *bundled* [subjected to pressure and tied tightly between boards] and sent to the *gathering* department, where they are assembled into books. Before they are gathered, the endpapers, if any, are *tipped* onto the first and last signatures, and any illustrations not comprising a separate signature are tipped, *inserted*, or *wrapped*, at the proper place.

■ *Tip*—Tipping means pasting onto a page with about ⅛″ of paste along the inside, or *gutter*, edge. Tips may be a single leaf or a 4-page fold (as are the endpapers). Pasting tips onto the outsides of signatures is simplest, in the middle of signatures is more difficult, and most difficult is tipping within a signature, which usually requires slitting open a fold by hand. Outside tips are done by machine, but the others are hand operations.

■ *Insert*—Inserting illustrations into a signature means placing 4 or more pages in the middle or elsewhere, thereby enlarging it by that many.

■ *Wrap*—Wrapping is the reverse of inserting; the illustrations go around the *outside* of the text signature. Mechanically, the process is the same as inserting and both are usually performed by hand. A wrap can be placed around certain of the pages within a signature (for example, around pages 5 and 12 in the 16-page signature described earlier in this chapter) but this is a slower operation.

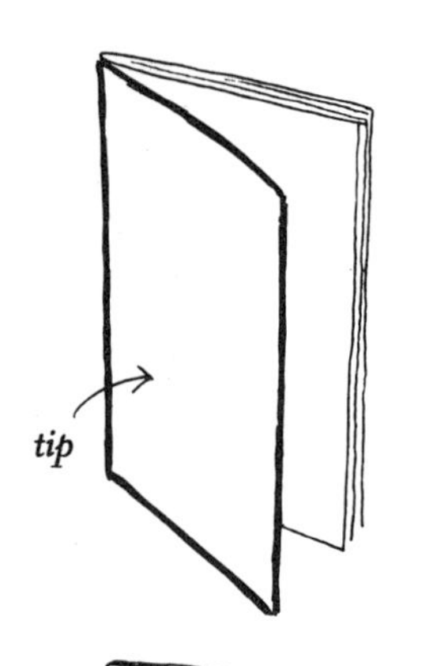

In some sewed books, tips are weaker than inserts or wraps because no stitching goes through them. To avoid tips it is possible to make 2-page (single leaf) wraps by leaving an extra ½″ of paper on the inside edge of the leaf to wrap around the signature, but this is not very practical for large edition binding, and the short pieces are unsightly where they protrude between pages.

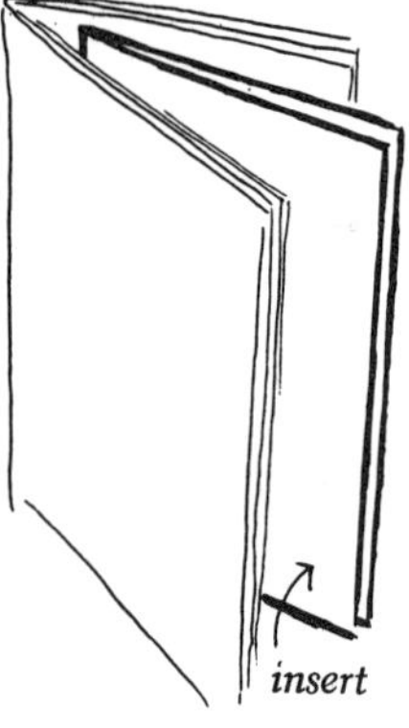

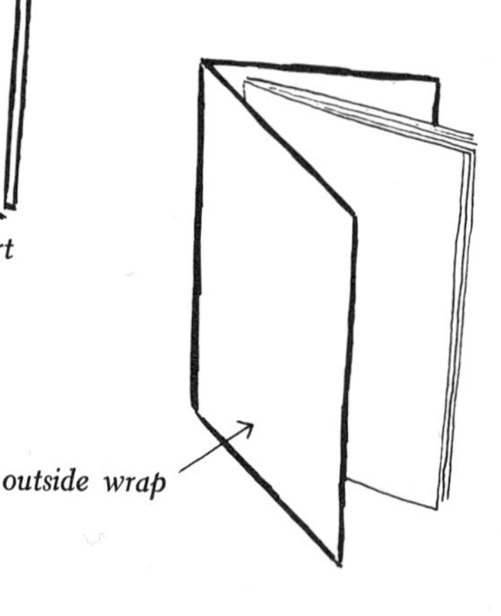

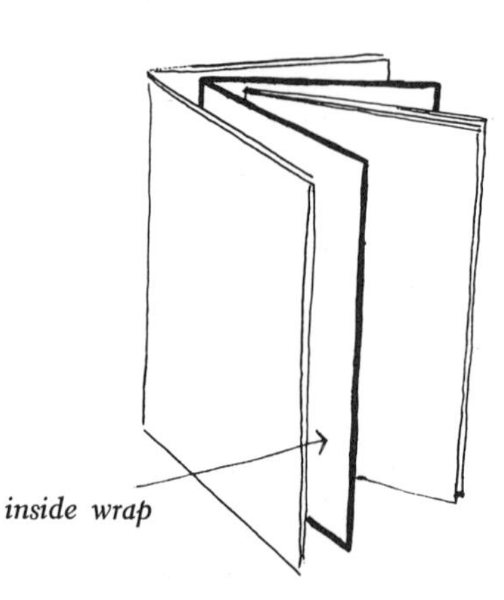

2 methods of reinforcing

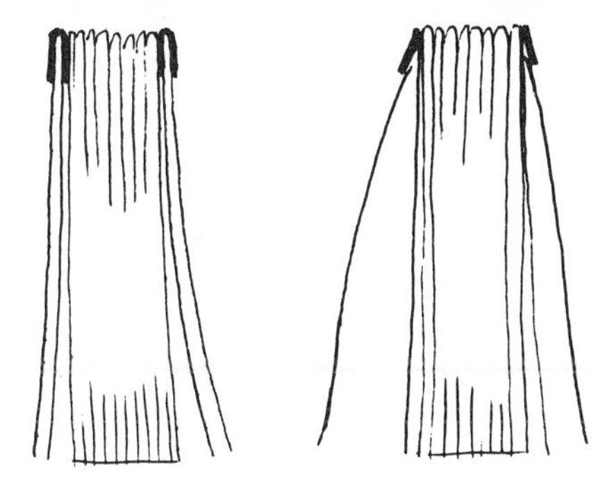

REINFORCING

Reinforcing of signatures, when required, is usually done at this stage. There are several methods. Generally, these consist of pasting a 1″ strip of cambric cloth along the back folds of the first and last signature after the endpapers are on, or pasting it on the outside of the endpapers without going around the signatures—depending on the sewing used. Sometimes, books are specially reinforced and bound for library use separately from the regular edition (*prebinding*). Libraries also have regular trade bindings *rebound* with extra reinforcement. Another kind of reinforcement is *whipstitching;* 1 or 2 extra rows of stitching on the first and last signatures. On very heavy books, 2 or 3 strips of cloth tape may be sewed across the back and extended onto the covers.

GATHERING & COLLATING

The completed signatures are piled in successive hoppers on the gathering machine. A mechanical arm takes a signature from the first hopper and places it on a conveyor belt, a second arm places a second signature from the next hopper on top of the first signature on the belt, and so on down the line until the book is completed. Thus, if the book has 10 signatures, the belt would always have 10 piles—one with all 10 signatures, one with 9, one with 8, and so on back to the first "pile" which would have only the first signature.

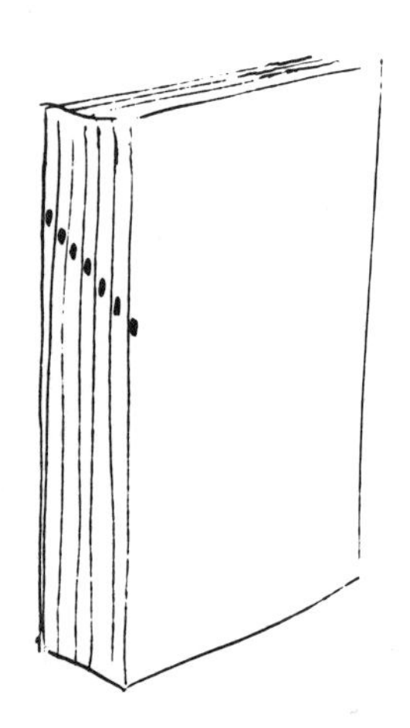

As the completed sets of signatures come off the machine, they are *collated* [checked for correct sequence and position]. In small editions this can be accomplished by an operator fanning through every fourth or fifth set to see that the first and last folios of succeeding signatures correspond, and that none are missing, duplicated, upside-down, or backward. Ordinarily, small marks (*collating marks*) are printed at certain places on the sheets, so that when folded, each signature has one along its back edge. A straight or diagonal line across the back results when the book is properly gathered, so any error is immediately apparent.

At this point, the process varies according to the kind of binding required, although some later operations are used in more than 1 method.

Case binding

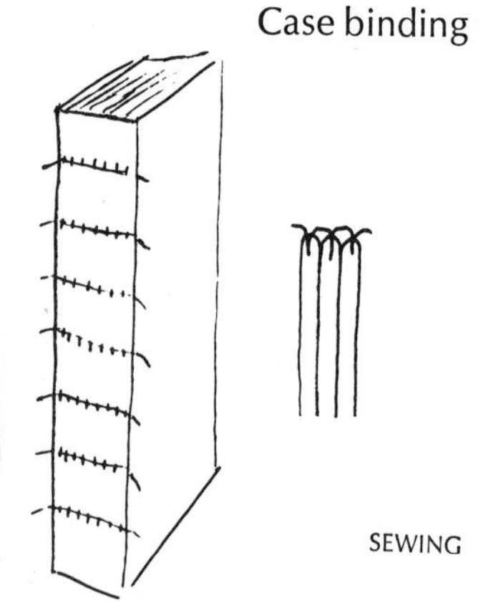

This is the conventional method of making a book, whereby the signatures are enclosed in a more or less rigid cover, to the inside of which they are attached by pasting the endpapers, or the first and last pages (*self-lining*). There are several variations in case binding, both in the manner of holding the pages together and in the nature of the cover. Any of these variations may be combined.

The pages may be held together (a) by sewing the signatures together, (b) by the use of wire staples, or (c) by adhesives (*perfect-binding*). These procedures follow immediately after collating.

SEWING

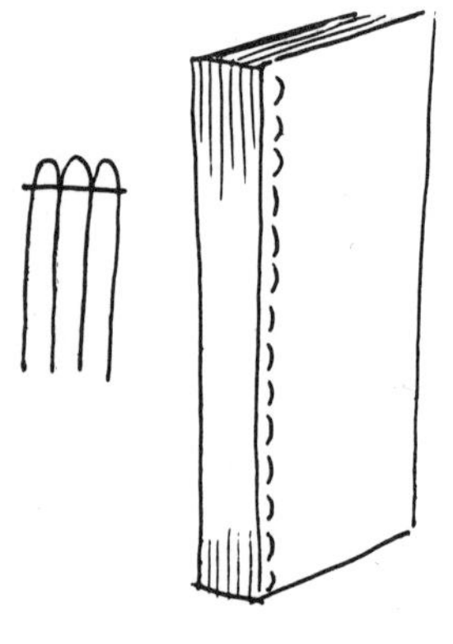

There are two methods:

- *Smyth sewing*—For trade books, this is the most common method. The thread is stitched through the gutter of each signature and passed through the other stitches at the back to join them. Being held this way, the pages are free to open without hindrance. The newer machines paste the back edge of the first and last signatures to the adjacent ones.

  If the book has only 1 signature and the stitching goes through the gutter it is called *saddle stitching.*
- *Side sewing* (*Singer sewing*)—The thread is passed through the entire book about 1/8″ from the back, just as it would be if sewed on a home sewing machine, as a hem is on a tablecloth. For books over 3/4″ bulk, another machine is used and the process is called *McCain sewing.*

WIRE STITCHING OR STAPLING

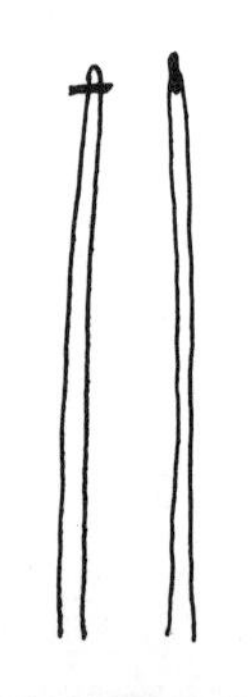

This is a cheaper method of holding pages together when there is just 1 signature. Two or 3 wire staples are passed through the gutter, as in a pamphlet (*saddle wire stitching*). *Side wire stitching* is similar in principle to side sewing, except that metal staples are used instead of thread. Side-sewed books have 2 wire staples put through them in the gathering machine to hold the signatures together for sewing, although these may be omitted on thin books.

PERFECT-BINDING

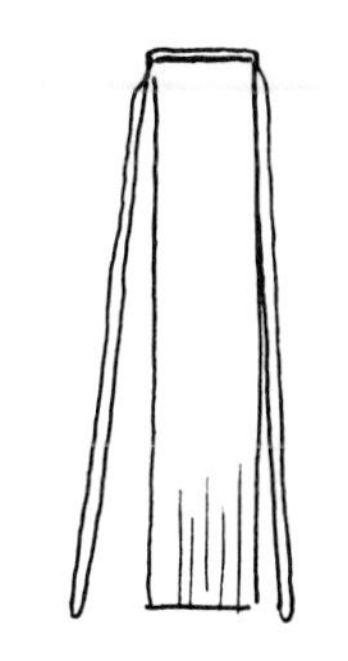

This method did not deserve its laudatory name until quite recently. The process consists of trimming off the folds at the back of the book and applying an adhesive to hold the pages together. Essentially, this is the same method as that used to make pads, and in its early days the results were about the same also—the pages were easily pulled out.

Subsequent improvements have made perfect-binding comparable in performance to sewed binding. There are many minor variations in the methods used, but they all involve trimming in such a way as to increase the amount of paper surface to which the adhesive can be applied—usually by notching or roughening the back of the book—and some kind of flexible, quick-drying adhesive.

SMASHING

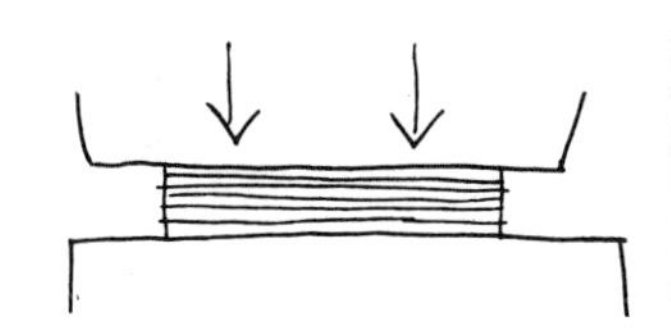

Sewed books must be given a heavy, rapid squeeze to eject air; compress the paper, stitching, and folds; and generally produce a compact unit. This is called *smashing* and is applied in a heavy press. During the perfect-binding operation, enough pressure is applied to the book to compress the pages firmly. No more is necessary because there are no folds left to hold air.

GLUING-OFF

This is the first operation in *forwarding.*

Even though sewed tightly, the back tends to loosen a little after smashing, so a thin coat of flexible glue is applied to hold the signatures in place. This is done by running the books back-down over a series of glue-carrying rollers, and then, usually, over a heating element that dries the glue so that it is hard enough to make the book firm in time for the next operation. Perfect-bound hardcover books are glued-off after the back folds are cut off and before the other 3 sides are trimmed. On these, a cloth lining is applied to the back.

TRIMMING

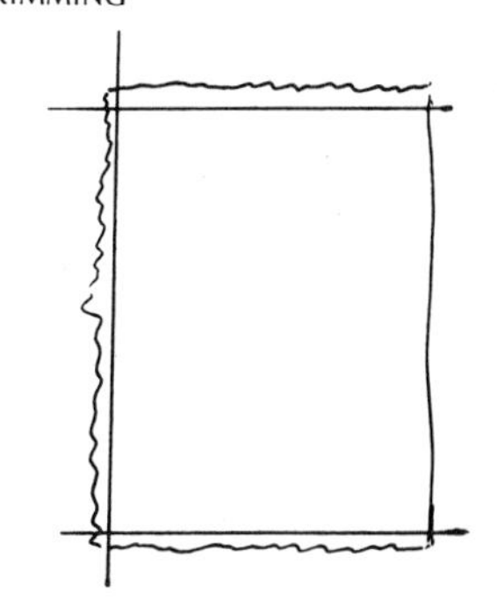

After being glued-off, the book is put into a trimming machine which trims (1/8″ approximately) at the *top* (*head*) *front* (*fore-edge*), and *foot* (*bottom*), thus opening all folds (or *bolts*) except those at the back. This is called a *smooth* (or *full*) *trim.* If a *rough trim* is desired at the foot, the knife takes off only enough to open the bolts, which are made to protrude slightly beyond the slit edges during folding. For a rough front, all folds are slit on the folder and there is no trim. The result is a more or less ragged edge somewhat resembling that of a book printed on handmade or deckle-edged paper. This adds about 1/8″ to the trim-size of the page.

EDGE COLOR

On case-bound books, the edge color is applied only to the top ordinarily. The color is an aniline dye and is sprayed on stacks of books about 1 foot high. The spray is directed at an angle from the back so that no excess color will get on the front. It may be applied by hand or by machine.

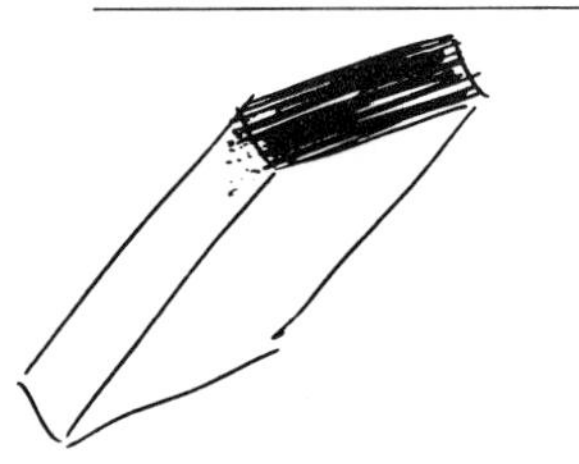

Gold edges are applied by hand in the same way as gold leaf is applied to frames. It is now possible to have an imitation gold applied at much lower cost by machine. The process is similar to the leaf-stamping operation used on covers (see "Stamping").

ROUNDING & BACKING

Both sewed and perfect-bound books are usually put through a machine which (a) *nips* the back to a uniform width, (b) rounds the back with a set of knurled rollers (thus producing the concave shape of the front), (c) clamps the book sharply *except* at the very back (the opposite of nipping), thus allowing the back to flare out slightly, and (d) shapes the back with curved backing irons.

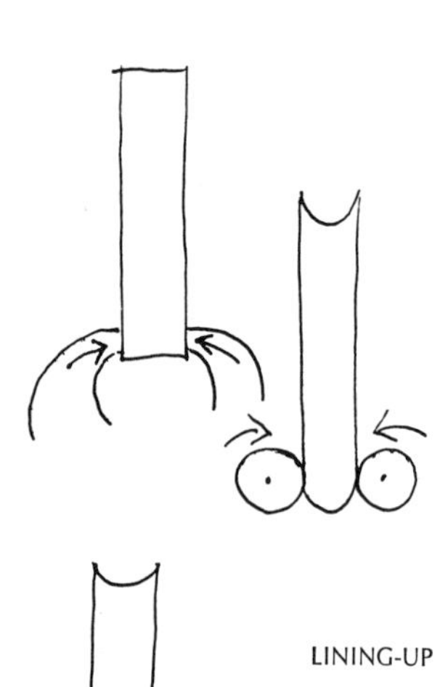

The ridge caused by the flaring of the back is called the *joint* and is very important to the structure of a book. It is at this point that the cover hinges and the pages bend when turned. The joint is also a locking device that tends to keep the book from slipping out of its cover. Books can be made with flat backs, but this is not practical when the bulk is more than about 1½", due to the loss of strength. Very thin books are usually made flat-backed, because there is not enough bulk for rounding and backing.

LINING-UP

This machine is usually combined with that which does rounding and backing. The books are carried along in clamps attached to an endless chain, along which each operation is successively completed. Sometimes, 2 books are carried in each position (2 up) for greater efficiency.

Lining-up is the major reinforcing process. First, a coat of glue is applied to the back. On top of this is placed a strip of *crash* or *super* [a gauze] extending almost the length of the back and about 1" over each side. Rollers press the crash into the wet glue and then apply another coat of glue on top of it. On this is applied a strip of tough paper cut to the length and width of the back.

The crash is very important, being the only link between cover and book other than the endpaper. On books requiring unusual strength, an extra-heavy crash (*legal crash*) or a double layer may be used. On a bound book, the crash can be detected underneath the endpaper.

Headbands are the strips of colored cloth that protrude slightly at the back on top and bottom. They are applied during lining-up, being glued to the back between the crash and paper.

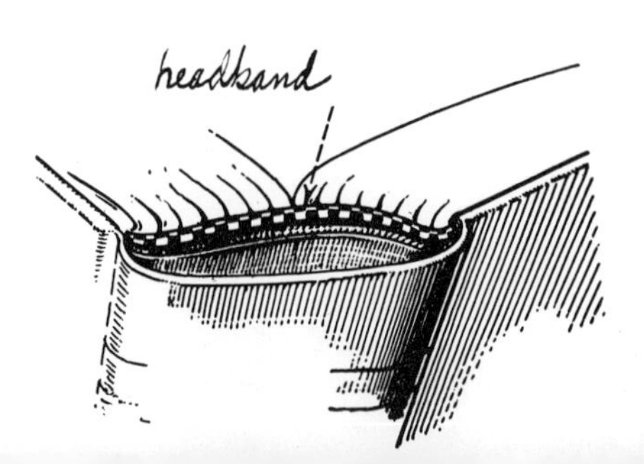

On completion of lining-up, the book is ready to be inserted in its cover. The cover is made while the folding, gathering, and forwarding are in progress, so that it will be ready at the same time as the book.

CASEMAKING

The conventional case (or cover) of a hardbound book consists of a more-or-less rigid board on each side and a strip of paper or board at the back, all covered with a decorative/protective material. The characteristics and varieties of these materials are discussed later in this chapter. The process of putting them together is *casemaking*.

The boards and the backstrip are cut to the height of the trim-size of the book *plus* ¼″—which provides for an overhang of ⅛″ at head and foot. The boards are made ⅛″ *less* than the width of the trim-size. The backstrip, for a round-backed book of normal bulk, is made ⅜″ wider than the bulk of the pages (*paper bulk*), to allow for the flare of the joint. For very thick or thin books, more or less than ⅜″ is added. For flat backs, the backstrip will equal the paper bulk plus the thickness of the boards. In a flat back, the backstrip is generally a rigid board rather than paper. This partly compensates for the lack of strength at the back and gives a neater appearance.

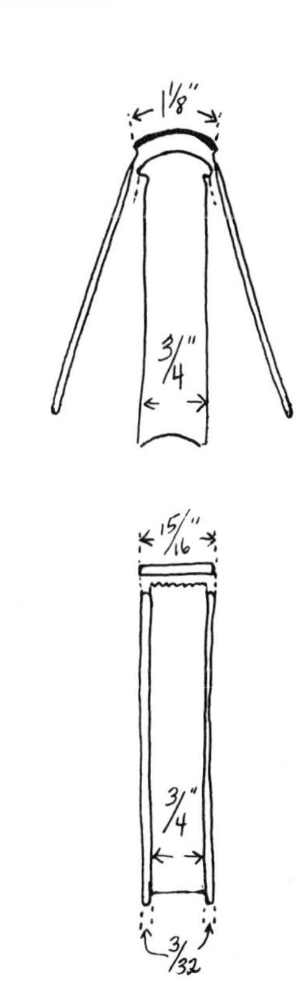

The cover material is cut to the height of the boards plus 1¼″—which allows ⅝″ at the head and foot for *turn-in*, i.e. for the material to wrap around the edge. In width, the material is made the width of both boards and backstrip, plus 1¼ turn-in, *plus* ¼″ for the joints on both sides. At the joint (or hinge) is a space of ¼″ between the boards and the backstrip. A diagonal cut is made at each corner of the material to prevent excessive bunching of the turn-in. Laid out in position for casemaking, the boards and cover material for a 7 x 10″ book, bulking ¾″, with a rounded back, would appear as follows:

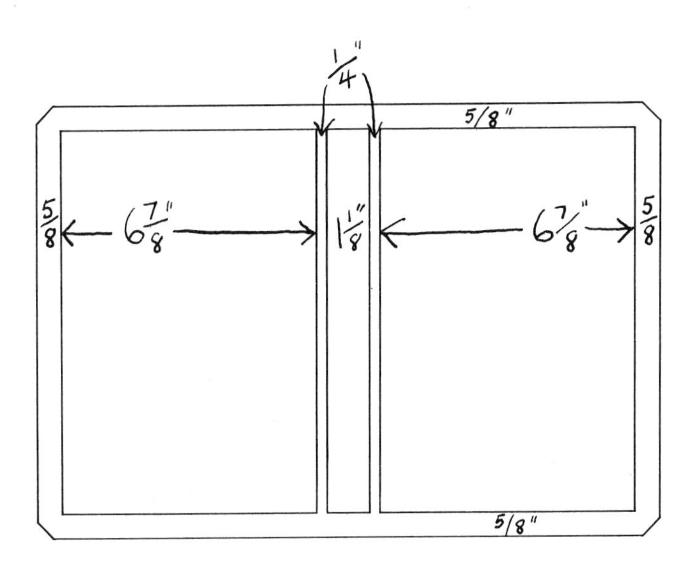

A cover such as this could be made in 2 ways: with precut pieces on a *sheet-fed casemaker,* or on a *web-fed casemaker* with only the boards precut, the cover material and backstrip paper being in rolls.

On the sheet-fed machine, the material is glued on its inside surface, the boards and backstrip are dropped onto the wet glue in the proper position, and small rollers push the turn-ins over and press them down, to complete the cover. This was a relatively slow operation until quite recently. New machines operate at about 4 times the speed of the old ones, thus equaling the production of web-fed machines.

In web-fed casemaking, the material passes over a glue roller and then, glue side up, under a hopper which holds the boards. Pieces of backstrip paper are automatically chopped off a roll to the proper length and dropped into place on the glued material. The boards are dropped into their positions at the same time. As the web moves along, the corners are cut, the material is cut off to the proper length, and the edges are turned in.

On some machines, the width of the web is the height of the material, so that board, backstrip, board, fall *successively* (*side feed*); on others, the web is the width, so the 3 pieces drop *simultaneously* alongside each other (*end feed*).

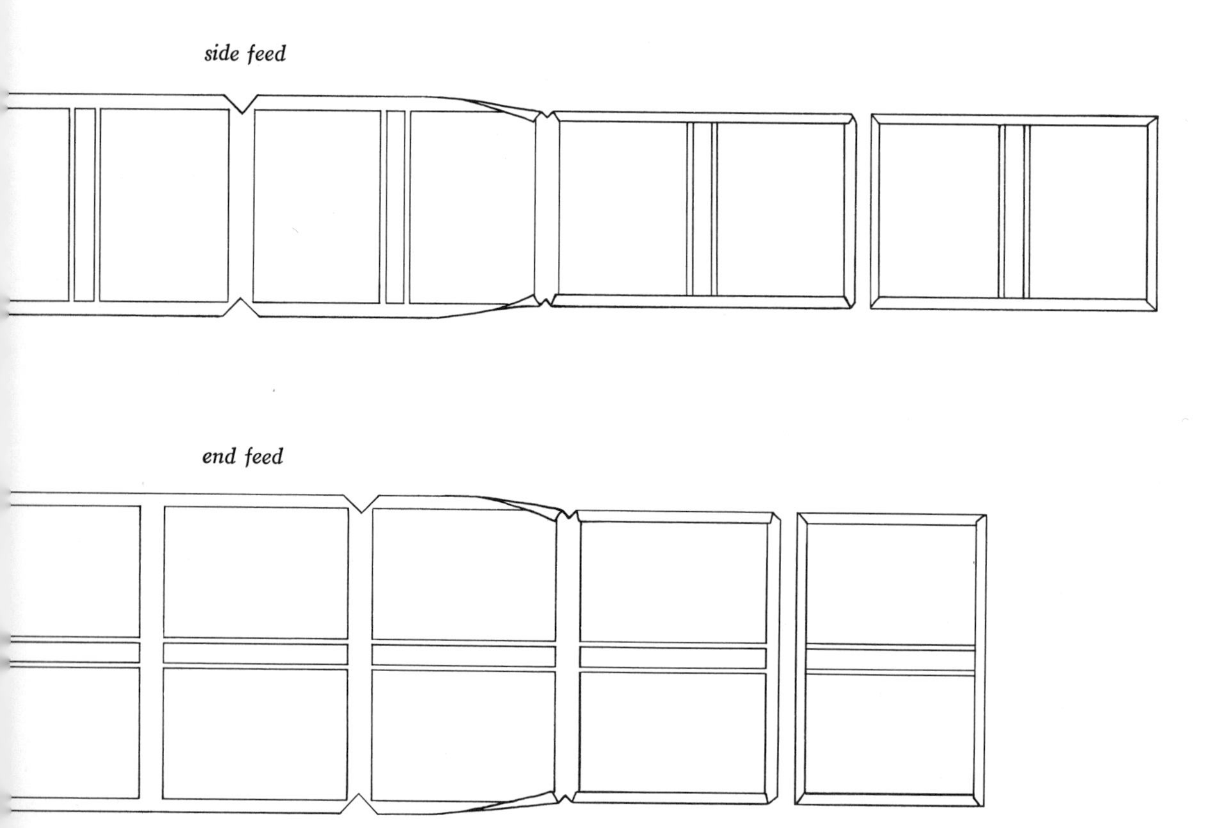

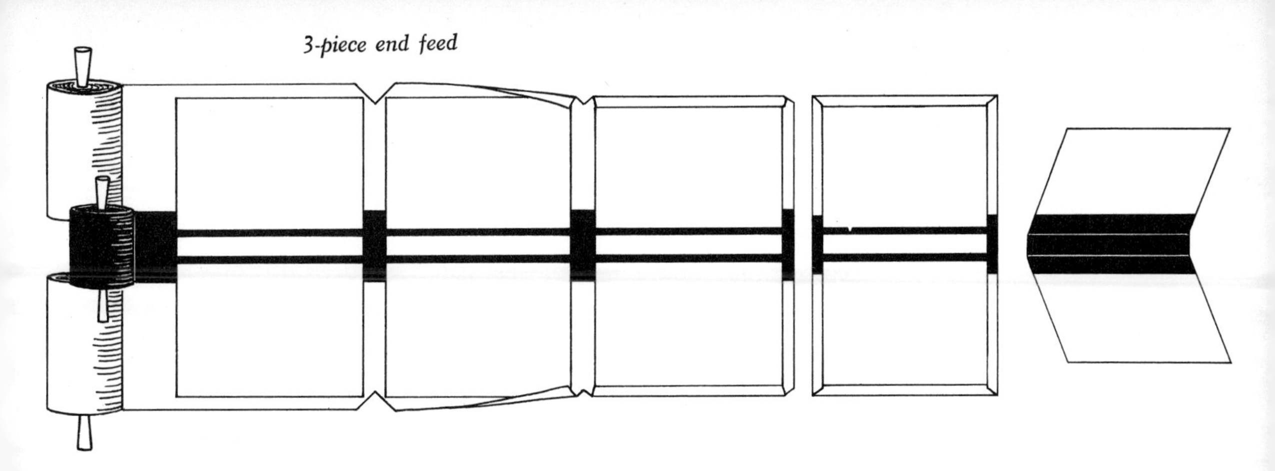

This distinction is of no significance when a cover is made with a single piece of material, but it is of primary importance if a cover is to be made with 2 or more pieces. When such covers are made by running material simultaneously from 2 or more rolls, it is obvious that on a side-feed machine the strips of material would run *across* the cover and on end-feed they would run *up* the cover.

The most common use of this technique is the 3-piece cover made on end-feed machines, with one material for the sides and another for the back (with some extending onto the sides and overlapped by the side pieces).

Almost any combination of materials is possible in this method, but each strip must be wide and strong enough to withstand the tension used, and to prevent difficulties caused by the almost 15-foot length of the web. For average materials, at least 2″ width is usually required, but more may be needed in some cases. Regardless of how much of the back material is supposed to *show* on the sides, at least ⅜″ should extend onto the boards to insure sufficient strength. It is, after all, this piece that holds the cover together and provides the structurally vital joint. The side materials, which have virtually no structural importance, may overlap the back material by any amount, with ⅛″ the minimum, to allow for inaccuracies in the casemaking.

The same method may be used on the side-feed casemaker, but here each piece forms part of the hinge and must have the requisite strength.

Multi-piece covers can be made on sheet-fed machines, but not in 1 operation. The standard 3-piece case is made by putting the back material on first, then putting the 2 side pieces on in a second run. While the use of more than 1 piece of material slightly increases the set-up and running time on a web-fed machine, the time (and cost) is actually doubled when a sheet-fed operation is required (CH.26).

Efforts have been made to find a less expensive way of producing covers, but the only prospect for important economy is in the direction of molded covers made of a single piece of material. For this purpose, plastics—mostly vinyls—are being used.

Despite the savings effected by the much simpler casemaking, the cost of these covers tends to be high because of the relatively expensive plastic. The problem here is the need to have flexibility in the joint and rigidity in the sides. This can be accomplished by molding a sheet of plastic with the necessary variations in thickness, but no cheaper material (of which paper is the most likely one) would have sufficient strength at the hinge if the thickness were reduced enough to provide flexibility. Experiments toward finding a suitable and cheaper material are in progress. "One-piece" plastic covers are made also by laminating pieces together instead of molding, often with a piece of board between layers of plastic. The edges are then *heat-sealed* [melted together].

Semi-rigid covers are made by using a single piece of plastic just heavy enough to provide some rigidity yet thin enough to bend. These are usually made with a paper adhered to the back in order to reduce the amount of expensive plastic needed (see "Binding materials"). In effect, such covers are virtually the same as paper covers, differing only in the way they are joined to the book itself and in the degree of rigidity. Even the materials are the same as some paperback covers, which have a thin sheet of clear plastic laminated to the printed paper. The difference then is only in the proportion of paper and plastic. Indeed, some "paperbacks" have been produced with covers of paper-lined vinyl. There is a tendency toward narrowing, if not eliminating, the distinction between case and paperback binding. This is discussed further in CH.26.

STAMPING

There are 3 methods used to apply lettering and other designs to covers: (a) printing the material before the cover is made, (b) printing on the cover by silk screen, and (c) *stamping* on the cover. The techniques of the first 2 methods are explained in CH.7 where the printing processes are discussed. (When the material is preprinted, the only special factor is the necessity of sheet-fed casemaking. It is possible to web-print the material and then make cases from the roll, but the problem of coordination requires extremely careful electronic controls, and this is feasible for very long runs only.) It is the third—and by far the most common—method which is described here.

There are 2 kinds of stamping: *cold* and *hot*.

- *Cold stamping* (*Ink stamping*)—This is very much like letterpress in that it involves the application of ink by impression with a raised surface. The basic difference is in the amount of impression. Where the letterpress plate or type lightly "kiss" the paper, the stamping press drives the raised image into the material hard enough to place the ink definitely below the surface. This is necessary to prevent the ink from getting rubbed away too quickly as the book is handled, slipped in and out of spaces between books on shelves, etc. The hard impression is needed also to flatten the relatively rough-surface materials used for book binding. A light impression on a natural finish cloth, for example, would transfer ink to the top of the threads only and not make a solid mark.

Ink stamping is done on a platen press differing only slightly from those used for printing. The stamping plate must be of hard enough material to withstand the heavy wear, but otherwise may be a letterpress plate. Special plates made for stamping are made of ¼″ thick material and are etched deeper than is necessary for printing. The extra thickness provides more strength and the extra depth allows for the deep impression in the material. These plates (*dies*) are discussed later under "Binding materials".

Because of the hard impression and frequently rough material, ink stamping cannot give the fine results possible in printing on paper. When the cover material is comparatively smooth, however, small type, fairly fine line drawings, and even coarse-screen halftones may be stamped satisfactorily. Light inks on dark materials are not usually satisfactory unless 2 or more impressions are used, although more contrast improves the results.

■ *Hot stamping*—This is used to apply *leaf*, for making *blank* impressions (*blind stamping*), and for *embossing*. The process is substantially the same as ink stamping, except that the die—which must be metal—is heated by contact with a heating element in the press. Heat is necessary to transfer the leaf from its carrier (see "Binding materials") to the material, and to help mold the material and boards in blind stamping or embossing. The amount of heat used varies from 200° to 275° according to the kind of leaf, the cover materials, and the kind of stamping.

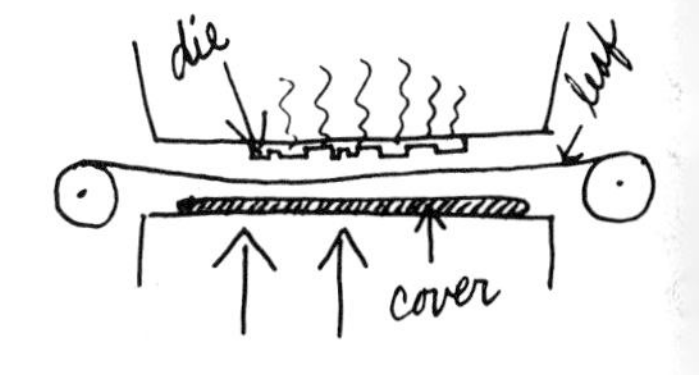

Leaf stamping once meant the application of genuine gold from small sheets or "leaves", and this is still the method used in making cover designs with hand tools. On a stamping press, a roll of leaf (metallic or flat color) just wide enough to cover the die is mounted on one side, and the leaf ribbon is drawn across the die by an arm on the other side, with the pigment side facing away from the die. The leaf is pressed against the cover by the heated die and the pigment is transferred. The pressure not only impresses the leaf below the surface, but forces the pigment into the weave or grain of the cover material. After each impression, the arm pulls the leaf just enough to move the stamped part past the die.

It is possible to mount several rolls of leaf of different colors on the press at a time, and stamp from all of them at each impression. (Some machines have side-feeds enabling them to run rolls at right angles to each other.) The number of colors is theoretically limited only by the amount of space available to mount the rolls, but the loss of time involved in mounting and running more than 4 or 5 is so great that it would probably be more economical to use half as many colors in each of 2 impressions. In making designs using multiple leaf colors in 1 impression, be sure that the printing image of each color is at least 5/16″ from that of any other color. Each ribbon must extend 1/8″ on both sides of the die to insure that all of it is covered, and another 1/16″ is needed for a divider to keep the ribbons apart. These paper-thin ribbons being pulled over a span of about 3 feet are not very stable—particularly if they are narrow.

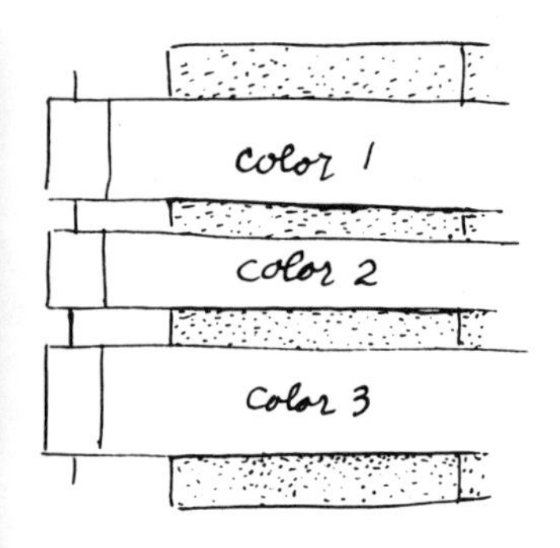

Blank or blind stamping is done by the same process as leaf stamping except that no leaf is used. The effect is caused by changes in color and texture of the material due to heat as well as by the impression. Because heat is required, blank stamping cannot be done together with an impression of ink (even if the ink could be kept from part of the plate) but is usually done with leaf stamping. To be effective, blind stamping must be impressed into the board as well as the cover material.

embossing

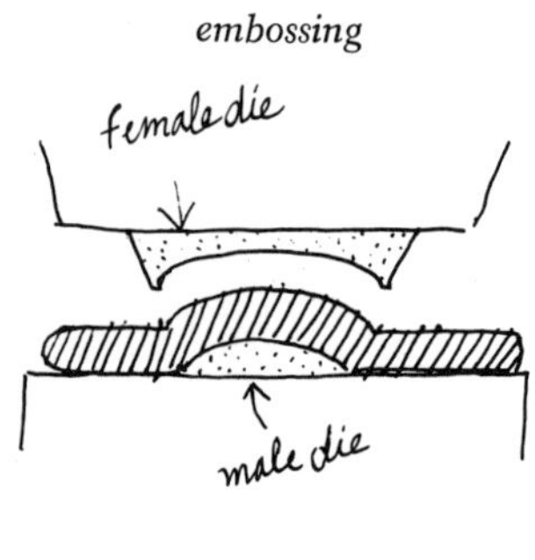

Embossing is similar to the other hot-stamping operations, but the image produced is raised *above* the surface instead of pressed into it. This usually requires use of a male and female die. The latter is stamped on top of the cover while the other is positioned on the press so that it will be under the cover when the impression is made. This means that a negative image will be pressed into the inside of the cover. If this is too large and/or deep, it can interfere with pasting the endleaf onto the board. Where the image is fairly simple, the male die may be omitted, using in its place a piece of cardboard cut to the proper shape. This saves the cost of a die (these are very expensive) and reduces the height of the embossing. The effect of embossing can be obtained without any embossing dies by making a negative-image or reverse die, i.e. a background is stamped, leaving the image raised on it.

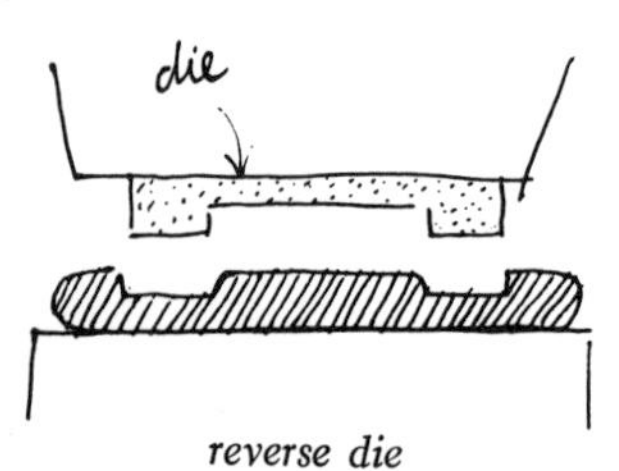

reverse die

When leaf has been used, each cover is given a light brushing with fine steel wool to wipe off the excess leaf. (This can cause smears if a dark-colored leaf is used on a very light material.)

CASING-IN

With both books and covers made, the next operation is *casing-in* [putting the book in its case or cover]. The books are fed into the machine back-up, astride flat sheets of metal. The endleaves are given a coat of paste just before the books pass under a hopper of covers. As each book goes through, a cover drops over it and is clamped from both sides, thus pasting the endleaves to the inside of the cover, with the crash inbetween.

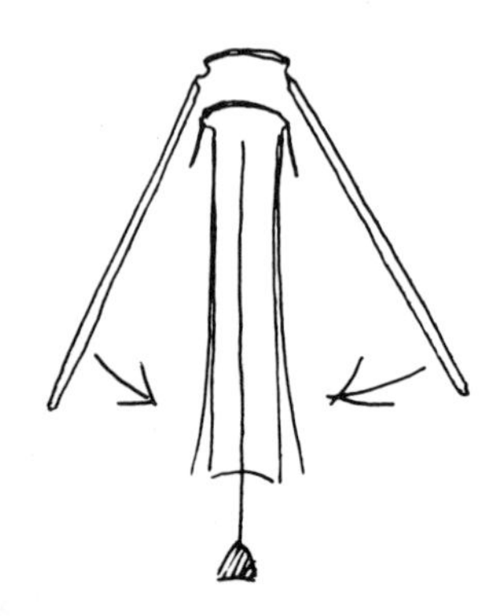

Casing-in a self-lining book is no different. The paste is applied to the first and last pages (where the endpapers would otherwise be) and these are pasted to the cover.

Before the covers are dropped into place they are formed by a heated bar, to correspond to the shape of the round-backed book.

Some books are made *tightbacked*, i.e. the spine of the cover is glued to the back.

BUILDING-IN

The cover would warp badly if the endleaf paste were permitted to dry by itself. To prevent this, the books are *built-in*. This is one operation that has been radically improved. The old method—still in considerable use—was to put the books between wooden boards which were then piled on other layers of books and boards up to about 5 feet. A projecting metal rim around the edges of the boards pressed into the joint to hold the shape. The pile was then kept under pressure for 6 to 24 hours while the paste dried.

There are now building-in machines which apply pressure and heat from both sides, accomplishing in seconds what formerly required a day. The basic principles of all building-in machines are the same, but they vary in the heat, pressure, and dwell used. This is important to know when using cover materials of differing thermal properties.

INSPECTION

A certain amount of inspection is done at each step in the binding process, but in spite of this some imperfections remain undetected, so a final check is made just before the books are wrapped. This inspection covers the entire range of possible faults—even those created by composition and printing. Composition errors will, of course, appear in all copies, but if serious enough (say, omission of the author's name from the title page) may cause rejection of the whole edition. Printing faults are also likely to affect many copies. Here the problem is usually battered type or *work-ups* [printing of nonprinting parts]. In binding, a great many things may go wrong but, because of the relatively slower speeds of binding machines and the numerous occasions for inspection and rejection, the faults at this stage are likely to be limited to a few copies. The most common problems are: sheets folded on a bias, corners folded in, inverted signatures, endpapers stuck together (due to oozing of excess paste), books cased-in upside-down, endpapers not centered or square in covers. Occasionally, imperfections in paper are discovered (holes, tears, stains, etc.).

Imperfect books are sent to the *repair department* where they are made acceptable, if possible. Skillful repair work can restore a remarkably high percentage.

JACKETING, SLIPCASING, & PACKING

Most books are given some kind of individual wrapping. Tradebooks almost always have a printed paper *jacket* [a separate wrapper, as distinguished from the cover which is attached to the book] or a clear plastic one. Technical and school books usually have a jacket of plain paper or *glassine* [a rather brittle, translucent paper]. Until about 1948 all jackets were put on by hand, but there are now jacketing machines in use. These can increase production greatly, but only on long runs.

It is important to provide instructions for positioning printed jackets on the books, because it is not always clear how they should fit. This is particularly necessary with off-centered designs, for there is a tendency to center the type on the spine of the book when wrapping.

If the books are to be inserted in *slipcases* [boxes] or individual mailing cartons this is usually done by hand, although very large editions may be cartoned by machine. In any case, these are fairly slow and expensive operations.

Expensive books are usually cartoned individually or in bulk cartons containing from 35 to 50 lbs. of books. Most books are packed on *skids* [wooden platforms] on which from 800 to 1000 average-sized books are piled, with a sheet of paper between layers. A wooden cover is placed on top and metal bands are wrapped around from top to bottom to keep the books under pressure, both to prevent warping and to keep them from slipping out.

Paperbacks

Paperbacks divide into 2 categories of significance to their manufacture: (a) *trade paperbacks*, which are sold through regular book outlets in quantities roughly comparable to hardbound tradebooks —say 6000 to 20,000—and (b) *mass-market paperbacks*, distributed through magazine outlets and printed in runs of 250,000 or more. The retail prices of these categories differ considerably, reflecting fundamentally different methods of production which are, in turn, related to the quantities involved.

TRADE PAPERBACKS

These are sometimes the same trim-sizes as hardcover books—often being printed from the same plates as a hardbound edition. The basic operations of binding are performed in the usual way. Most of these books are perfect-bound, although many are sewed—particularly when the run is small. The sewed books are fed into a machine which applies an adhesive to the back, drops a preprinted paper cover into place on the book, then trims book and cover together. Sometimes the books are smashed first. If an edge stain is used, this is sprayed on after trimming.

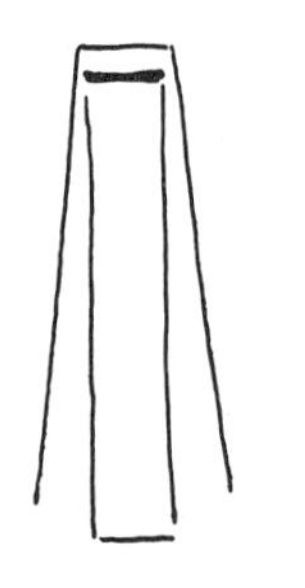

When paperbacks are perfect-bound, they go directly from collating to the binding machine, which trims off the back, applies an adhesive, and then completes the operations described above.

MASS-MARKET PAPERBACKS

To describe the process of binding mass-market paperbacks it is necessary to refer to their printing, because the entire manufacture of these books is integrated. It is only because they are so efficiently produced that they can be sold at such low prices.

The most advanced paperback production equipment can take a roll (or rolls) of paper at one end and turn it automatically into bound books at the other. The rotary press has a fully coordinated folder built in, which feeds signatures to a gathering machine. A binding machine takes the gathered signatures and completes the books (as described for perfect-bound trade paperbacks) at a rate of about 200 per minute. In quality, the books produced in this way are not always perfect, but they are remarkably good under the circumstances.

Mechanical binding

This term refers to bindings using a mechanical device, not to a binding process. In fact, mechanical binding is much less automatic than case binding.

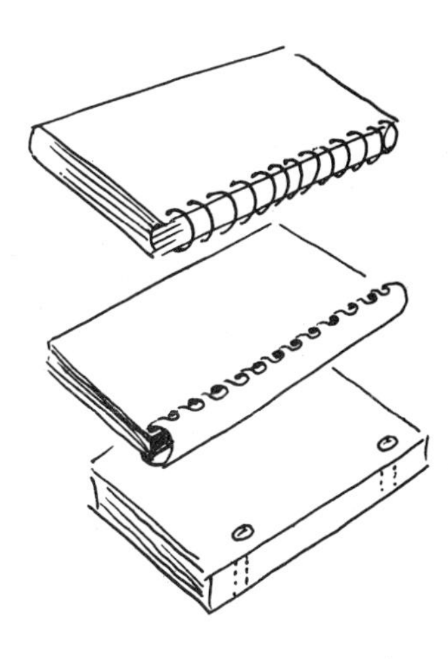

There are many kinds of mechanical bindings, both metal and plastic. All of them involve a device that joins single sheets by passing through holes on 1 edge. Some snap on, some wind through the holes, some have posts or rods, others have rings, etc.

Although the mechanical devices differ considerably, the binding process varies only in the way that each is attached. The basic operations of folding and gathering are the same as in all binding. The gathered books are then trimmed on all 4 sides, holes are punched through the pages, and the metal or plastic binding apparatus is attached. There are no endpapers needed on mechanically bound books, but the covers—2 separate pieces—are gathered with the signatures.

Slipcases, plastic jackets, & cartons

SLIPCASES

Slipcases are the open-end boxes in which books are sometimes sold and referred to as "boxed". Usually, 2 volumes are boxed together, but sometimes 1 is presented in a slipcase alone, and occasionally 3, 4, or even more may be in a single box. The construction varies according to the number and weight of the books.

Slipcases are made of boards similar to those used in hardcovers and are covered in paper of about the weight and strength of a good text. The box is made of 2 pieces of board, *scored* [blank stamped along the folding line], folded, and held together with paper tape. The cover material may be preprinted or plain. In the latter case, there is usually a printed label pasted on the side(s) and/or edge. Sometimes the covering is put on in several pieces, with the printed label constituting 1 or more of them. The material is turned in about ½″ on the front edges.

For extra-heavy books, some panels may be reinforced with another layer of board. It is customary to die-cut half-moon finger openings on the front edges to facilitate removing the book, but this is not as necessary with a heavy book, which is inclined to come out of its own weight.

The standard kind of slipcase is usually made by machine, but special variations are almost always hand operations. Especially on small runs, the 15 to 20¢ cost of an average slipcase can easily double when a special requirement must be met.

PLASTIC JACKETS

Clear plastic jackets are made of acetate in several thicknesses. The most used is 5 point (.005, or 5 thousands of an inch), but 7½ and even 10 pt. may be used when the book is very heavy and/or very expensive. In all cases, the folds must be preformed with heat. The material is too resilient to fold cold without springing open, and if a cold fold is made too hard it is likely to crack. This is true to a lesser extent of 3 pt., but this weight is too thin to be heat formed. Because of the forming, it is necessary to give the supplier a bound dummy of the book on which to base his measurements. If the jacket is only 1/16″ off-size, it may not be usable.

CARTONS

Mailing cartons for individual books must be able to protect their contents well enough to bring them to their destinations in perfect condition. Particularly when the books are expensive, they will be returned if damaged in transit due to inadequate packing. The rigors of going through the mail are severe enough for average-sized books, but very large and heavy ones are subject to considerable stress. (Mechanically bound books are a special problem.)

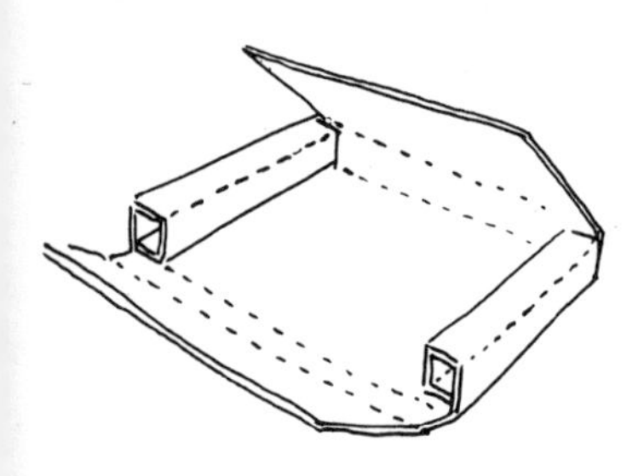

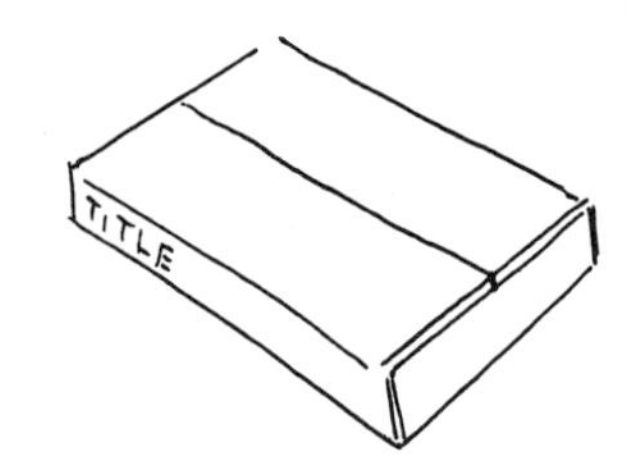

Numerous attempts have been made to achieve maximum protection at minimum cost, but the most successful would seem to be the corrugated paper "bumper end" carton. It is made from a single piece and die-cut. The ends are folded over 4 times to make bumpers that effectively protect the corners of the book—and it is the corners that take the most abuse in mailing. The sides are turned over on top, so that only 1 edge need be taped closed.

The danger here is having the book damaged if the recipient tries to cut the tape at the top. This can be solved by placing an extra piece of corrugated paper—or board—on top of the book before the flaps are closed, but this is an added expense. The problem doesn't exist in the conventional carton, whose end flaps are on top of the book rather than being folded to make bumpers.

There are 2 weights of corrugated paper in general use for this purpose, 200 lb. test and, for extra-heavy duty, 275 lb. test. These may be obtained in the standard brown color or in a mottled white. Printing is done on the cartons when flat, using soft rubber plates. The results are fairly crude.

Binding materials

In cooperation with the various state agencies that buy books for public elementary and high school use, as well as with the American Textbook Publishers Institute, the Book Manufacturer's Institute (BMI) has established a set of minimum standards for making books to be used in schools. This has relieved the textbook purchaser of having to determine acceptability in each case, and has simplified the problem for publishers and manufacturers. The BMI standards cover almost all aspects of production, but among the most significant features are those having to do with binding materials. In general, these requirements are in excess of what is necessary for satisfactory performance in tradebooks, but they are often met in making tradebooks of interest to libraries. Library books are not ordinarily treated as strenuously as elementary-school books, but they are used continually over long periods, and the librarians, understandably, want them to last as long as possible.

The BMI specifications are revised frequently as conditions change.

COVER MATERIALS—CLOTH

For hundreds of years, animal skins—vellum, leather—were virtually the only materials used for book binding. In the 19th century, some decorative papers were used on sides to make "*quarter-bound*" [3-piece binding] and "*half-bound*" [3-piece plus separate corner pieces] books. It wasn't until the latter part of the century, when mass production of books by machinery came about, that leather became obsolete. The individuality of animal skins does not lend itself to large-scale automatic processes. Thus leather was replaced by cloth, which is not only relatively uniform, but which may be produced in rolls for use on web-fed casemaking machinery. However, leather is still used for soft covers on bibles.

The cloth used for book binding is entirely cotton, despite the use of such terms as "linen" and "buckram". The material without any processing is called *greige goods* (pronounced gray) and comes in various qualities and grades. These are measured mainly in terms of the weight of thread and *thread count* [the number of threads per square inch]. In 1936, the U. S. Dept. of Commerce established specifications for grades of cloth from A to F. After World War II, however, the demand for cheaper cloth and the competition of paper substitutes (which came into being when cloth became scarce during the war) inspired the book-cloth manufacturers to produce a lower grade—and then, a few years later, a still lower grade.

The way that the greige goods are processed varies also. The main distinction is in the *filler* used. Some cloth is filled with a composition consisting chiefly of starch, while others have some plastic—usually pyroxylin or vinyl—in them. The starch-filled cloth is easily damaged by moisture, while the *plastic impregnated* has enough water resistance to take wiping with a damp cloth. BMI standards for schoolbooks call for at least a B grade plastic-impregnated cloth.

Some cloth is *plastic coated* rather than impregnated. These materials are just as water resistant as the others, as long as the coating lasts. BMI specifications provide for the use of coated grades of cloth also.

Book-cloth finishing is done by running the material through various vats and rollers that apply the color and surface characteristics. The chief distinctions are between *natural finish, vellum finish,* and *linen finish.*

In vellum-finish cloth, the goods are dyed first. Then the filler is applied to both sides of the material. The face is given a coating that includes the coloring, while the back has sizing suitable for the adhesives used in casemaking. To make a linen finish, the goods are undyed and the face coating is scraped so that the white threads show partly through. Steel rollers smooth the surface and emboss if required. Natural-finish cloth is dyed, then is filled and sized from the back only, leaving the face in its soft, natural state.

Rolls are put up in widths of 36, 38, 40, and 42″, which makes it possible to cut out for almost any book economically. The usual length of a roll is 250 yards.

The prices of cloth are quite uniform from one supplier to another. They range from about 37¢ per yard (38″ wide) for the poorest grade to about $1.25 per yard for the best. In A grades and better, most materials may be obtained plastic-impregnated, at about 5¢ per yard more than starch-filled. The price per yard varies with the size of the order, going down 1 or 2¢ in each larger quantity bracket.

The cloth manufacturers stock a large number of colors and finishes of several grades of material and can usually deliver an order within a few days. They will make special colors and finishes for orders of reasonable size. Most companies stock white cloth specially prepared for lithographic printing. Sample sheets (11 x 15″ or 12 x 18″) and swatch books are available from the principal manufacturers—of which there are less than a dozen.

COVER MATERIALS—PLASTIC

The plastic materials available now are mostly vinyls of 4 to 7 pt. thickness with backings of paper. The backing provides rigidity to enable working the material on bindery machines, and it simplifies the problem of gluing. Vinyl is not without problems, however. While it *can* be fabricated with almost any qualities desired, it is difficult to keep these qualities in balance without creating undesirable features. For example, if the material is made to resist the heat used in stamping and building-in, it may lose too much cold resistance (*cold-crack*) and shatter when a carton of books is dropped on a loading platform in midwinter. Other problems sometimes encountered are stretching, sticking together, repelling ink or leaf, etc. These can be and have been overcome, but not without some effort. Pyroxylin and other plastics are also being used as binding materials, usually in combination with paper.

COVER MATERIALS—PAPER

Paper was used widely as a cover material when cloth was scarce during World War II. For 1-piece covers it was found to be adequate for tradebooks of small to average size, where no hard use was involved. Libraries, however, objected strenuously. When cloth became available again, the use of these papers continued, because of their economy. Even when the lowest grades of cloth were introduced, their price was still double that of the cheapest paper substitutes. The best of the papers are still below the price of the cheapest cloth.

There are 2 kinds of paper used in binding. One is the kind mentioned above, which is strong enough to be used for 1-piece cases, the other is used only for the sides of 3-piece cases. The former kind was at first an 80 lb. kraft paper with a casein coating. These go under such trade names as *Mactex, Skytex, Buckraft,* etc., are available in colors, and are usually embossed with leather- or cloth-like textures. They sell for about 15¢ per yard. A better grade, at about 20¢, is made of kraft paper, often with some resin impregnation, and a coating of lacquer or pyroxylin. These are sold as *Duroid, Kivar, Sturdetan, Permakote,* etc., and are strong enough for most tradebook purposes.

There are some paper materials with special formulations that make them unique. One is *Elephant Hide,* which has a marble-like appearance, considerable strength, and surface resistance to moisture, soiling, and scuffing—without any coating. This material is manufactured in West Germany by a secret process. It comes in a large number of colors and patterns of unusual appearance, is strong enough for most tradebook uses, and sells for around 25¢ per yard. Another material is *Linmaster,* made in Scotland of especially tough impregnated fibers. It too requires no coating to perform satisfactorily and comes in colors with or without embossing. It is in the same price range as Elephant Hide.

Several lines of cheaper binding papers sell for around 10¢ per yard. These are dyed-through kraft papers with some resin impregnation but without coatings and are adequate for small books with light handling probability. The papers in this group (*Duroid* 30, *Permalin,* etc.), represent the minimum quality acceptable for 1-piece cases.

In addition to the lines mentioned there are a number of others with special finishes and patterns. Some lines have a considerable variety of effects available, both printed and embossed.

All of the products mentioned thus far are sold in rolls—generally 38 or 40″ wide—or in sheets. While they are intended primarily for 1-piece covers, they can be and are used as sides of 3-piece cases. Any paper of about 70 lb. substance and reasonable strength may be used on sides, as there is no structural requirement, but the only lines classified as binding papers are those available in rolls.

Until the 1940s, when web-fed casemaking made it possible to produce 3-piece covers economically, there were no papers available in rolls, except on special orders. Since then, several of the better text papers have been made available in rolls in their most suitable colors—Curtis' *Tweedweave* and *Stoneridge*, and Strathmore's *Grandee*. These are 80 lb. text papers of superior printing qualities and appearance, but their price is low in comparison with even the cheapest papers made for 1-piece bindings. They are put up in 25 or 26″ rolls, but their price on a square yard basis is about 10¢. Tweedweave is available with some printed patterns (*Tweedprints*) at a few cents more per yard.

Also available in rolls are *Multicolor* and *Colortext*, 2 lines of colored stock developed primarily for endpapers, but very satisfactory for sides, and even usable as 1-piece bindings in some circumstances. These are slightly lower in price than the text papers mentioned above. Both the text paper and endpaper lines are colored through. Neither have any coating.

There are presently several lines of papers being made with latex saturated cellulose fibers and pyroxylin coatings. These can perform as well as cloth in practically all respects and are designed for use on textbook covers.

COVER MATERIALS—PAPERBACKS

A 10 pt. coated-one-side stock is used for most paperback covers. Such paper may be obtained in all grades. It is flexible enough to fold, yet provides reasonable protection (considering price) for the pages. Less expensive, although not as scuff resistant, is an uncoated stock of the same thickness. It costs less, not only because it has no coating but because it requires no varnish or other finish over the printing.

There are several papers being used now which are tougher and thicker than the regular stocks and are intended to provide longer life for the book (Kivar No.3, Lexitone, etc.). Their cost is several cents more per copy on an average trade paperback edition.

New cover material lines and modifications of existing lines are in almost constant development. Contact with suppliers and regular reading of trade periodicals are necessary to keep abreast of these changes.

ENDPAPERS

Endpapers have distinctive and significant strength requirements, since they are the main agent in holding hard cover and book together. All material sold as endpaper stock is made to specifications required by the BMI standards for schoolbooks, which call for an 80 lb. kraft. For a discussion of endpaper use, see CH.26.

DIES

For many years the best dies for leaf or ink stamping were made of brass. They were hand-finished, cut to more-than-adequate depth, and had excellent resistance to long-run pounding. They may still be the best dies, but they have been challenged on every score by others, and they are most vulnerable in the matter of price.

To stamp cleanly on a fairly rough-surfaced material a die should be at least .040″ deep in all but the smallest areas between lines. It is not possible to etch brass this deep and retain the definition of edges, so, after transferring the image to the photosensitized metal, a very shallow bite is taken first, and the rest of the depth is routed out by hand—using power tools and hand gravers. If the work is skillfully done, the result is a die with sharp edges and very little of the shallow stepping often seen in fully etched plates. This handcraftsmanship is an increasingly expensive commodity, and a search has been under way for the past 20 years or so to find a cheaper way of producing dies of satisfactory quality.

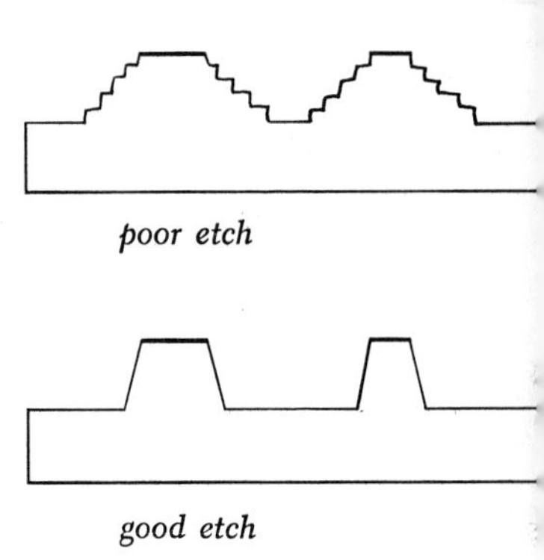

For short runs, an extra-heavy electro called a *binder's electro* was the first answer to this need. This plate has an extra coating of copper and is backed up with lead to ¼″ thickness. However, the backing metal tends to squash, and the etching is not deep enough to begin with, so these dies are not reliable for more than 2 to 3000 impressions under good conditions. Besides, unless the design is all type, a line cut must be made first and this adds to the cost. Binders' electros are rarely used now.

For *very* short runs (a few hundred), it was common practice to stamp with an ordinary line cut. The depth was only about .025 and the metal was softer than copper.

The first promising innovation was the *magnesium die*, which could be etched to .040″ by the mechanical etching machine (CH.7). Introduced in the late 1940s, magnesium was widely used as a cheap substitute for brass dies until its faults became apparent: (a) the metal tends to deteriorate in air unless specially treated, (b) while its hardness gives it long life (though not nearly as long as brass), it also makes for sharp edges that tend to cut the cover material, and (c) there is considerable stepping to reach the proper depth.

A later entry was the *Micrometal die*. This is made of the metal now generally used for line cuts, which is a harder alloy than the old one, and is etched on the mechanical etching machine to depths up to .0100″. The etching is not only deeper but is more nearly vertical than magnesium's. The metal is not as hard as magnesium, however, and is not comparable to brass.

More recently, a *copper alloy die* has come into the field and this may provide the answer. The metal is claimed to be harder than brass and it etches very well. At this writing there has not been enough experience in the use of these dies to draw conclusions, but the indications are very promising.

Brass dies will always be needed for embossing, as it is necessary to sculpt the subject in bas relief—both positive and negative—and this must be done by hand. (Even a pantograph engraver requires an original sculpted by hand.)

A broad comparison between the cost of brass dies and etched dies is not possible because the basis of pricing is different. The largest component in the price of brass dies is hand labor, and this varies according to the size and complexity of the subject. Etched dies are priced on a straight area basis, regardless of the nature of the copy. Conceivably, a very simple subject of large area might be less expensive in brass than in Micrometal. However, taking as a comparison the die for the spine of an average book, with many small characters in a small area, the etched die comes out considerably cheaper; if a complicated ornament or drawing is involved, the cost of brass becomes prohibitive. The difference in price among the various etched dies is not very significant.

All of the dies mentioned so far are metal, because only metal can conduct the heat used in hot stamping. For ink stamping, the die may be of any material of requisite hardness—and not as much hardness (or depth) is needed as for the other. This brings in the possibility of using plastic duplicate or etched plates (CH.7). In some experiments, these have shown a tendency to warp.

It is impossible to rate the various dies in terms of impressions, because there are a number of variables involved. A die may give 10,000 satisfactory impressions on one job but only 6000 on another. The material being stamped, the nature of the subject, the heat required, the speed of stamping, all affect the die's performance. A more elusive variable is the amount of wear inflicted during the setting-up process. An initial miscalculation of pressure needed may give the die a pounding equivalent to a thousand impressions after the pressure is properly adjusted. Accidental feeding of 2 covers can have the same effect.

LEAF & INK

The ink used for stamping is similar to printing ink, but is heavier and thicker. More ink is deposited than in printing and there is proportionately less absorption by the material, so more drier is used to hasten air-drying. This gives the ink a shiny look. If desired, a flatter look is possible, but this requires running at slower speed. Special inks are required for printing on plastic or plastic-coated materials.

Leaf is a paper-thin (or thinner) layer of colored mineral powder or metallic powder laid on a gum and wax base, which holds it to a carrier of either glassine or plastic (acetate or mylar). Over the layer of powder is a layer of resin which bonds the pigment or powder to the material on which it is stamped. Leaf is made up in master rolls 24″ wide and 400 to 600′ in length. These are cut into narrower rolls as needed by the stamper. Plastic backing conducts the heat better and results in sharper stamping. Glassine backing is more effective where heavier deposits of leaf are required, as on panels. Special *panel leaf* is available with an extra thickness of pigment.

Metallic leaf includes not only the conventional gold in several shades, but aluminum, bronze, and a number of metallic colors. These were subject to rather rapid deterioration (fading or darkening) until anodyzing was introduced a few years ago. They are now available both ways. The anodyzed imitation gold is supposed to keep its appearance almost indefinitely. The old imitation gold is inclined to tarnish in a few years—depending on the materials with which it comes in contact.

Colored pigment leaf varies considerably in its stamping qualities. There are chemical differences that prevent some leaf from "taking" on certain materials: the amount of pigment needed to cover varies with the color; the degree of heat needed varies with color, backing, and lot; and the colors vary greatly in their light fastness. On top of this, the performance of leaf varies according to the manufacturer. It is advisable to make sample covers whenever possible (CH.26).

The variation in heat required is particularly significant when covers are being stamped with more than 1 color per impression. Sometimes, the quality of one part of the stamping must be sacrificed for another.

Each leaf supplier has a card showing samples of the colors carried in stock. The cards, the names, and the numbers vary, but the colors are about the same from one to another. Special colors can be made, but only for large orders.

COATINGS & LAMINATIONS

It is usually necessary to apply a finish to protect a printed surface on cover materials. There are some materials, such as natural finish cloth and antique paper, that absorb so much of the ink that they need no protection because the normal abrasion of use would not penetrate below the ink. Also, there are special inks of such hardness when dry that they resist scuffing to a considerable extent. Whether these inks are adequate protection or not depends on the amount of wear to which the book will be subjected.

There are 2 kinds of protective finish. One is the application of a transparent liquid coating, of which there are many kinds, the other is *lamination* [adhering a sheet of clear plastic to the surface of the base material]. There is also "liquid lamination", which consists of applying a layer of plastic in liquid form, but this is really more coating than lamination.

Coatings may be applied by spraying, by roller, or by a printing plate. The least expensive coating is the *press varnish* [a coat of varnish applied on a printing press just like an impression of ink]. There are specialized plants called *finishers* which can apply a large variety of varnishes, lacquers, liquid plastics, and other concoctions designed to provide protection for various materials in varying degrees. It is always best to ask the finisher to recommend a coating for a particular job.

Sheet lamination is quite expensive, about 10 times the cost of press varnish, but it gives the maximum protection and a glossy finish matched only by an acetate jacket. The only hazard in lamination is the tendency of the plastic sheet to come loose. For this reason it is not advisable to laminate on a rough material. The smoother the base, the firmer the adhesion.

In using protective finishes, particularly on color process printing, take account of the slight discoloration they cause—varying from almost none with lamination to a distinct yellowing with varnish. Consider also the possibility of *using* the varnish as an overall film of color, at no additional cost. This is available on a press varnish. Any color may be used.

It is important to inform the printer of the finish to be used, as special inks are required in some cases.

BOARD

There are 4 kinds of board used for hard covers:

- *Binder's board*—This is the best and the most expensive. It is made much like paper, as a solid sheet of fibers, and is less likely to warp or crack than any other. BMI standards require this board for textbooks.
- *Chip board*—This is made somewhat like binder's board but it is not as dense and is made not more than about 65 pt. in thickness. While it is the cheapest board, it is relatively weak and is little used for tradebooks.
- *Pasted board*—It can be made in any thickness, being 2 or more layers of chip board pasted together. This is the kind used for most general book purposes.
- *Red board*—This is a thin, tough, flexible board used for "limp" or flexible covers, mainly on books meant to be carried in pockets.

The boards used in most books are between 70 and 90 pt. in thickness, with 80 to 85 the most popular size. Red board is usually 36 pt.

THREAD, CRASH, & LINING PAPER

These 3 items are selected and purchased by the binder, but it is useful to know that extrastrong grades of each are available when their use is indicated. The decision to use heavy grades should be made in consultation with the binder. An alternative in the case of crash and paper is to double the amount of regular weight. Sometimes nylon thread is used rather than heavier cotton thread, to avoid excessive bulking at the back. There are, however, some technical problems connected with nylon thread that tend to limit its use.

ADHESIVES

This too is a technical matter best left to the binder. Production people should be aware, however, of the very large range of adhesives available and the need to fit the adhesive to the job. Particularly in perfect-bound books, the adhesive is all-important.

Adhesives fall into several categories; the *pastes* (similar to library paste) used to adhere endleaves to cover, the *glues* used to adhere cover material to boards, and the *flexible glues* used in backing (gluing-off) and perfect-binding. Considerable experiment has been carried out to find the ideal adhesive for perfect-binding. The range has extended from the animal glues originally used in bookbinding to "hot-melt" glues made of plastic compounds. The problem is to find an adhesive that is fluid enough to penetrate the interstices of the paper fibers, that dries fast enough to match the speed of the machines, that is very strong and flexible when dry, and will not become brittle and crack with the passage of time.

HEADBANDS

Headbands are made in long strips of cotton cloth about ⅝″ wide. The cloth is like a good canvas and has a rolled edge, which is sometimes woven with colored threads, making a pattern of alternating stripes. Some headbands are solid colors. About a dozen choices are usually available. Headbands may be regular or *mercerized* [having a silky gloss].

11 | Preparation for camera & press

General

The key word in this area is *accuracy*. Neatness is highly desirable —and its absence can cause some problems—but it is possible to produce the desired results with sloppy work *if it is accurate.*

The preparation of copy is essentially the same for all kinds of material and all processes. There *are* differences, and these will be taken up later, but the basic considerations are similar and are discussed in this section.

CAMERA COPY

There are 2 kinds of camera copy: line and continuous tone.

■ *Line copy*—This is photographed with maximum contrast—that is, every mark is solid and everything in the background is eliminated entirely. Even where there is the appearance of intermediate tones, as in halftone screens, benday tints, etc., there are really only solid dots or lines with white space between.

Thus, the essential characteristics of line copy are sharpness and contrast. Each dot, line, or mass should have clearly defined edges and every mark should be as close to black as possible, the backgrounds as close to white as possible. Anything short of the ideal black against white necessitates a compromise in the camera work, and there will be a loss of quality in the result. Faint lines and gray areas *can* be picked up, dark backgrounds *can* be dropped out, but the measures required to compensate for deficiencies in the copy will create other deficiencies in the result. To some extent, these problems can be overcome by skillful etching, finishing, etc., but it is best to avoid the problems by providing good copy.

■ *Continuous-tone copy* (photographs, etc.)—This copy cannot be reproduced exactly, but something pretty close to perfection is theoretically possible. However, to achieve the best results it is necessary to have an ideal combination of perfect plates, paper, and press work, and these are rarely available. It must be anticipated that some loss of fidelity will result, so the copy should be of the highest quality possible. While some qualities lacking in copy can be faked by the platemaker, it is much better (and cheaper) to start out with good subjects.

Each piece of copy has its own requirements and characteristics. Following are some notes on the most frequently used kinds:

▪ *Reproduction proofs*—The sharpest proofs are made on a gloss-coated paper, but most cameramen prefer dull-coated stock because it makes less glare. Examine repros carefully for broken letters, etc. Proofs are not necessarily first-rate just because they are called repros. Reject those that are not sharp and clean.

▪ *Photostats*—The main problem with photostats is distortion caused by shrinkage of the paper in drying. Some attempt is made in the camera work to compensate for this, but the trouble is that the shrinkage is irregular. For most purposes, the distortion is negligible, but it can be serious where register is involved. The larger the size, the worse the problem.

Don't expect good duplication of continuous-tone copy by photostat. The process is primarily a means of reproducing line copy cheaply. To get good line copy duplication, ask for *glossy prints* and indicate that they are for reproduction. However, use original copy whenever possible, as even the best stats are 2 steps away and there is some loss in each step. Out-of-focus prints should be rejected. *Matte* [soft finish] *prints* are cheaper and are good enough for dummies and sketches.

▪ *Photographs*—For good reproduction, monochrome photographs should be glossy prints, preferably with a wide range of tones from light to deep shadow. The reproduction process tends to flatten out the tones (the lights get darker and the darks get lighter), so it is best to begin with rich contrasts.

Everyone knows that one shouldn't write heavily on the back of a photograph or use paperclips without adequate padding, but a large proportion of photographs carry the bas-relief marks of those offenses. Don't.

▪ *Line drawings*—The time to worry about the suitability of drawings for line reproduction is before they are made. Experienced professional illustrators need no warning, but those who are not familiar with the problems of reproduction should, when possible, be told the basic considerations:

(a) Use *black* ink, paint, or pencil on white paper.

(b) Faint lines won't show in the reproduction (except pencil lines that shouldn't).

(c) All lines tend to get heavier in printing.

(d) Reduction may cause small spaces to close up completely, but it is best to provide for some reduction, as this tends to minimize imperfections.

(e) The printed result will probably be off-black on off-white.
(f) When register is involved, use accurate register marks.

■ *Continuous tone drawings and paintings*—The same requirements as for monochrome photographs. For discussion of color copy see "Color printing" in CH.7.

■ *Screened photoprints*—A contact print on paper of a screened halftone negative is known as a *velox*. It looks like a proof of a halftone plate. Being just black dots and white paper it can be used as line copy, so it is possible to save part of the cost of halftone engravings (CH.7) by having a velox made (by a photoprint company) and then a line cut. This is effective only when coarse screens are used (up to 100). Finer screens require copper engraving so there is no saving. Also, there is too much loss of quality with finer screens. Most photoengravers charge a penalty for velox copy to discourage its use.

Another advantage in using veloxes is the opportunity to incorporate them in camera copy with other elements—thereby saving high stripping and finishing charges. They also enable the original artist to do dot retouching rather than leaving this to someone else.

SCALING

Scaling [determining the final size and shape of reduced or enlarged copy] is a simple matter, once understood. There are 2 methods—1 mechanical, the other mathematical. The mechanical one seems easiest, but it is slower and less useful for complex problems. Both methods are described below:

■ *Mechanical scaling*—This is based on the geometric fact that all rectangles of the same proportions have the same diagonal, i.e. a rectangle 8 x 10″ will have the same diagonal as one 4 x 5″, 6 x 7½″, etc.

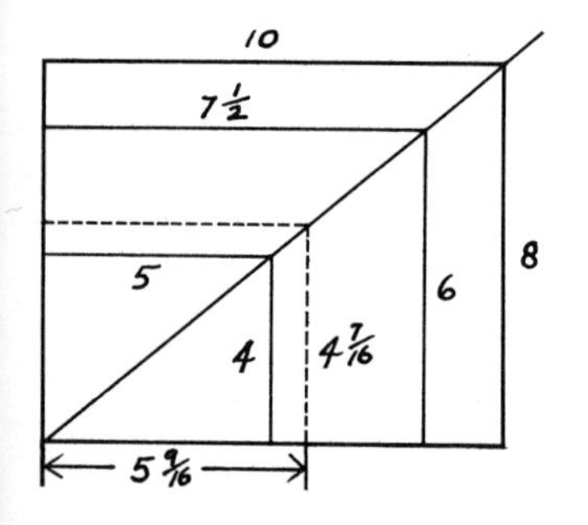

Thus, to reduce a horizontal 8 x 10″ photograph to a width of 5⁹⁄₁₆″, lay a sheet of tracing paper over the copy and draw a line between diagonally opposite corners. Then measure 5⁹⁄₁₆″ along the 10″ side and draw a line from this point perpendicular to the edge. When this line touches the diagonal you will have the height of the reduced picture.

It is possible to buy, and very simple to make, a transparent plastic device that eliminates the need for drawing lines and measuring. This is very desirable because there is much room for error in the mechanical process.

■ *Mathematical scaling*—You don't have to be good at mathematics to use this method, because it is really just another mechanical process. The basic principle is mathematical proportion, but with the use of an engraver's *proportional scale*, or slide rule, it is simply a matter of setting 2 dimensions in alignment, and then finding the fourth by reading it on the scale opposite the third. So, to find the height of an 8 x 10″ picture being reduced from 10″ to

$5\frac{9}{16}$″ wide, align $5\frac{9}{16}$ with 10, then find 8 on the same line as 10. The number opposite 8 will be the answer ($4\frac{7}{16}$). Not only will you have the dimensions, but you will be able to read off the percentage of original (linear) size of the copy after reduction (55+%) and the fractional proportion (9 to 5) at the same time. These are extremely useful for economical *ganging* [combining for simultaneous shooting] of pictures with identical focus.

Be sure to get an engraver's slide rule calibrated in eighths (for use with inches) rather than the engineer's, which is divided into tenths (and has other complicated scales not needed in this work). A slide rule seems rather formidable at first, but with a few minutes' practice you can do simple problems very rapidly, and complicated ones with hardly more trouble.

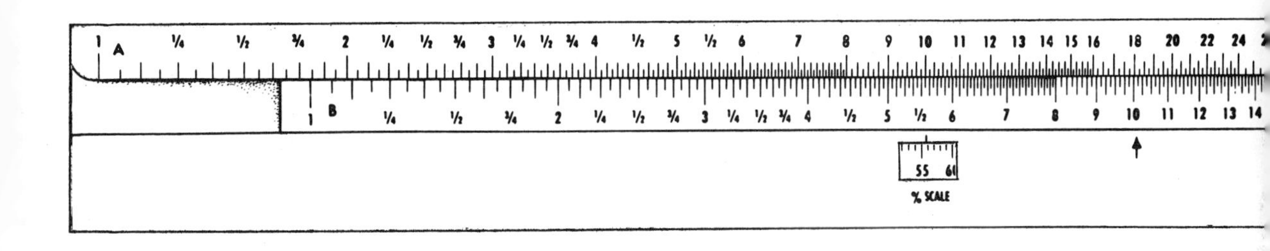

MECHANICALS

A *mechanical* is a piece of camera copy consisting of more than 1 element, arranged and marked for maximum accuracy and economy in platemaking. Economy in this case means minimizing the amount of camera and laboratory work required. To this end, it would be best to combine all the elements of each intended printing plate into 1 unit, which could be photographed in a single shot and the film exposed onto the plate without further handling. This is not always possible, but the closer you can come to the ideal the better.

There are 3 requirements for single-shot copy:

(a) each part of the copy must be in the same scale,

(b) the parts must be in the proper position in relation to each other, and

(c) there must be no part that requires a different screen or exposure than any other.

If part of the copy does require a different screen but is in the same scale as the remainder, it can be placed in position and the cameraman will shoot the copy twice—once for the screened copy, once for the other. The 2 negatives will then be combined to achieve the desired result. In practice, *artwork* [photographs, drawings, etc.] is usually larger than the finished size, and is not in position with type—which is usually *same-size*. This situation is discussed later in this chapter.

If one part of the copy overlaps another, it can be pasted on a transparent acetate overlay in the correct relative position. Whenever overlays are used, there should be at least 3 widely separated register marks on the base copy, and corresponding marks on the overlays. If there is no overlapping and all copy is in the same scale it is better to put everything on 1 board. This eliminates the need for register marks and results in maximum accuracy. Preparation of color copy is discussed in CH. 7.

There are numerous tricks of the trade in making mechanicals. These can be learned by experience, talking to experienced hands, and reading books on the subject. Copy can be adhered with rubber cement, tape, a melted adhesive (*dry mounted*), or by use of pressure-sensitive adhesive-backed paper. Squaring can be done with a T square, a light-table, or a transparent grid device. Each method has its advantages and disadvantages. The only important thing is *the result*—which should be accurate, secure, and clean copy. Remember that paper edges, cuts, cement excess, dirt, or anything else visible that is not part of the copy may be picked up by the camera.

MARKUP

Even perfect copy will not bring a good result if it is not marked properly. Instructions must be clear and complete. And remember, what may seem clear to you may not be clear to someone else—particularly if he is being rushed. Everyone has a tendency to omit what seems obvious, forgetting that these things are not obvious to someone unfamiliar with our *intentions*. To compensate for this tendency, try writing your instructions as though they were directed to an idiot. You might be surprised to find that you have no more trouble from confused instructions—and no one will complain.

Here are some of the markings that should appear on camera copy (when appropriate):

- *Register marks*—Place them outside the copy.
- *Indication of bleeds*—Write "Bleed" wherever one occurs. (Extend bleed copy 1/8″ outside trim.)
- *Indication whether line or halftone.*
- *Size of halftone screen* (110 screen, 120, 133, etc.)
- *Size and tint of benday screen* (85 screen, 20% tint, etc.)
- *Trimming guides*—Make clean, fine lines *outside* the copy.
- *Folding guides*—Same as above.
- *Dimensions*—Clearly indicate whether sizes and distances are before or after trim.

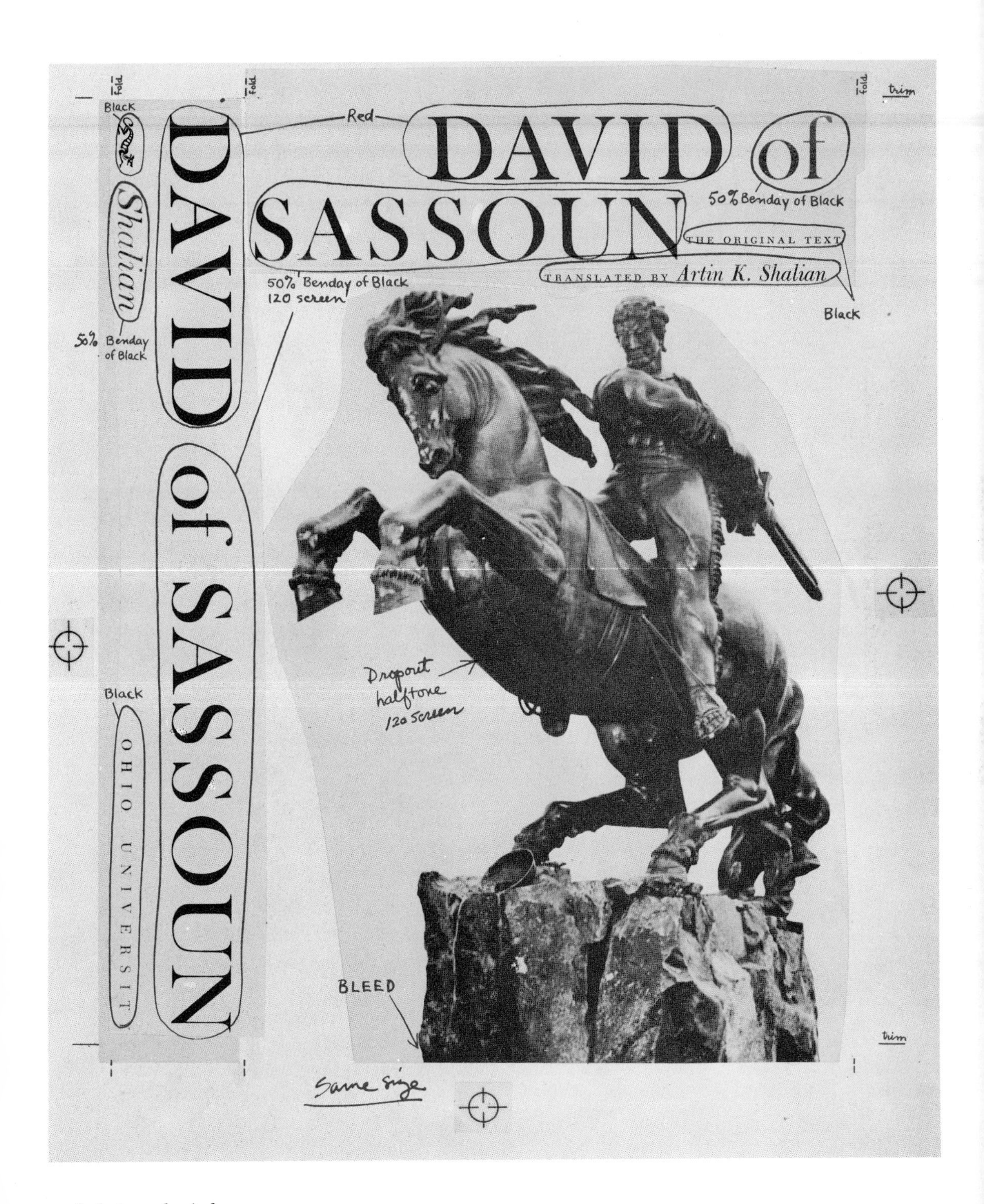

marked-up mechanical

▪ *Scale* (same-size, how reduced or enlarged.)—This is a confused area. Cameramen work with the relative percentage in *linear* size of the finished engraving to the copy, i.e. if 8 x 10″ copy is to be made 4 x 5″, the percentage is 50. If 8 x 10″ becomes 12 x 15″, the percentage is 150. Same-size is 100%, etc. Ideally, everyone would use this system and there would be no trouble. However, some say "reduce 50%" in the first instance and "enlarge 50% in the second. Others say "reduce 1/2" and "enlarge 1 1/2 times" (1 1/2X). Still another method—and probably the safest in view of the confusion possible with percentages—is to use proportions. Example 1 is expressed as "reduce 2 to 1" and the second is "enlarge 1 to 1 1/2". Another advantage of this system is its flexibility. For example, "reduce 17 to 9" can be instantly translated into percentages with an engraver's proportional scale.

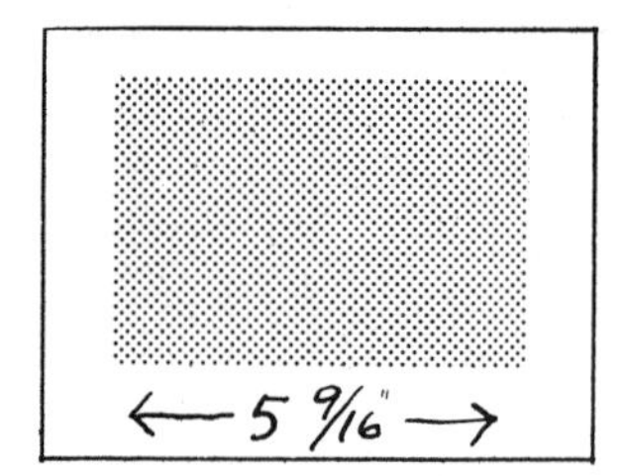

Whatever system you use, it is best to let the engraver know about it in advance. With work coming in marked in several ways, it is understandable that he might become confused.

When practicable, give the actual dimensions to which the copy is being reduced or enlarged. A dimension with arrows pointing outward on each side (← 5 9/16″ →) indicates that the entire copy is to be made that size in that direction. If the copy is to be reduced so that a certain *part* of it is to become 5 9/16″, a mark should be made in the margin opposite each end of the part concerned, and the indication 5 9/16″ BM (Between Marks) written between them.

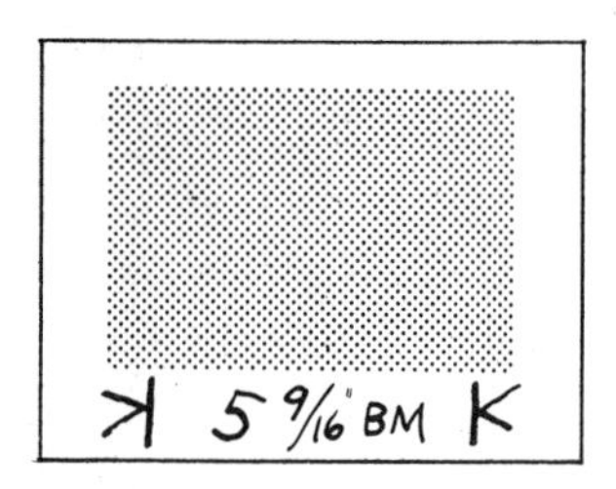

In no case should more than 1 dimension be given, unless the engraver is permitted to *crop* [cut away part of the picture] as necessary to maintain both (as when cuts must align). Even then, he should be told *how* to crop. In general, it is best to indicate 1 dimension and scale the subject so that the other dimension will be correct after reduction or enlargement.

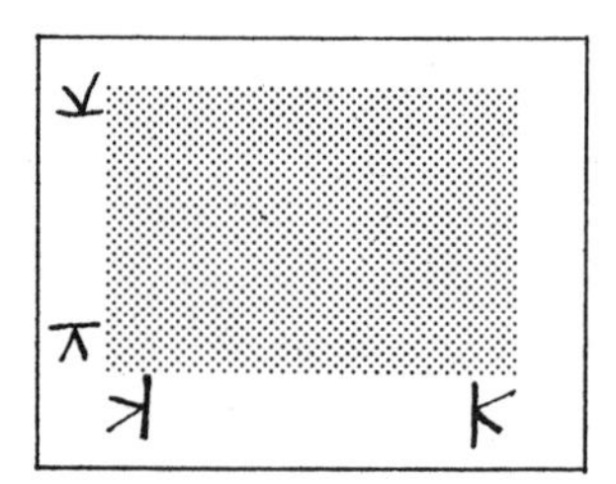

▪ *Cropmarks*—These should be clean lines in the margin indicating the places for cutting. An arrow should point to the mark in the direction of the portion of the picture being retained. If there is no margin, attach a slip of paper to the edge. Cropmarks on the back of a picture are a source of trouble.

▪ *Color*—Indicate which color for each part of the copy. Supply a sizable (at least 1 x 2″) swatch of flat, even color.

▪ *Silhouetting*—unless the outlines are obvious, make a tissue overlay and indicate how the silhouetting is to be done.

▪ *Mortising, Notching, etc.*—The clearest way of indicating their position is by use of an overlay.

All markings except register, trim, and fold marks—which must be black—should be made in color so that they will stand out and not be confused with copy. Light blue is best for markings that should not photograph. On photographs, use a grease pencil or tempera paint. Ballpoint pens make permanent marks.

Text and illustrations—letterpress

Ordinarily, the only preparation for camera involved in letterpress books is in ordering engravings for illustrations. If captions or other lines of type are to be included in the cuts, be sure to consider the effect of reduction on legibility and typographic relationships.

Remember to allow for a small shoulder (about 1/32″) even on adhesive-blocked cuts. This is important when cuts are planned to butt together or credit lines are expected to lie close to the pictures. Sometimes it is best to have 2 or more units mounted together on 1 block, in order to have the proper space between.

When pages are to be prepared for photomechanically made letterpress plates, the procedure is the same as preparing copy for lithography or gravure. Otherwise, only makeup (CHS.5,24) is involved. Preparation of letterpress plates or pages for press is discussed in CHS. 24 and 25.

Text and illustrations—lithography & gravure

Here it is best to make a mechanical for each page. However, if there are no more than 2 elements on each one, or if none of the elements can be shot together, it is usually sufficient to make a dummy (CH.21).

To make a page mechanical, the outline (untrimmed) is drawn in light blue lines and each same-size element pasted into place. If, for some reason, any item cannot be pasted in position, the platemaker will shoot it separately and strip-in the negative. (This is more expensive than pasting it in the copy.) The page is then marked with all instructions—including 2 *margins* [the distance from an edge of the page to the nearest element on it]. One margin must be the top or bottom, the other, the inside or outside.

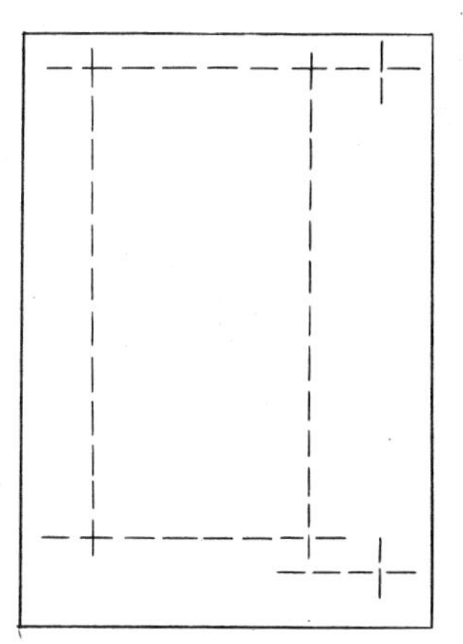

In either a dummy or a mechanical, when giving the distances between elements on a page (in which some, but not all, are pasted in position), at least 1 vertical and 1 horizontal measurement is omitted. This permits minor inaccuracies to be absorbed. The omitted measurement is usually one of the outer margins in each dimension, but not necessarily. Shown are 2 alternatives.

50 James Ensor

Magic Musicians

50 James Ensor

Magic Musicians

When a whole book is being prepared for camera, it is worth having blank sheets printed (in light blue ink) with the outlines of the page and whatever guidelines, corners, etc., would be useful in speeding the pasteup and increasing accuracy. The printing can be avoided by working on a light-table, with a transparent guide sheet taped to the glass.

Silk screen

The preparation of copy for silk screen is the same as for any other photomechanical platemaking process.

Preprinted hard covers

The only difference in copy preparation between preprinted hard-covers and other kinds of printing is in positioning the copy on the material. For the dimensions of cover material see CH.10. Of the ⅝″ allowed for turn-in, about ⅛″ goes around the thickness of the board and the rest is on the inside of the cover. Copy that is meant to bleed at the edge of the cover should extend to ¼″ (or less) from the edge of the sheet. This will mean that about ⅛″ of the copy will be covered by the endpaper.

Paperback covers

In width, the trimmed cover for a flush-trimmed paperback (CH.10) is the trim-size of the book, doubled, with the paper bulk added. Some people add ¹⁄₁₆″ to the paper bulk to allow for some loss in going around the corners at the back. The trimmed cover height is the same as the trimmed page size. The *un*trimmed cover has ⅛″ more on all 4 sides because it is put on the book before the pages are trimmed. If there are any bleeds, an additional ⅛″ must be added to the copy on that side. Be sure that the proper placement of the cover on the book is made clear to the bindery, if the design does not do so itself.

Jackets

Copy for jackets must have ⅛″ more on top and bottom than paperback covers, because of the overhang of the boards. On the front edge, bleeds should extend at least ⅛″, and preferably ¼″, past the edge, as the bleed should go around the thickness of the cover so that no white paper shows. The extra ⅛″ is desirable because jackets are not always accurately wrapped on the books. Copy that bleeds on the back edge of the spine should extend ⅛″ past the spine onto the back cover for the same reason. Jacket dimensions for a book of 7 x 10″ trim size, ⅞″ paper bulk, and round back would be as shown at left. See also discussion of cover dimensions on page 163.

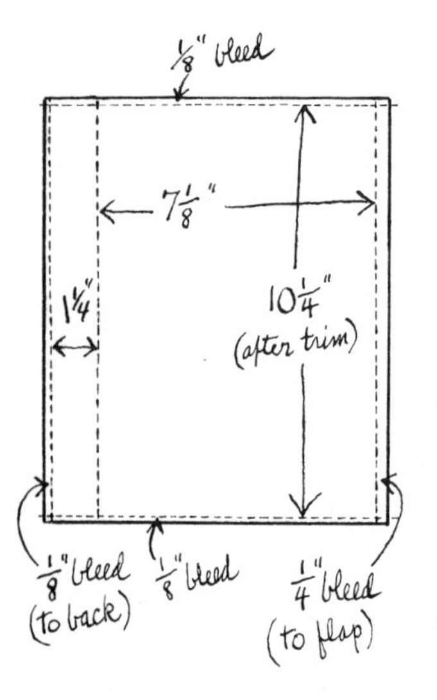

Preparation of the press layout for a jacket is essentially the same for letterpress and lithography. The position of flap and back-cover copy is given relative to the front cover and spine.

Again, if the position of the spine on the book is not perfectly obvious, have a proper indication printed on the sheet.

All the processes for making stamping dies (except the binder's electro) begin with photography, so the procedures for preparing camera copy apply. The requirements are the same as in making line engravings, except that some kinds of dies can be etched to various depths, so it is sometimes necessary to indicate the depth desired.

Dies and Stamping

Layouts for cover stamping are much the same as for jacket printing, except that only the front cover and spine are (usually) shown. Proofs of the dies are positioned in a layout showing the edges of the front cover and spine, including any division of cover material (CH.10). The dimensions are as indicated for preprinted covers, except that there are no turn-ins here. Remember that there is a space of ¼" between the spine and the front and back cover boards (the joints), in which no stamping can be done.

The position of each die is indicated by measurement in inches from an outer edge of the cover and/or an edge of the spine. Where there is more than 1 impression, overlays should be used as in multicolor printing. Dies should be kept at least 1/16", and preferably more, from the edges of the spine. The stamping operation is not as accurate as printing, and the inaccuracies of casemaking sometimes add to the error. The stamping layout for this book is shown.

¼"
BOOKMAKING
Marshall Lee
BOWKER
3/16"
1 9/16"
The illustrated guide to design & production
1 7/16"
ANODIZED GOLD FOIL
BLIND STAMP

12 | Estimating cost

A basic knowledge of the subjects covered so far is satisfactory for most readers of this book because: (a) the rudiments are all that can be absorbed at one time, (b) there is no need to know more because you are not actually having to do the things described (such as operating a photosetter or folding machine), or (c) where you *do* have to apply this knowledge you can usually get help from the suppliers involved. You *should* know more, but this knowledge can come in time as you gain experience.

Estimating cannot be done properly without a *thorough* knowledge of the subject, and a thorough knowledge of the art of estimating. It is simple enough to use a table or chart to arrive at the cost of basic operations and sometimes this is very useful information, but once details, complexities, and variations enter the picture, nothing less than an intimate acquaintance with all aspects of the problem will keep you out of trouble. Approximations are extremely dangerous in cost estimating. The profit margins in both book manufacturing and publishing are very small, and a slight error or miscalculation can easily doom your company to a loss. A seemingly minor deviation from the usual procedure in any operation may turn out to be a major problem, involving the use of a larger machine, a hand operation, or a time-consuming adjustment.

Because estimating requires more knowledge than can be gotten from this (or any one) book, and the consequences of even a small error can be disastrous, this chapter makes no attempt to enable the reader to perform the function himself. The information given is meant simply to provide enough familiarity with estimating to make it possible to deal effectively with those engaged in it. No reliance should be placed on your own estimates until you have had much practical experience in book production and in estimating itself.

Finding the probable cost of materials is relatively easy, but even this has booby traps. Price increases, penalties, extra charges, spoilage allowances, shipping charges, taxes, over- and under-runs—any or all of these can cause trouble for the unwary estimator. It is in estimating the cost of manufacturing processes, however, that the real dangers lie. The time required to perform a routine operation is known—but how long will it take to make up that special running head, or to make ready to print those unusual illustrations, or to insert books in that special carton? Not even the man in the shop knows exactly how much time these things will take, and your guess is likely to be less accurate.

A rough guess about cost is usually worse than no figure at all. No important decisions should be based on such guesses, because they could be, and usually are, wrong. There is a tendency to guess *under* the actual cost—which may lead to the obvious disaster—and rough figures obtained from a professional estimator are likely to be high—which may discourage a perfectly sound project. Professional estimators usually decline to give rough estimates at all, but if pressed they generally add a substantial percentage to their own guess in order to cover themselves. Even when a figure is thoroughly understood by both parties to be only a guess and not a contract, bad feeling often ensues when the bill comes to more than the guess. Moral: Don't operate on anything but a formal estimate in writing.

This warning having been given, it must be admitted that publishers often want and use rough estimates in the early stages of planning a project. These frequently are in the form of comparisons with the cost of previously published books, and sometimes they are prices on dummy specifications, but in either case they are based on actual costs, not guesses. However, the danger remains, because the new book will rarely come out like either the previous one *or* the dummy specs. Such preliminary figures can be very helpful, provided they are used with caution—and are replaced by detailed estimates before final decisions are made.

Some of the estimating problems and practices encountered in each area of bookmaking are discussed in the sections that follow. Additional information on costs is included in the chapter dealing with each subject.

Composition

There are 2 kinds of composition prices. One is the page price based on emage (CH.5). Emage is computed by multiplying the *overall* width and height of the text area in ems of the type size—the overall area being a rectangle parallel to the edges of the paper, with its sides encompassing the *outermost* elements included in the makeup. Thus, although the text itself on this page is 24 picas wide, the *overall* width is 33 picas, because it includes sideheads set on a measure of 8 picas, plus 1 pica separating them from the text. If the running heads were above the text, the overall height would include them. If there is an illustration on the page, it is included in the overall dimensions, even if it bleeds. (Actually, the emage on these pages did *not* include the sideheads and illustrations, for they were pasted and stripped in later, rather than being made up with the text.) The emage in a given area *increases* as the type size *decreases*. (A page of 8 pt. type costs more than a page of 10 pt.) This is because there are more characters per area, therefore more type to set.

HUMAN WELFARE

democracy, that it is a system of principles and not of rigid rules, that these principles must be reinterpreted as times and conditions change, and that the need for new interpretation and application will always exist.

Clearly, therefore, in speaking of democracy, the Committee is not thinking merely of the form of our institutions and organizations, which are but means or instruments for men's requirements. To identify present forms too closely with democratic ideals is to make idols of the forms, thereby hindering their improvement for the service of mankind.

In times of uncertainty many people tend to resist change, in the illusion that democracy and its institutions are made more secure by an unchanging order. This, we believe, strikes at the very heart of democracy by denying to it the right to grow. For democracy's greatest strength lies in its ability to move constantly forward in action toward the increasing fulfillment of people's needs and the greater achievement of its goals. It is man's faith in this ability which assures the survival of democracy.

DEMOCRACY ON CHALLENGE

During its investigation the Committee was constantly reminded that democracy is on challenge in the world today. A great new foundation can thus most appropriately make its entrance into human affairs with a reaffirmation of democratic ideals and with the expressed intention of assisting democracy to meet that challenge and to realize its ideals.

The crisis in the world today requires that democracy do more than restate its principles and ideals; they must be translated into action. We must take affirmative action toward the elimination of the basic causes of war, the advancement of democracy on a broad front, and the strengthening of its institutions and processes. National conduct based solely upon fear of communism, upon reaction to totalitarian tactics, or upon the immediate exigencies of avoiding war, is defensive and negative.

[21]

Emage

11/18 Times Roman x 30

30
12
360 pts
+ 42 pts overhang
402 pts overall width

36.5
11) 402.0 37 Ems wide

30 Lines
18 pt
540 pts
+ 36 pts running head
+ 48 pts folio
624 pts overall depth

56.8
11) 624.0 57 Ems deep

57 – 11 pt Ems deep
x 37 – 11 pt Ems wide
399
171
2109 Ems overall

The emage basis is used for books in which the pages are mainly straight text. Prices on such material are simple to calculate, as book compositors have certain charges per thousand ems for each size. The rates (for hot-metal composition) are based on normal setting speeds for normal copy and include makeup. There are many variations of these base rates, but they too are quite specific. The main ones are:

■ *Leading*—The rate is based on 2 or more pts. of leading. If less, there is a penalty because there are then more lines on the page. For 1 pt. leading, 5 to 10% is added. For *solid* lines [no leading], the penalty is 10 to 20%.

■ *Thin faces*—Some unusually thin faces carry a penalty because the emage rates are based on a normal number of characters per pica. For these faces, the emage is based on 1 size smaller than that being set (11 is figured as 10, 10 as 9, etc.).

■ *Minimum area*—Pages of less than a certain emage (usually 1000) are charged at the rate for that minimum, because of the extra handling required where there are so many pages for the total emage.

■ *Complicated work*—Usually, there is a separate rate for fiction and nonfiction, assuming that nonfiction will be slower in setting and proofreading because of proper names, unfamiliar terms, and more complicated makeup. The difference is about 10%. An extra penalty is charged when the text is unusually broken up by cuts, tables, formulas, etc. This varies greatly, depending on the kind of typesetting machine used.

■ *Difficult copy*—A penalty, which may go as high as 25%, is charged for setting copy that is difficult to read, as this slows the setting and proofreading. Such copy may be a heavily corrected Ms, a faint copy, negative photostats, extremely small type, etc.

■ *Foreign language*—The penalty (50 to 75%) charged for setting foreign language copy (including dialect) usually depends on how familiar the language is to the compositor, the availability of typesetters and proofreaders adept at the language, and the number of special characters required. In some cases it is better to take such work to specialized compositors.

■ *Poetry and plays*—Poetry aligned at the left is usually charged at 110% of the base rate, centered poetry at up to 125%. Plays, or play-style material (court testimony, interviews, etc.) are usually 115 to 125% of the base rate. The penalty varies according to how the characters' names are treated.

■ *Mixer* (CH.5)—Where there is only occasional need for type from different magazines on the same line, it probably pays to have the odd type cut in, but where such lines occur frequently in the copy, the entire job is usually set on a Mixer at 1½ times (150%)

the base rate for emage. Use of some photocomposing machines can greatly affect this cost.

- *Double column*—Two-column pages carry a penalty on the makeup time. This varies with the complexity of the work and the kind of machine used.

In general, penalties are charged on only the penalty copy itself, but when this constitutes a major portion of the Ms, the entire job may be billed at the penalty rate. The penalties are also cumulative. For example, a page of double-column, foreign language, centered poetry could be charged at 2 times base rate.

Bear in mind that each compositor has not only his own base rates, but his own rules for varying emage rates. While the above list is useful as a guide, it is necessary to check individual suppliers. The BMI issues a printed list of Trade Customs which forms the basis for most practices.

The other basis for billing composition is the *time charge* [a price based on the time required to do the work at a certain hourly rate]. Prices are based on time charges when the copy is too varied to use the emage basis. The relatively low emage rates are justified only by the efficiency in setting large amounts of fairly straight text. While these rates can be adjusted to cover more complicated work, they are no longer applicable when the amount of straight setting falls below a certain point.

Compositors are reluctant to give estimates of time charges, usually stipulating that such figures are only estimates and not firm prices. Understandably, when firm prices must be given, the estimator adds enough to cover any miscalculation.

Frontmatter [pages preceding the text] and part-title pages (CH.14) are usually charged at a standard multiple of the text-page price. This is essentially a time charge, based on the average cost of setting and making up such pages, which are sometimes very simple and at other times quite the opposite.

Chapter openings (CH.18) are usually priced according to the typographic arrangement used. Practices vary from one compositor to another, but there is generally one charge for machine-set lines and another for hand-set lines, with an extra charge added if the makeup is unusually complicated.

Sometimes, there is no charge for individual machine-set lines if they are in a face and size being used in the text, but if a different magazine is required, a nominal charge is made. This is usually the price of 1 hour's work, and is based on the time needed to change magazines *plus* the work of casting every mat and checking the proofs to be sure that no incorrect or damaged mats are present.

Usually, no extra charge is made for subheads, captions, or running heads (CH.18) since they are covered by emage, although additional charges are sometimes applied when machine changes, letterspacing, or complicated makeup are involved.

There is usually an extra charge for any type that appears on a machine-set line but is not from the same magazine. The greatest cost occurs if the slug or film must be cut to insert the other type. The charge is somewhat less if the special type can be cast on the same slug by inserting pi mats by hand (CH.5).

In general, there is a major difference in the cost of setting machine-type and hand composition. Linotype costs only a few cents per line, while hand-set type may cost $2 to $4 per line for smaller sizes of display, and more for larger sizes. Monotype in text sizes costs somewhat more than Linotype and, in display sizes it is charged as hand-set type. Ludlow is also charged as hand-set type, even though it is cast on a line slug, because the mats are assembled by hand. Because each photocomposing machine has unique capabilities, the cost of this composition depends on the nature of the work. What is easy for one machine is difficult for another.

The trade customs of compositors entitle them to charge extra for almost anything that is not straight text setting—and some do, but others prefer to cover these extra costs in their emage rates. Most use a combination of both methods of pricing. This should be considered when comparing price estimates.

Because they are based on volume production, the hourly rates of book compositors are much lower than those charged by typographers doing advertising work. The latter can deliver high-quality work on short notice, and offer a large choice of typefaces, but the staff and facilities needed to supply such service (customarily required by ad agencies) call for higher prices.

The price of composition includes the cost of a certain number of proofs—usually 2 galley, 2 page, and 1 set of foundry or plate proofs—a total of 5. Additional proofs are charged at a price per proof. Repros, acetates, or other special proofs are not included in the composition price. In photocomposition the cost of proofs varies somewhat, depending on the kind of product delivered by the machine (negative or positive film or paper print).

As there is much variation in the method of making up pages with photocomposition products, the emage price often includes only typesetting and proofs, with a separate price for makeup. Typewriter composition prices are often on a line basis, varying according to the size of type and length of line.

Plates

The price of plates of any kind is based on area, with a different unit price charged for line and halftone copy. Letterpress plates usually carry a penalty for *open work* [pages in which there are large blank areas] because of the extra routing needed to prevent the open areas from printing.

In letterpress, the charge is for individual page plates. In offset lithography and gravure, the individual page size is not significant, it is the size of the form that counts. Therefore, elements on the pages within the form need not be close together for economy (CH.7).

offset lithography plate area

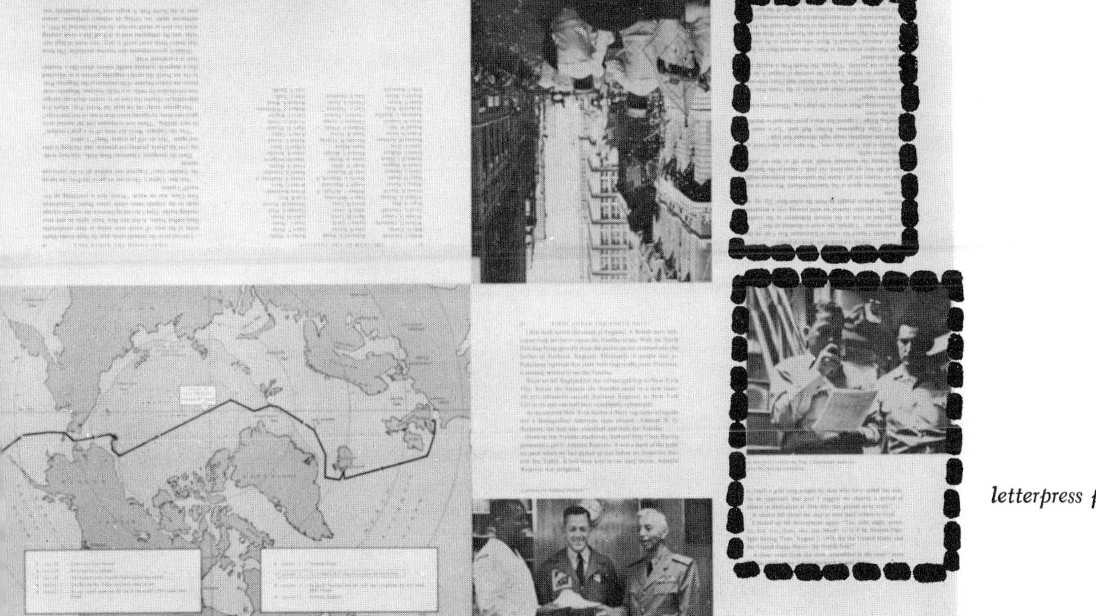

letterpress plate areas

Printing

The price of printing consists of the charge for makeready plus a price per thousand impressions, which is based on the cost of operating the press during the time required, i.e. the pay of the man or men operating the press, amortizing the cost of the machine, the rent or taxes on the space it occupies, and general overhead (lights, bookkeeping, maintenance, etc.). Except for parts of the last item, the cost increases with the size of the press.

The ink cost is relatively minor and quite uniform from one job to another, so it is included in the basic price for printing. Occasionally, when an unusual amount of ink is required, a separate charge is made. When more than 1 color is used there is a charge for washing the ink out of the press each time (washup), but this is a negligible amount on a large run and is usually not noted separately.

While all forms of printing are estimated on the basis of makeready plus impressions, the relative importance of each factor varies from one process to another and according to the specifications of the job. For example, more time is needed to make ready a letterpress type form with pages of inch-thick metal than an offset form consisting of 1 thin sheet of aluminum; a form of straight text can be made ready and can run faster than one containing color process; a form of 32 pages can be made ready faster than one of 64 pages; the high speed of rotary presses and perfectors reduces the importance of impressions in relation to makeready time; in general, the shorter the run, the larger makeready looms in the price.

Although the printer's cost per thousand impressions is the same for the first thousand (after completion of makeready) and the tenth or hundredth thousand, the price per thousand usually decreases somewhat with larger quantities. The main benefit of long runs, however, is in reduction of the unit cost of makeready.

There is also an advantage in larger forms, up to a point. It doesn't take nearly twice as long to make a 64-page form ready as a 32-page form, so it is usually cheaper to have fewer, larger forms. This is not always true, however, since the time of a larger press is worth more than that of a smaller one. On a very large, fast press and a short run, the much higher cost of makeready time may make it more economical to run more forms on a smaller press, as there is little advantage in the speed.

The price of lithography and gravure printing includes the plates. Usually, they are quoted as a separate item, and they should be, in order to permit comparison with letterpress—where the plates, if any, are usually estimated separately with the composition price.

Paper See CH.8.

Binding Estimating binding costs is much more complex than figuring printing prices, as there are many more operations and materials. The price quoted by binders is a unit price (per copy) according to the size of the run, usually without any itemization. There are a great many items involved and not one of them accounts for a major part of the cost. About 20% of the total is materials, and these costs don't vary much in the normal range of quantities used. The cost of operations is, as in printing, divided between makeready, or setting-up, and running, but due to the much slower speeds of binding equipment, the setting-up costs are relatively small compared to running time, even in average editions of 5 or 6000. Consequently, there is not much difference in the unit cost of binding a small edition or a large one. Only in extremely small quantities is there a really appreciable difference. Editions under, say, 2000 become quite expensive because the setting-up cost is spread over so few copies. For example, it might cost 36¢ per copy to bind 5000 copies, 35¢ for 10,000 and 34½¢ for 50,000—a spread of only 1½¢—but the price for 1500 copies would be 42¢.

The only items of material large enough to be worth calculating with a view to saving money are the cover material, which may account for about 10% of the total price, and the endpapers, which may amount to about 5%. For 1-piece covers on a 6⅛ x 9¼" trim-size book, about 10 covers can be cut out of a running yard of material, including spoilage. Thus, using a 45¢ material, the cost per book is about 4½¢, a 30¢ material means 3¢ per book, etc. Using this rule of thumb it is quite easy to estimate the effect on unit cost of any change of material. In estimating 3-piece covers, each material is figured separately.

To find out the cost of a material used on part of a cover, divide the width of the piece into the width of the roll, then divide the height of the piece into 36″, multiply the 2 answers and you have the number of pieces that will cut out of a running yard. Divide this number into the price per yard to get the price per piece. Thus, a 5 x 7½″ (trim-size) book with a 2½″-wide strip of cloth showing on the backbone and sides would require a piece 3″ wide (to allow each side to overlap ¼″) and 9″ high (CH.10). The 3″ would cut 14 times out of a 42″-wide roll and the 9″ cuts 4 times out of a yard of length. This gives 56 pieces (4 x 14) per yard. If the cloth costs 56¢ per yard, each piece costs 1¢. If the backbone were 1″ wide, the side pieces would each be 5″ wide x 9″ high. If the sides were a paper from a 25″ wide roll, the 5″ would cut out 5 times and there would be 4 pieces 9″ high out of the yard length. This would provide 20 pieces or 10 books (2 sides per book) out of a running yard. At 10¢ per yard, the sides would cost 1¢ per book. The total cost of cover material is then 2¢.

The cost of a 1-piece cover of the cloth used for the backbone would be 4⅔¢, i.e. the width of the piece is 12½″, which cuts out 3 times from a 38″ roll (with ½″ waste) and the 9″ height comes 4 times out of the yard, making 12 pieces per yard. Divided into 56¢ this comes to $.0466.

Endpapers are each twice the untrimmed page size. Thus, on a trim-size of 5 x 7½″, each untrimmed page is 5⅛ x 7¾″, so each endpaper is 10¼ x 7¾″. Endpapers are cut from sheets, not rolls. Remembering that the grain should run with the fold (7¾″), this size would cut out of a 26 x 40″, grain-long, sheet 10 times (2 times 10¼″ out of 26″ and 5 times 7¾″ out of 40″) with some waste. From here, the cost would be calculated as for any other paper (CH.8).

The labor costs in binding divide roughly into: (a) sheetwork—folding, gathering, sewing, (b) forwarding—trimming, backing, etc., (c) casemaking, (d) stamping, (e) casing-in, and (f) wrapping. The items vary in amount and proportion of the total binding cost, according to each book's characteristics and the length of the run. Some of the alternatives are discussed in CHS. 16 and 26, but a general picture of unit costs for an average book might be somewhat as follows:

sheetwork:	about 12½	cents	
forwarding:	about 7½	"	
casemaking:	about 3	"	
stamping:	about 2	"	
casing-in:	about 5½	"	
wrapping:	about 4½	"	
makeready:	about 3	"	(includes all operations)

To the total of 38¢ for labor would be added about 3¢ for materials other than the text paper and the cover material. Thus, if the latter were 5¢, the total binding cost would be about 43¢. The prices would vary also according to the individual binder, the kind of equipment used, and when the work is done.

To the above should be added a figure for packing and shipping, as these are customarily in the binder's price. Where packing is on skids and delivery is local in bulk, ¾¢ should be enough. For packing in bulk cartons add about 3¢, including the cartons. For individual carton packing, figure at least 8¢ for labor and between 9 and 20¢ each for the cartons, depending on the size of the book, the number of copies, and the design of the carton. Where individual carton labeling is to be done by the binder, there is an additional charge of about 3¢, including delivery in bulk to post office. There is no charge for skids if they are returned.

CAUTION: All the cost figures given in this chapter (or elsewhere in this book) are provided for the reader's *general information*. They are composite prices prevailing at the time of writing and are subject to variation according to time, locality, the individual supplier, and various special circumstances.

13 | Schedules & records

Schedules

In making books for publishing, an essential, vital part of the problem is to get the books made not only well and economically, but efficiently. This means getting books finished in time to be published as scheduled. The financial success or failure of a title may hinge as much upon *when* it is published as any other factor.

There are 2 problems in the choice of a publication date: (a) deciding on the time when the book is likely to be best received by reviewers, booksellers, and public and (b) relating publication to the needs of the house for income to cover expenses. The latter is, for all but the smallest publishers, a relatively minor consideration, but once the decision is taken the apparatus of distribution is set in motion—a catalogue is printed, advertising is prepared, salesmen are briefed and go selling, orders are taken—and any change in schedule means a major upset.

THE HAZARDS

Even if only 1 title is being produced, the problem of keeping a publication date is formidable—but when 50 or 100 are in work simultaneously, nothing short of high efficiency (and a generous helping of luck) will succeed. If the pub date is set before the Ms is completed, as is often the case, there is a good chance that the Ms will be late. The author may become ill, be distracted by pressing personal matters, run into an unexpected difficulty in writing, go abroad on a windfall fellowship, or decide that the Ms is no good and rewrite it. Once he turns it in, it may require considerable editing, checking, or examination for libelous material. When released by the editorial department, the Ms goes to the designer—who may find it a problem because it is not clearly organized, incomplete, or economically impractical. The problems solved and design worked out, the Ms goes out for composition, where it may be delayed by a busy compositor or set in the wrong size by mistake. Once in galleys, it goes back to the author, who may delay its return for any of the reasons mentioned before or another one. These hazards hold true for paging as well. Before the book gets on press, any one of a number of calamities may strike—loss of proofs in the mail; loss or damage of plates in transit; strikes; late delivery of illustrations, engravings, or paper; receipt of a new chapter from the author; etc., etc. Delays caused by a busy printer are to be expected, and there could be plate *batters* [injuries] on press. In the bindery, another delay is likely as the binder tries to fit the job into *his* schedule, and the possibilities for small and large disasters during binding are multiple. These are some of the reasons for missing a publication date even *if* the production department operates efficiently.

Another production obstacle is the concentration of publishing activity in seasons, which everyone in book publishing deplores, but the problem of distributing books through such a large country makes it difficult to do otherwise. It is more convenient to have 1 sales conference at which all the salesmen are briefed on the season's list than to brief them individually on a few titles at a time. As the salesmen are scattered from Maine to California, it is not feasible to bring them together more than 2 or 3 times a year. These factors, combined with the massive emphasis on the Christmas gift market, tend to perpetuate the practice of producing books in batches.

This throws a heavy strain on all production facilities in the months prior to October, when most fall books are wanted, and a somewhat lighter rush is concentrated in the midwinter months when the spring lists are being prepared. Fortunately, most publishers see the disadvantages of this arrangement and are trying to spread their publications more evenly through the year.

THE TIME REQUIRED

It is customary for tradebooks to be manufactured in time for delivery about 6 weeks prior to pub date. This gives the publisher time to ship books to all parts of the country, and to send them to reviewers enough in advance to enable appearance of reviews at or about publication date.

A book of average size and no problems *can* be produced in about 3 weeks—if everyone concerned puts all else aside. The normal time needed is about 4 months. Complicated manuscripts, high-quality production, slow proofreading, require still more time. Thus, an average book should go into production not much less than 6 months before the publication date desired, to make allowance for unforeseen problems.

A realistic production schedule for an average book (about 320 pages of fairly straight text in an edition of 5 to 10,000) might run as follows:

analysis, design, sample pages	2 weeks
composition	3 "
reading galleys	2 "
page makeup	2 "
reading pages	1 week
correction and plating	2 weeks
printing	2 "
binding	3 "
total	17 weeks

Although it is possible to make the book in less time, it would be dangerous to allow less unless the manufacturer were to give a firm promise of an earlier completion date—and even then there are too many possibilities for delay (as noted earlier) to depend on the date.

PROMISES & PRESSURES

Generally, a supplier of services will not give a definite schedule until the job is in hand for production, for he has no way of knowing what work will be in his plant when the job does come in. For a very big or important job he may give a firm date in advance, but this obviously means that some other work will be pushed aside if necessary. Since you are just as likely (at some time) to be on the receiving as well as the pushing end of this treatment, it is best to avoid asking for such promises. The hard truth remains, however, that with the best of intentions and the most efficient planning, circumstances beyond your control sometimes make a crash program necessary. The object in bookmaking is to insure that such cases are the exception rather than the rule.

With a great many jobs in work at the same time—and conflicting pressures from all sides—the supplier may easily fall behind on any one job. While it isn't wise to push him too hard too often, a gentle reminder at proper intervals is quite necessary. Knowing just when and how to do this is vital for a production manager. It is best to prod when there is still time to get the job done on schedule if the supplier has been delinquent, but late enough to give him a reasonable chance to get going. On a long-term job, occasional, well-timed reminders are in order. Written reminders are effective and not as distracting as phone calls.

Records

The number of details involved in producing even 1 book is astonishing, the problem of keeping track of several in various stages of production is overwhelming, unless systematic records are maintained.

It would be nice to be able to say that a simple chart is sufficient, but it isn't. To be effective, a record system must cover every detail, and this means that a progress chart should provide a place for each item of production. Anything not carried on the chart is very likely to be overlooked at some point.

There are as many ways of arranging production records as there are people keeping them—and any system is good if it works. The basic idea is to provide a space to be filled when a particular operation is completed, so that the blank spaces are reminders of what is not yet done. This would be relatively simple if all operations were successive, but there are many things to be done concurrently, and the problem is to get them all done when they are needed. At one particular moment, for example, all of the following may be in progress on 1 title:

text in composition,
frontmatter copy coming from author,
foreword being written,
Library of Congress number applied for,
illustration engravings being made,
a missing illustration being made,
paper for text being made,
paper for illustrations ordered,
binding design out for approval,
bulking dummy being made,
jacket plates being made,
jacket flap copy being written.

This list is not an exaggeration, but a common occurrence. And if ordering something were sufficient to get it done, the problem would be complex enough; but each item must be followed up or it may be late and hold up the entire job.

It is not possible to record the progress of *every* detail of production, yet every detail must be somehow covered. For example, if no entry is provided for the receipt of halftone blueprints, a space for noting receipt of the cuts will be a reminder that something is due from the engraver, and a call to him will reveal the state of the job. The more records kept the better for accuracy—but keeping up records takes time too, and a small staff is usually not able to make all the entries desirable. Each office must find its own compromise.

On the following page is a typical record form. Note that spaces are provided for the dates when various items are *due,* as well as the dates they arrive. A considerable amount of work is needed to maintain such records, but it is better to use such a form and fail to keep it perfectly than to use an inadequate form.

In addition to a chart on which the progress of each book is recorded in detail, it is desirable to keep a chart showing the general progress of all books in work. This enables determining at a glance the state of the whole list in terms of the seasonal publication schedule.

PRODUCTION SCHEDULE

TITLE:	PUB DATE:	BOUND BOOK DATE:
AUTHOR:	TRIM SIZE:	QUANTITY:
EDITOR:	No. PAGES:	BULK:

COMPOSITOR:	BINDER:
PRINTER: type/plates/litho	JACKET PRINTER:

COMPOSITION	DUE	ACT
Ms to design		
Sample pgs IN		
" " OK		
Estimate IN		
" OK		
Ms & comp ord OUT		
Galleys IN		
" ret		
Castoff IN		
" OK		
Frontmatter OUT		
" pfs IN		
" " ret		
Pg pfs IN		
" " ret		
Rev gals/pgs IN		
Rev pfs ret		
Index OUT		
" pfs IN		
" " ret		
Foundry pfs IN		
" " OK		
Plate pfs/repros		

MATERIALS	DUE	ACT
Text ppr ord		
" " IN		
Insert/endppr ord		
" " IN		
Jacket ppr ord		
" " IN		
Bdg material ord		
" " IN		

PRINTING	DUE	ACT
Dum & ord to ptr		
Mechanical to ptr		
Pg blues IN		
" " OK		
On press		
Sheets to bdy		

ILLUSTRATIONS	DUE	ACT
Illustrations IN		
" to cam		
Blues/engr pf IN		
" " " OK		
Caption copy OUT		
" pfs IN		
" " ret		
Repros IN		
Pg blues/pg pf IN		
" " " " OK		
Dum & ord to ptr		
Sheets to bdy		

JACKET	DUE	ACT
Jacket design ord		
" " IN		
" " OK		
Mechanical to ptr		
Blues/engr pf IN		
" " " OK		
Flap copy to ptr		
" " pfs IN		
" " " ret		
Repro/plate pf IN		
Dum & ord to ptr		
Jackets to bdy		

BINDING	DUE	ACT
Bdg design IN		
" " OK		
Dies ord		
" IN		
Ptd cover:mech IN		
Mech & ord to ptr		
Blues IN		
" OK		
Sheets to finish		
" " bdy		
Sample covers ord		
" " IN		
OK & ord to bdy		
Bound books		

MISC

Each title should, of course, have its own folder containing a copy of every proof or document relevant to the book's production. Although there is a good chance that the world will collapse under the weight of all the records being accumulated, it is better to keep anything that *might* be useful than to throw it away and need it later. A system of periodic destruction of old files will keep the accumulation from getting out of hand, and microfilming is the answer to permanent filing of important documents.

Most filing systems in production offices are based on letter-size files, but if you are starting a new system, it is not a bad idea to use legal-size files, which are a little larger and very handy where large proofs, sketches, etc. are to be kept.

The most important records in book production, besides those needed to keep schedules, are those concerning expenditures of money. Sometimes an order is given in the course of a conversation, and this may be sufficient for the supplier, but to keep the records straight, a formal order on a numbered order form should be executed. Besides the copy or copies required by the bookkeeping department, at least 1 copy of all orders should be made for the records of the production office.

There are 2 main reasons for keeping such records. One is to compile figures on production expenditures for the needs of management, the other is to check against any inquiry involving an error in the records of another office. In the latter case, the inquiry may offer the order number, the date, or the name of the job. Your orders may be filed according to any 1 of these, or 2, or all of them. While maximum efficiency would require 3 kinds of files, there are not likely to be enough inquiries to justify this. If 1 file is kept, it should be according to title, as this is the most generally useful.

Incidentally, it is customary for book manufacturers to file jobs by title, so, even though Mss are referred to by author in publishing houses, confusion is minimized by using the title outside the house. The chances of a publisher having 2 authors of the same name on 1 list are small, but suppliers deal with perhaps 30 or 40 publishers, and the chance of a duplication of authors' names is considerable. Even when titles are similar, an abbreviated form can be made distinctive.

For a discussion of preparing composition orders see CH.19. Printing orders are covered in CH.25 and binding orders in CH.27.

C

PROCEDURE

14 | Analysis

The process of design has 3 steps:

(1) Analysis of the problem.

(2) Consideration of the possible solutions.

(3) Selection of the best solution.

Essentially, this is the process of problem-solving. Design is the name given to problem-solving in certain fields, of which bookmaking is one. If the 3-stage process is not carried out, the result cannot be called design.

The application of stock solutions to unexamined problems may produce superficially adequate results at times, due to coincidence, but over a long period there will be many more failures than successes. For that reason, this book offers *guides to procedure*, rather than rules. Rules can be found in stylebooks, but they are primarily to help beginners produce usable work or at least avoid the worst mistakes—they cannot produce excellent design. A few rules are given in this book, but they are related to principles rather than procedure.

With experience, it is possible to shorten the distance between (1) analysis and (3) selection. Repeated encounters with 1 kind of problem enable a designer to instantly reject some solutions and move swiftly toward others. It may even appear at times that the middle stage of the design process has been omitted entirely, just as it may seem that the transmission process from nerve-ending to brain has been omitted because one shouts in pain immediately upon touching a hot object. In both cases, the speed of the action makes it imperceptible, but the action takes place.

Even intuition can be comprised by the analytic process, since creative intuition will not produce answers of value unless preceded at some time (however far back) by analytical effort. The intuitive process will be discussed in the next chapter, now we are concerned with analysis.

The problem in bookmaking

The characteristic of book publishing that makes it perpetually interesting—and confounds the conventional businessman—is its multiple purpose. A single book may be an object of commerce, a work of art, an act of faith, and an article of practical use—or a half dozen other things. The problems of bookmaking reflect this diversity.

Every book presents 3 kinds of problems: (a) mechanical, (b) commercial, and (c) editorial.

- *The mechanical problem*—Turning the Ms into an efficient and economical book.
- *The commercial problem*—Producing a book that is suited to its market, aids sales, and can be sold profitably.
- *The editorial problem*—Creating a book that properly expresses the author's message.

There is some dispute as to the legitimacy of a designer's concern with the editorial content of a Ms. There is a school that would consider the analysis completed once the mechanical and commercial problems had been examined.

Another school holds that the design must do as much as it can for the author—that it must support visually what the author is saying verbally. (See "Schools of design" in CH.2.) If the latter view is valid, then there *is* an editorial problem in bookmaking. This book proceeds on that assumption, leaving it to the reader to use or ignore references to the editorial aspects.

The esthetic element has not been omitted. It is implicit in the 3 factors named, but is subordinate to them. Esthetic success should not be achieved at the expense of any of the basic aspects although, paradoxically, some books cannot achieve success mechanically, commercially, or editorially unless they succeed esthetically.

Mechanical analysis

An analysis of the mechanical problem of a Ms is known variously as *a character count, breakdown,* or castoff. Breakdown is probably the most apt term, for there is more involved than just a character count, and castoff is properly applied to the process of counting the number of pages in galley proofs.

A breakdown is a division of the Ms into various kinds of material, with each kind counted by the most suitable method. There are 4 ways of counting: (a) by characters, (b) by lines, (c) by units, and (d) by pages.

CHARACTER COUNTS

Character counts are used to determine the amount of material in continuous prose copy. The text of the Ms itself is usually counted by this method.

Authors and editors use "word counts" in measuring the size of a Ms, but this is an inaccurate method, even disregarding the fact that there are often kinds of material that must be counted in other ways. Consider the varying vocabularies used by different writers—or even the same writer dealing with different subjects. A book on sociology, for example, will probably have a higher proportion of long words than will a novel. One writer may average 5.5 characters per word while another may average 6.1. This is a difference of only 10%, but in a 320-page book the difference means 32 pages. There is also a possibility of error when an author makes his word count. If he estimates an average of 10 words per line and it is actually 9.5 he is off another 5%, or 16 pages. There are other errors inherent in this method, so it would be best for editors to use character counts and encourage authors to do the same.

In a character count, each letter, number, punctuation mark, word-space, and sentence-space is counted as 1 unit. On a standard typewriter, the widths of all characters and the single space are identical. In type, the widths of characters and spaces do vary, but there are so many in a page that the average for a particular size of a particular face can be assumed to be the same in all cases (some exceptions are taken up later). There are 2 sizes of type on American standard typewriters: *pica* and *elite*. The pica width is 10 characters to the inch and the elite is 12 characters per inch. Justifying typewriters and those having characters of varying width must be treated as typesetting machines for character-count purposes.

← 1" →	
Bookmaking:T	*(elite)*
Bookmaking	*(pica)*

▪ *The text*—To make a character count of straight text, first determine the average number of characters per line in the Ms. This is the most crucial estimate in the analysis because it is multiplied thousands of times and any error will carry to the final result in proportion. As we have seen, even a few percentage points of error mean a substantial number of pages in the book. Unfortunately, it is not easy to estimate accurately the average characters per line. In typescript, although the uniform character width makes it simple to determine the number of characters in a line, the varying width of line presents a problem. Assuming that the entire Ms was typed by 1 person on 1 machine with the same width of line setting, the problem is fairly small. The usual practice is to draw a line down the right side of the page at what is optically the midpoint between the longest and shortest lines (not including paragraph endings). This line would represent the average width. A more accurate method is to actually measure the number of characters on each line of the page and take a mathematical average. This is not an excessive amount of work in order to arrive at such an important figure.

If, as is more likely, the Ms has been typed by various people and machines, the average characters per line found on the first page

On just such a night, seven years before, Chrysis had left
the land of Gennesaret. She remembered it well. They were five men,
sellers of ivory. The long tails of their horses were adorned with
parti-colored tufts. They had met the child at the round edge of a well...

Before that there had been the blue lake, the transparent sky, the
light air of the land of Galilee.

Her mother's house was surrounded with pink, flax-plants and tamarisks.
Thorny caper-bushes pricked childish fingers when she went to catch butter-
flies... She could almost see the wind in the waves of the pine grasses....

The little girls bathed in a clear brook where there were red shells
under flowering laurel: and there were flowers upon the water, and flowers
all over the fields, and great lilies grew upon the mountain, and the line of
the mountain was that of a young breast....

Chrysis closed her eyes and smiled a faint smile which suddenly died
away. The idea of death had just occurred to her. She felt that she would
be conscious until the last.

"Ah!" she said, "what have I done? Why did I meet that man? Why did
he listen to me? Why did I let myself be caught in this trap of my own
making? Why is it that, even now, I regret nothing?

"To love or die: that is the choice God gave me. What have I done to
deserve punishment?"

Fragments of sacred verses came to her from her childhood. She had not
thought of them for seven years. They now returned one after the other
with implacable precision, to define her life and predict her penalty.

A typescript page with a line drawn at the width of the average line.

can be used only as long as the typescript is similar to that page. Wherever a change occurs, a new average figure must be found.

When counting characters in printed copy (anthologies, reprints, etc.), the width of line is uniform, but the number of characters in the lines will vary (up to 10%) because of the justification process (CH.5). However, if enough lines are counted (there is no easy method, each character and space must be counted), an accurate average can be found. A count of about 20% of the lines on a page can reasonably be projected to that page and all pages set like that one. This should be repeated *at least* once in every 100 pages, as it is likely that more than 1 operator set the book. Machine composition can be set *tight* or *loose*, and a difference of 4 or 5% in the average characters per line is very possible. For example, when a good operator gets a bad break that will result in too wide spacing, he will reset several lines to overcome the problem. Another operator will simply space out the line and go on.

When an average character count per line has been determined, multiply this figure by the number of lines of text. To find the latter, multiply the number of lines per page by the number of *full* pages (if they have the same number of lines), and add to this the number of lines on *short* pages—usually chapter openings and endings. If there are spaces in the MS (around chapters, subheads, etc.) they are subtracted from the line count.

If the Ms has varying numbers of lines per page, either count enough pages to get an average or, better still, count the number of lines on each page and total them. This is not too difficult with the help of an adding machine. (On standard typewriters, double-spaced lines measure 3 to the inch.)

The problem is very simple with printed copy because the number of lines per page will be uniform. However, count several pages to be sure you have a normal one. Some pages may be made a line short or long to avoid widows. (CH.5).

Until this point, it has been assumed that the Ms is clean and orderly. Unfortunately, this is not always so. Some handwritten corrections are almost always present, and usually these may be disregarded as they probably cancel out each other, but there *are* Mss with heavy handwritten corrections, pasted-in strips of copy, extensive deletions, etc. About all that can be done is to make a careful, page-by-page guess as to the effect of such irregularities. Don't make a guess for the Ms as a whole, there is too much room for error.

Sometimes it pays to send a very dirty Ms back to the editorial department for retyping. Weigh the compositor's penalty (CH.12) against the cost of retyping—and the loss of time in slowed setting and proofreading against the time needed for retyping. Often, the time element means more than the money involved.

A rough character count can be made by determining the number of characters on a typical page and multiplying by the number of pages in the Ms, with the short chapter opening and closing pages subtracted. In a perfectly typed Ms of straight narrative text such a count would be adequate, otherwise it should be used with caution. To make an ideal character count, each line should be counted and the totals kept chapter by chapter.

Any prose part of the Ms which might ultimately be set in a style different from that of the main text should be character-counted separately. If you count everything in with the text, you have no way of knowing how the length of the book would be affected if you should decide to set some part of it in a different size type, a narrower measure, or with different leading. The kinds of copy that usually require a character count are:

- *Extract*—This is quoted material that is not run in with the text.
- *Appendix*—An appendix may be any kind of copy, but when it is prose it should be counted separately.
- *Introductions*—A long introduction is usually set as part of the text, but there is no harm in counting it separately. Short introductions to parts and chapters should always be separated, preferably piece by piece.

▪ *Notes*—Whether arranged as footnotes or in a group at the end of the book, notes are a separate item.

▪ *Foreign language*—This may be extract or part of the text, and should be so designated. It is mainly for pricing purposes that foreign language is counted separately (CH.12).

LINE-FOR-LINE COUNTS

Any line of copy that will definitely begin a new line on the printed page and will definitely not extend beyond 1 line may be counted as *line-for-line* copy. Obviously, it is necessary to know how many characters per line the printed page will have in order to make such a count, but an approximation is usually sufficient. Where the copy is clearly less than the probable number there is no problem. Where it is clearly more, but certainly not more than twice the number, 2 lines are counted. In borderline cases, guesses must be made—and these should average out to the right amount.

There are several kinds of line-for-line material and these should be counted separately. This method is used wherever possible, as it is more accurate than a character count. Some of the most frequently encountered line-for-line material is described below:

▪ *Conversation*—Short lines of conversation and other lines in text (courtroom testimony, questions and answers, etc.) which will definitely set as 1 line of type should be counted and the number subtracted from the text line count.

▪ *Poetry*—Some poetry has a large number of lines of about 1-line width. Take a guess at the possible number of characters per line in the printed book, and make a paper strip of the proper width. All wider lines should be counted as 2. Stanza breaks are counted as 1 line each.

▪ *Tables*—Tables in the text should be counted separately from those in an appendix, as you may want to set them differently. For pricing purposes, tables are usually grouped and counted according to number of columns.

▪ *Glossary*—If the definitions are brief, this can be counted line for line, otherwise it is best to make a character count.

▪ *Bibliography*—Some bibliographies have descriptive paragraphs for each title. These should have a separate character count, while the book titles can be counted line for line.

▪ *Lists*—If the list is typed double column, the line count should note this. Should you decide later to set the lists in single column, the line count would be doubled.

▪ *Subheads in text*—Where the subheads are long enough to average more than 1 line, a line count should be made in addition to the regular heading count (see below).

UNIT COUNTS

Sometimes it is necessary to know only *how many* of a particular kind of material is in the Ms, rather than how many characters or lines there are. This is true mainly of elements of space, or elements surrounded by space. In such cases, the space that can be allocated in the printed book is variable, so it is more important to know the number of elements there are than how much space they occupy in the Ms.

- *Subdivisions*—Count the *number* of part-titles, chapter titles, section titles, and subheads—giving each class of subhead a designating number and a separate count. Do not count lines or characters.
- *Spacebreaks*—These are usually 1 or 2 lines each. They should be counted and the proper number of lines subtracted from the overall line count for the text. Then list only the *number* of spacebreaks.
- *Units*—The number of occurrences (or units) of each kind of material within the text should be counted. For example it is not enough to know that there are x number of characters of extract, or y number of lines of poetry, you must know *how many times* extract or poetry occur, because you may decide to have some space before and after each quotation and/or poem, and you must be able to compute the amount of space involved. (100 lines of extract may be 2 quotations of 50 lines each, or 50 quotations of 2 lines each.)

It is necessary to make some estimate of the number of occurrences of footnotes, if they are to appear beneath the text, because you will need some space to separate the two. This is difficult to do with any accuracy, because you can't know how the notes will occur in the page makeup. A reasonably good way of figuring this is to count all the footnotes and then, if there are fewer notes than pages of Ms, assume that each footnote will fall on a separate page. If there are more notes than pages, assume that there will be footnotes on every page in the book. You are not likely to be exactly right, but you probably won't be too far wrong.

PAGE-FOR-PAGE COUNTS

In the frontmatter and sometimes in the *backmatter*, there will be material that will obviously fit on 1 page in the book. The *half-title* [usually the book title set in small type on the first page], the title, the copyright notice, the dedication, a brief acknowledgment, a small contents page, etc., need not be counted for characters and lines. Simply note their existence. The same is true for any such page in the text, such as a full-page table or chart. Make a character or line count only where there is any possibility that the copy will run more than 1 page.

INDEX

If the Ms is a printed book, there is no problem. Simply count the number of lines, making sure that you count the lines in each column, not per page. With a new Ms, you can only guess. As a rule of thumb, allow 1 page of index to every 40 pages of Ms with average copy, 1 to 30 for a Ms with very many names and/or technical terms, 1 to 50 for one with comparatively few. Check your guess with the editor and use his figure if it differs from yours.

ILLUSTRATIONS

This is usually the most difficult part of a mechanical analysis. It is certainly the most difficult to discuss in general terms, because there are so many possible situations.

The first step is to divide the illustrations into: (a) color process, (b) monochrome halftone, (c) monochrome line, and (d) simple color, halftone, and line, as each kind has its own technical requirements. Then, make a tentative determination of the approximate amount of space to be occupied by each illustration, even if it can be only a rough guess, somewhat as follows:

(a) color process:
  8 full page
  6 half page
(b) monochrome halftone:
  6 full page
  19 half page
  23 quarter page
(c) line cuts
  52 half page
  67 quarter page

You may be surprised to find how naturally illustrations will fall into such size-groups at a glance. The space might not ultimately work out as you guessed, but it is very useful to have an estimate such as this to start from.

TABULATION

All information of the mechanical analysis (breakdown) should be tabulated in an orderly and useful form. This tabulation will become a tool in creating the book, so it should be typed for maximum efficiency. Include whatever data may be of some use. There is nothing lost if you don't use a particular figure on your breakdown sheet, but it is very frustrating to need something that isn't there. For convenience, note the Ms page on which each kind of material first occurs.

It is a good idea to type all items to the left, so that the right side of the sheet can be used for inserting the calculated number of pages for each one. If you draw lines across the page under each item there is less danger of overlooking one. On the opposite page is a specimen breakdown sheet. Note that the tabulation is according to parts of the Ms or kinds of material, with the character, line, page, and unit counts for each listed together (c = characters, L = lines, pp = pages). This makes it possible to take all elements into consideration in deciding, for example, how many pages to

TITLE: *Example*
Ms pp: 339

DATE: 12/2/11

FRONTMATTER
half title__pp, title__pp, cpyrt__pp, ded__pp
preface 2762 c
contents 44 L
introduction 5250 c
TEXT:
538,050 c
103 L
EXTRACT: (p.67)
5892 c
POETRY: (p.29)
129 L
14 units
PLAYSTYLE: (p.162)
1264 c
10 L
4 units
TABULAR: (p.212)
42 L
12 units
BIBLIOGRAPHY: (p.318)
4922 c
53 L
INDEX:
allow__pp
FOOTNOTES:
1640 c
14 units
ILLUSTRATIONS:
halftone:75
line:28
SUBDIVISIONS:
part titles:3
chapters:8
A heads:18
B heads:41
spacebreaks:19

allow for a bibliography containing material counted in several ways.

Commercial analysis

There are many possible commercial considerations, but the main ones are:

(a) the size of the first printing and binding (edition),
(b) the nature of the intended audience, and
(c) the kind of distribution anticipated.

These, and whatever other commercial problems there may be, must be fully considered so that the design and production of the book will contribute to a financially successful publication. The actual sale of the book is not the only commercial consideration. Even with the sale of a large number of copies, a book will not be profitable if it is not well planned in terms of its particular conditions of distribution.

SIZE OF PRINTING & BINDING

The publisher's decisions as to how many copies to print and, of these, how many to bind, are based less on the cost of production than on his estimate of the book's sale. He can hold down the unit cost through a large printing, but there will be no profit if he is left with most of the books unsold.

Most books are printed in relatively small quantities. Yet, it may take the same amount of time to make a job ready to run, the same investment in machinery, the same amount of floor space, the same amount of editorial and administrative work, and the same cost in composition and plates for a run of 5000 as for one of 50,000. Obviously then, the design and production plans for a short run must be quite different from those for a long one.

If the printing is small, more economy in *plant cost* [items not affected by size of edition, i.e. composition, plates, illustrations, etc.] is required. If the printing is large, the expenditures for composition and illustrations are less significant than the cost of materials, hand operations in binding, and other items that remain about the same per unit regardless of the size of the edition. A small edition might make it possible to take advantage of a special lot of paper or cloth at a good price, but a large one will permit you to order a special color, size, or finish without penalty. (Remember that a later printing may be too small for a special order. Have a satisfactory substitute in mind.)

A decision to bind only part of the edition printed has limited effect on design or production planning. Usually, a large majority of the edition is bound, and it is worth ordering materials for all at the same time. Also, it is common practice to carry the sheetwork (CH.10) through the whole edition and hold back only the remainder of the binding operations until sales justify completion.

Ideally, the bookmaking departments participate in discussions concerning the size of the first printing. In any case, the management's thoughts in this matter should be thoroughly investigated as part of the commercial analysis.

THE NATURE OF THE AUDIENCE

Who are the potential buyers and readers of a book? They are not always the same person. The buyers of books read by young children are usually adults, as are the buyers of schoolbooks and most reference books for the young. Books for all kinds of readers are bought by libraries. A large proportion (perhaps half) of the books purchased in bookstores in America are not read by the buyers but are intended as gifts. In such circumstances, any design considerations based on audience must have 2 aspects: 1 for the buyer and 1 for the reader.

Examine the characteristics of both groups. What are their occupational backgrounds? What kinds of education have they? What is their social and economic status? What are their tastes and prejudices? What are their ages? What physical disabilities might they have?

These are not impertinent questions. The answers will affect your decisions. Size and kind of type, shape and weight of the book, durability, dirt resistance, style of typography, quality of materials, number and kind of colors, number and kind of illustrations—these and other design factors are subject to modification according to audience requirements.

For example, take a book on retirement activities for the financially secure. The reader will be past middle age, so the type should be a bit larger than average (CH.6). Durability is obviously not too important here, but light weight would be appreciated by the older readers, particularly those with such ailments as arthritis and palsy which frequently limit manual powers. Presumably, good quality materials and attractive but restrained colors would please the potential readers as well as the younger friends and relatives who are likely to be buying the book as a gift. The economic status of the reader suggests a retail price that would make such an approach feasible.

DISTRIBUTION

Most books are sold in several ways. Each method of distribution has its own needs and these must be known so that they can be met. Some of them are indicated below.

- *Bookstore sales*—These usually require attractive jackets and are helped by illustrations and attractive visual elements in general. In most cases, it helps to have as large and thick a book as possible, unpleasant as the thought may be.
- *Mail-order distribution*—This suggests a lightweight package to keep down postage, although certain kinds of mail-order books

must be large and lavish to succeed. In any case, weight should be controlled to avoid going just over a postage weight bracket. Damage in transit is also a factor to consider.

- *Library sales*—Here, a strong binding is important. The librarians have definite, practical views on binding specifications.
- *Textbook sales*—Elementary and high school books usually require a lot of color and illustrations. They must meet BMI standards of material and manufacture (CH.10).
- *Gift sales*—Usually made through bookstores, these suggest large size, extensive use of color and illustration, high quality materials.

Sometimes, the demands of several methods of distribution conflict and have to be reconciled. At other times, the commercial requirements may not be apparent from the Ms alone. For instance, an editor may anticipate subsequent books on the same subject by the author of a new Ms, with the thought that they might eventually be sold as a set or series. Knowing this, a designer will avoid an arrangement of the title which would not be adaptable to another, will avoid the use of odd lots of material which cannot be obtained for the subsequent volumes, etc. Question the editorial and sales departments to learn what the commercial problem is.

Editorial analysis

Visual support of the author may be mostly practical—taking the form of good organization and a clear presentation of the material. The support may be mostly esthetic—consisting of subtle suggestion of mood and atmosphere. In almost all cases there will be a combination of both. The most practical book, if well designed, will have a functional beauty that grows naturally from its sense of order and fitness—just as in a fine bridge or aircraft. At the other end, even a novel or a book of verse must be made to perform satisfactorily. No amount of atmosphere or graphic beauty is sufficient if the practical problems are unsolved.

In order to make an accurate and effective visual presentation of the text, the designer must become completely familiar with the Ms and must clearly understand the author's intentions. The designer's attitude toward the subject may be different from the author's, but his job is to present the writer's approach—not his own. Whatever of the designer's personality or viewpoint appears in the result may be only a residual, inadvertent by-product of his effort to express those of the author.

READING TECHNIQUE

It is necessary for a designer to develop techniques for quickly extracting the essence of a Ms, and rapidly learning what he must know about it. No method is perfectly satisfactory if it does not include reading the entire Ms, but this is usually impossible, so a compromise must be made.

In fiction, an effective method is to read the first 18 or 20 pages, then read 2 or 3 pages at intervals of about 30, and then read the last 6 or 8. In this way, one can usually learn the setting and atmosphere of the story, feel the style of the writing, catch the general development of the plot and discover the ending. With practice, a fairly accurate reading of a 350-page Ms can be made in about an hour. From the standpoint of pleasure, this is a very unsatisfactory way to read, but this is a sacrifice the designer must make. It is important to maintain an alert and flexible approach, however, as some stories are so constructed that a misleading impression might result from a strict adherence to this system.

Nonfiction in narrative form can be read in about the same way. A writer will usually explain his subject and premises in the beginning and state his conclusions at the end. A spot check through the body of the text will give the general drift of the story or argument, as well as the feel of the author's style. If the Ms is composed of several parts by the same or different writers, each piece can be studied in somewhat the same way, reducing the number of pages read in proportion to its length.

Nonfiction of complicated organization or varied content should be examined page by page. The text will have to be read to the extent necessary to understand its organization, intent, and style, and each page must be seen, to insure that every problem has been observed.

There are many kinds of Ms and no one study procedure can be effective for all. In principle, the idea is to sample where a sample is sufficiently revealing and examine in detail where necessary. Read prefaces, forewords, and introductions—even if you can't read anything else. For some reason, people are inclined to bypass these, but this is usually a mistake. By its nature, such a piece is a statement considered too important, significant, or special to include in the body of the text. Here, the author often explains his purpose and/or summarizes the content of the text. Here, another writer often throws light on the character or background of the author and his work. These are insights which would usually require a considerable amount of other reading to achieve—here is the equivalent, in many cases, of a chat with the author.

Whatever method is used, enough study and analysis of the Ms must be carried out to determine the exact nature, feeling, and intention of the book. At some point prior to making decisions the designer should check his interpretation with the author or the editor. At the very least, he should compare his impression with the one carried by some advertising or catalogue copy prepared for publication. A briefing of some kind, oral or written, will often have to substitute for a thorough reading of the Ms, because of insufficient time.

In conclusion

It is not a bad idea, particularly when learning, to make a brief written summary of your commercial and editorial analyses. Even in the form of rough notes, such a summary will help clarify your thoughts and fix them in your mind. Remember, *in making an analysis you are not to draw any conclusions about the book you will design.* At this stage you are only to *learn* about your problem. Before you *decide* on anything you must go through a process of consideration, in which all the levels of consciousness and intuition are brought into play.

15 | Creative solutions

The creative problem

In book design, the creative problem is to interpret and indicate the nature of the content. The indication *must* be accurate, it *should be* interesting and pleasing. In an exceptionally successful book the accuracy is such as to create a profound sense of fitness, the design is interesting to the point of being intriguing, and pleasing to the point of being beautiful.

Every Ms has a certain character, and this can be analyzed and interpreted. Whether simple or complicated, the character of the work can be expressed in more or less abstract visual terms. Some books are more easily expressed than others, some appear to be almost impossible to express. Certainly, it is unreasonable to expect that the total aspect of any book can be rendered graphically. Yet, it is probably better to tend deliberately in the right direction than to leave the tendency to chance—with the likelihood that it will go in the wrong direction.

The designer's creative problem is somewhat like that of the abstract painter—to communicate in terms that will reach the subconscious levels of the viewer's mind, where response will be automatic reaction rather than conscious thought. The reader may be quite unaware of design in books, but he cannot escape being affected by elements that establish character and mood. Modern psychology confirms the power of subconscious impressions to modify states of mind, or attitudes. A striking, if rather frightening, demonstration of this principle, is the use of subliminal communication to implant ideas. (In the course of a motion picture or television show an unrelated message can be repeatedly flashed on the screen so rapidly that the viewer is not aware of its existence, yet he responds to its content.) The designer must exploit the psychological devices that can help him create a receptive atmosphere for the author's work.

Any decision affecting the physical aspect of the book can have expressive value. Every physical attribute contributes to the total effect and helps create the character and atmosphere of the book. It makes a difference whether any part or the whole is delicate or strong, gay or somber, large or small, simple or complex, thick or thin. Even the format can be significant. For example, a different reaction to the sight and feel of a book will result if it is squarish and chunky than if it is tall and slim. The relation of weight to size has a definite effect.

In fact, no element of a book's appearance can fail to have some character and therefore some effect. It is the job of the designer to mobilize all these elements so that their sum, and each one of them, will contribute to a successful solution of the creative problem. At the same time, the creative solution must avoid conflict with the mechanical, commercial, or editorial requirements. Indeed, it should be in complete harmony with them.

The creative process

To reconcile the sometimes divergent needs of the various aspects of bookmaking, decide first on what *should* be done creatively, then modify these decisions as necessary to accommodate the practical considerations. In other words, plan the ideal first and retain as much of it as you can. This works better than any other procedure because the creative process functions best when it is free of practical considerations. The moment you accept mechanical or economic limitations, your imagination tends to freeze. Not that it merely restricts itself to the practicable—it tends to act as though the limiting walls were made of glass, and it swings in a cramped arc far short of those walls. This is a safe enough procedure, but it precludes any chance of extending the possible. From the experience of civilization we know that even modest advances have usually been the result of expeditions well beyond the practicable. To remain always within the walls leads to stagnation and sterility.

For the best results in conceiving ideal creative solutions, it is necessary to tap the creative forces within us. Merely recalling routine devices and standard arrangements will not produce anything but stock solutions. The processes of rational mental effort will not produce a creative solution unaided. Usually, the automatic mechanisms of the mind will set the creative process in motion, and it will help to some extent—but it is much better to consciously invoke the force and utilize it fully. If a man falls into deep water he will automatically thrash his arms about in an effort to avoid drowning, and he may succeed, but he is much more likely to succeed if he knows how to swim.

After reading and studying the Ms, put it down and relax. Let your mind create associations at random. From these associations, try to recall everything from your experience that is related to the subject—sights, sounds, smells, textures, people, places, pictures, words, colors—anything and everything. Then, if possible, let some time pass while you do other things. A few hours might be enough, but overnight is better. During this time, the conscious thoughts associated with the subject will seep down into the lower layers of consciousness, arriving eventually at the region in which the creative forces originate. The contact of subject matter with creative force produces ideas and imagination. The natural tendency of such impulses is to rise to conscious awareness and, when they do, we speak of "inspiration" and "intuition". Sometimes, these impulses burst into the open despite any obstacle. More often they must be given receptive conditions or they will remain unborn, or arrive in weakened and misshapen form.

The most propitious condition for creativity is an utterly blank mind. Such a state invites ideas just as a blank sheet of paper invites drawing or writing. Far from being a simple matter, achieving a blank mind is quite difficult. Our minds are filled with a lifetime of impressions and thoughts, and these are constantly in motion. The mystics of the East, particularly Tâoists, take considerable trouble to develop an ability to wipe their minds clean at will. Some of the greatest works of Asian art are attributed to the creative powers invoked while in such a state. The technique is simply a process of narrowing down the field of mental activity by concentrating on a single point. Eventually, the concentration is complete, and the mind engaged with nothing but a single point of light, a distant mountain peak, or some other isolated focus. From here, the mind goes into a suspended, trancelike state in which even the point of concentration is eliminated. This is, obviously, similar to the process of hypnotism, and indeed it might be termed self-hypnotism. A master can put himself instantly into such a trance, even without a concentration point, but this takes years of effort and a lot of will power.

You may think that this is Oriental mumbo-jumbo having nothing to do with you or your work. Not so. For one thing, what the Asians have known for thousands of years is now being "discovered" by modern science. The psychological studies of the past 80 years tend to confirm the understanding of creativity outlined above. Also, unless you intend to exclude creativity from your work (and this is your choice) it is essential to understand and enter into the creative process.

Of course, you can't sit in your office staring for hours at a distant mountain peak or anything else. You would either be fired or carried off in a padded wagon. Nor are you likely to find there the peace and quiet essential to total concentration. The fact is, the conditions of modern business are unsuited to creative activity. Nevertheless, create we must, and there is really no substitute for the creative process, so an effort must be made to utilize that process.

To begin, not every Ms warrants, or can be given, a major creative effort. Also, the creative process is not an either/or matter—it will operate to the degree in which you participate. So if you can't put yourself into a catatonic trance, you can at least shut your eyes and try to concentrate on the darkness for a few minutes. If this fails to produce good enough results, you might get an inspiration in the middle of the night or while dozing on the train. The point is, you must take *positive action* toward freeing your imagination if you want the best results. You simply have to recognize the limitations and work within them. True, not everyone has a fertile imagination and the seeds you plant may not sprout—but the evidence suggests that there is a lot more creativity in most people than is apparent.

The objective of this creative effort is a clear, sharp visualization of the ideal finished book, in all its details. Even though the practical result may not resemble this ideal, the technical facilities available today make anything possible, if not always feasible. But, as time progresses, more and more becomes feasible.

The creative means

With the desired result visualized, begin to assemble the devices with which to achieve that effect. These devices include all the elements of visual art, used with the insights of psychology as well as the intuition of the artist. The most effective and accessible tools are: (a) *symbolism,* (b) *color,* and (c) *texture.* It is by suggestion that we elicit the reader's subconscious reactions, and these 3 devices are rich in suggestive power.

SYMBOLISM

The use of symbols has vast possibilities, not only for suggestion but for graphic effects. If the symbolism used is visually satisfactory, its effectiveness as symbol is not essential. Therefore, the first principle in the use of symbolism is: it must look good. The symbol will sometimes be obvious, sometimes obscure. If it looks good and is obvious, it will surely be effective to some degree—and it doesn't matter how much. If it looks good and is obscure, the worst that can happen is that it will be ineffective as symbol, but again, it doesn't matter. This is not to imply that it is unimportant whether or not symbolism is effective. The point is that if it fails as symbol it does no harm, provided it is visually satisfactory. In such cases, the symbol is no more than decoration, but it is perfectly justified if it is good decoration.

Whether the symbol is obscure or obvious, it should be used imaginatively. By treating it in a creative way, you impart the special quality that makes the symbol a meaningful part of the book. The illustrations opposite are examples of such treatment.

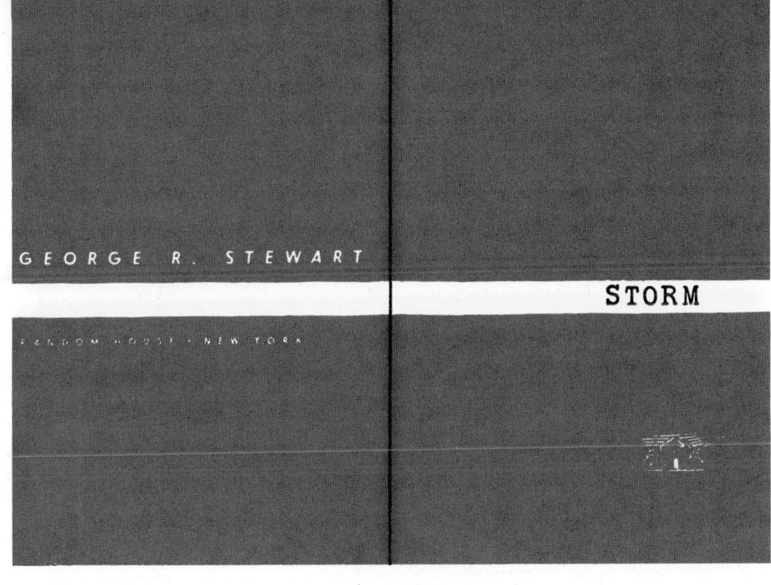

The telegraph tape, a symbol of urgency associated with disaster, is used imaginatively by Ernst Reichl. The background tone was printed in color.

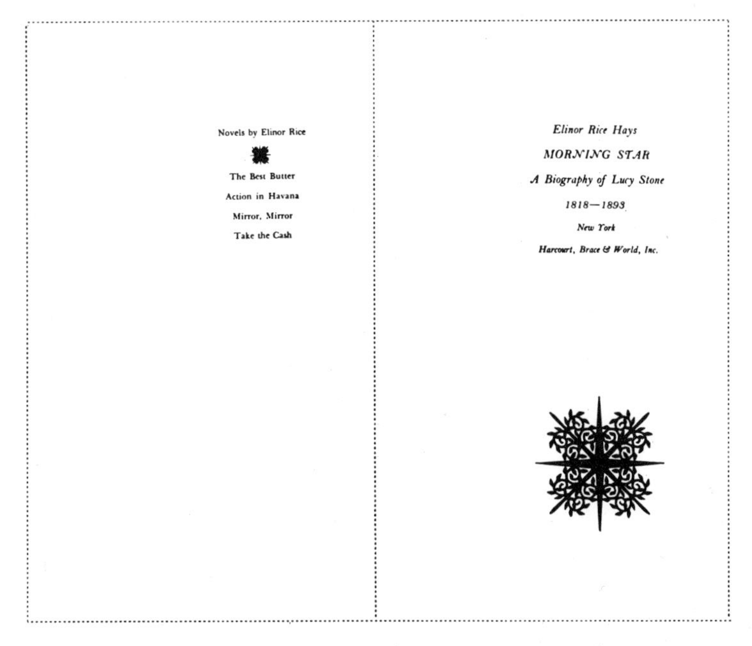

The obvious symbol as handled by Betty Anderson creates a fresh, evocative, and handsome spread.

The degree of subtlety required of symbols depends on the nature of the Ms. When the subject of the text is factual and its approach direct, a literal or representational symbolism is appropriate. A book of belles lettres or any text with a romantic quality, shaded meanings, or indirect allusions would call for a more subtly suggestive symbolism. Turn the page for illustrations of symbolism well related to text in this sense.

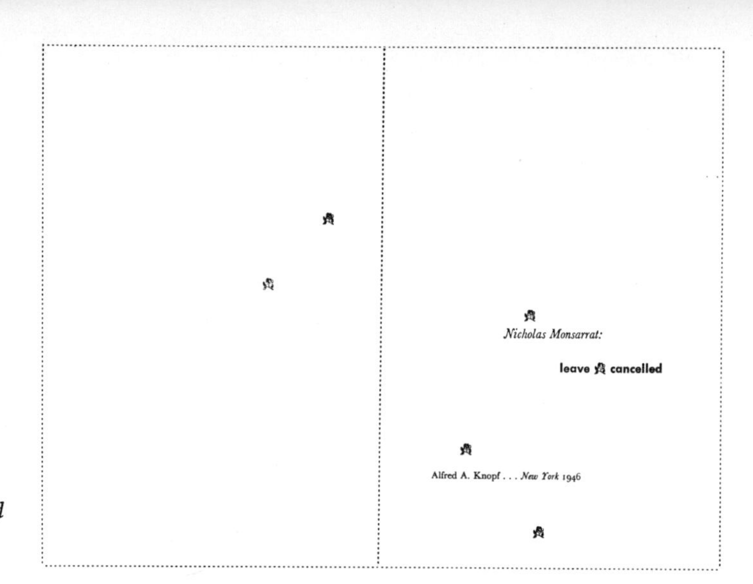

Scattered roses are appropriate symbols for this novel designed by Paul Rand—

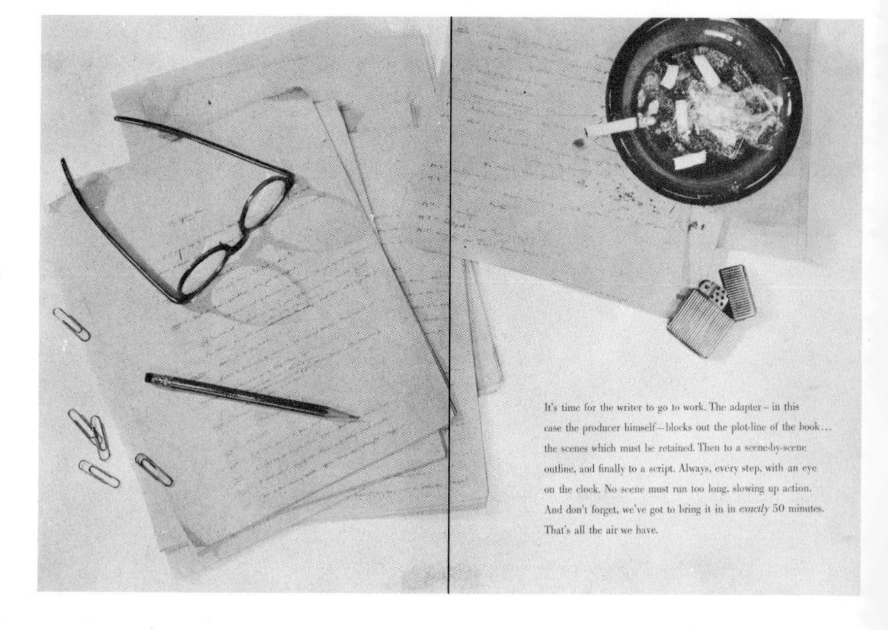

and the artifacts of conference are suitable for this factual account of how a radio program is made. Design by William Golden.

The symbols used may represent any aspect of the book. They might be related to the subject, they might be associated with the mood, the atmosphere, a plot, a character, or perhaps the author. Their purpose is to suggest salient features of the Ms, as part of the effort to create a book that accurately reflects and reinforces the author's message.

It is important to keep symbols in balance. If a symbol becomes dominant in the graphic arrangement, it should be related to the dominant characteristic of the book. The relationship of symbols to each other must reflect the relationship of the elements they represent. The total effect of the symbolism in a design must be a true indication of the basic character of the book.

Search the Ms for symbols used by the author. Sometimes a writer will inadvertently repeat a theme, at other times the motif will be consciously employed. Poets, of course, are entirely at home with visual images, and they are usually known for their favored symbols—W. B. Yeats for his golden birds, towers, trees, etc.; Edith Sitwell for her roses, drums, and so on. Sometimes, the book's subject will be a person with whom some symbol is associated. For example, see the following illustrations showing the use of characteristic symbols for Debussy and Stravinsky. Where no readily apparent symbol is present, the designer must create appropriate symbols from a study of the editorial analysis.

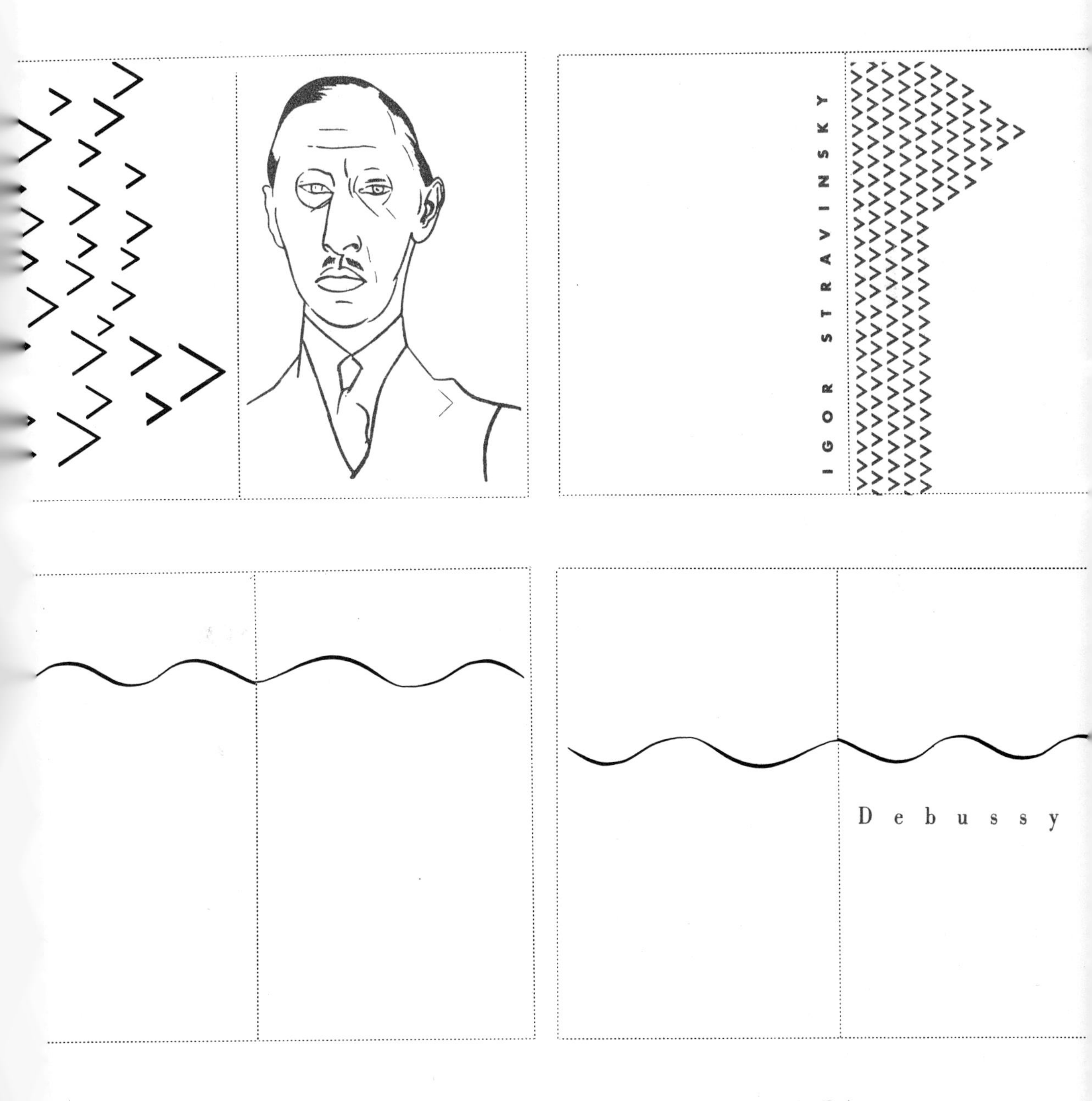

The sharp, staccato symbols of the Stravinsky book and the undulating line in the Debussy volume suggest the characteristics of each man's work. Both designs by Merle Armitage.

The range of possible symbols is virtually unlimited. Symbolism in graphic form is illustration, and the broad graphic possibilities are suggested in CH.9. The symbolic values of color and texture are discussed later in this chapter. The shape of the book or the proportions of a text page can be symbolic. Even the sequence and placement of illustrations can have meaning. In an edition of Bernal Diaz' *Discovery and Conquest of Mexico* designed by the author, some of the illustrations consist of drawings of Mexican and Spanish weapons of the period. Pages of Mexican weapons occur where the Aztecs were ascendant, Spanish weapons where Cortez triumphed. The weapons are in profusion when the battle waxes and are few when it wanes. The effect is somewhat like the offstage clash of arms in a play.

48 THE CONQUEST

to do them any harm, but were willing to give them some of the things we had brought with us and to treat them like brothers, and we prayed them not to begin a war as they would regret it, and much else was said to them about keeping the peace. However, the more Aguilar talked to them the more violent they became, and they said that they would kill us all if we entered their town, and that it was fortified all round with fences and barricades of large trunks of trees.

Aguilar spoke to them again and asked them to keep the peace, and allow us to take water and barter our goods with them for food, and permit us to tell the Calachones[1] things which would be to their advantage and to the service of God our Lord, but they still persisted in saying that if we advanced beyond the palm trees they would kill us.

When Cortés saw the state of affairs he ordered the boats and small vessels to be got ready and ordered three cannon to be placed in each boat and divided the crossbowmen and musketeers among the boats. We remembered that when we were here with Grijalva we had found a narrow path which ran across some streams from the palm grove to the town, and Cortés ordered three soldiers to find out in the night if that path ran right up to the houses, and not to delay in bringing the news, and these men found out that it did lead there. After making a thorough examination of our surroundings the rest of the day was spent in arranging how and in what order we were to go in the boats.

The next morning we had our arms in readiness and after hearing mass Cortés ordered the Captain Alonzo de Ávila and a hundred soldiers among whom were ten crossbowmen, to go by the little path which led to the town, and, as soon as he heard the guns fired, to attack the town on one side while he attacked it on the other. Cortés himself and all the other Captains and soldiers went in the boats and light draft vessels up the river. When the Indian warriors who were on the banks and among the mangroves saw that we were really on the move, they came after us with a great many canoes with intent to prevent our going ashore at the landing place, and the whole river bank appeared to be covered with Indian warriors carrying all the different arms which they use, and blowing trumpets and shells and sounding drums. When Cortés saw how matters

[1] Calachiones (?)

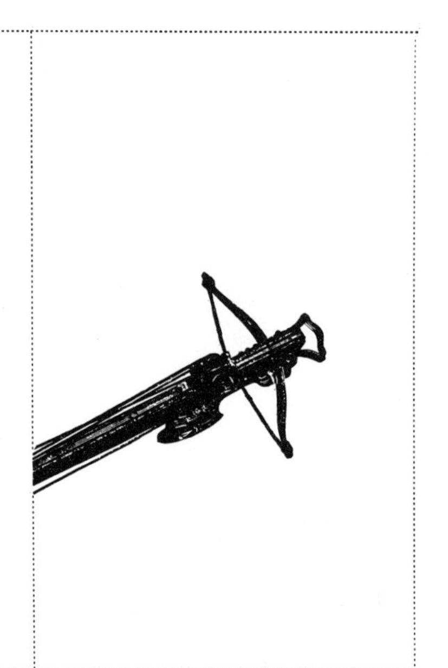

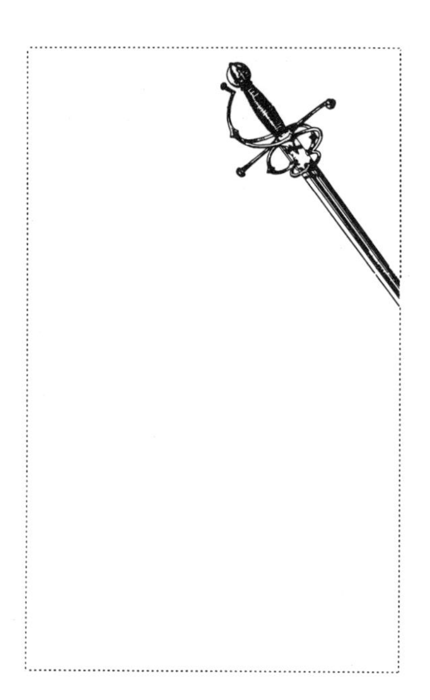

300 THE CONQUEST

that they had taken from him the Indian women he was bringing and had given him two wounds and that if he had not let the women go, the Mexicans would have captured him, and would have put him in a canoe and carried him off to be sacrificed, and that they had broken down a bridge.

Let me go on and say that Cortés promptly ordered Diego de Ordás to go with four hundred soldiers, and among them most of the crossbowmen and musketeers and some horsemen, and examine into what the soldier had reported, and that if he found that he could calm the Indians without fighting and disturbance that he should do so.

Diego de Ordás set out in the way that he was ordered with his four hundred soldiers, but he had hardly reached the middle of the street along which he was to march, when so many squadrons of Mexican warriors fell on him and so many more were on the roofs of the houses, and they made such fierce attacks that on the first assault they killed eight soldiers and wounded all the rest, and Diego de Ordás himself was wounded in three places, and in this manner he could not advance one step further but had to return little by little to his quarters. During the retreat they killed another good soldier named Lyscano who, with a broadsword, had done the work of a very valiant man.

At that moment, while many squadrons came out against Ordás, many more approached our quarters and shot off so many javelins and stones from slings, and arrows, that they wounded on that occasion alone over forty-six of our men, and twelve of them died of their wounds; and such a number of warriors fell upon us that Diego de Ordás, who was coming in retreat, could not reach our quarters on account of the fierce assaults they made on him, some from the rear and others in front and others from the roofs.

Little availed our cannon, or our muskets, crossbows and lances, or the thrusts we gave them, or our good fighting, for although we killed and wounded many of them, yet they managed to reach us by pushing forward over the points of our swords and lances, and closing up their squadrons never desisted from their brave attack, nor could we push them away from us.

At last, what with cannon and muskets and the damage we did them with our sword-thrusts, Ordás found an opportunity

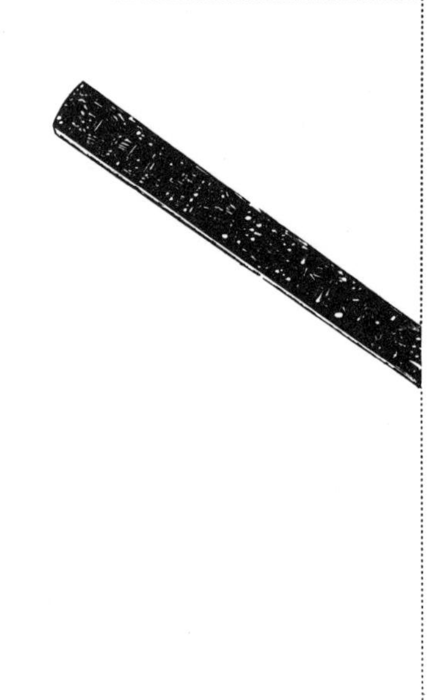

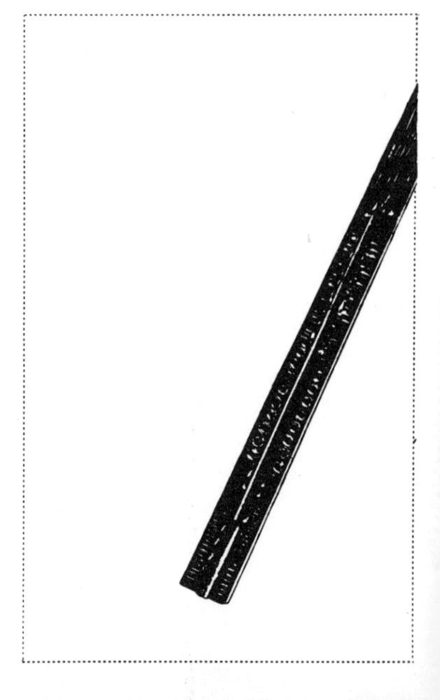

298 THE CONQUEST

many squadrons of Indians were approaching to set fire to his quarters he sallied forth to fight them, and he ordered the cannon to be fired, but it did not go off, and after he had made a charge against the squadrons which were attacking him, and many Indians were bearing down on him, while he was retreating to the fortress and quarters, then, without fire being applied to the cannon, the ball and the small shot was discharged and killed many Indians; and had it not so happened the enemy would have killed them all, and they did on that occasion carry off two of his soldiers alive.

Another thing Pedro de Alvarado stated, and this was the only thing that was also reported by the other soldiers, for the rest of the stories were told by Alvarado alone, and it is that they had no water to drink, and they dug in the courtyard, and made a well and took out fresh water, all around being salt; in all it amounted to many gifts that our Lord God bestowed on us.

† LXXXVII

When Cortés saw that they had given us no sort of a reception in Texcoco, and had not even given us food, except bad food and with bad grace, and that we found no chieftains with whom to parley, and he saw that all were scared away and ill disposed, and observed the same condition on coming to Mexico, how no market was held and the whole place was in revolt, and he heard from Pedro de Alvarado about the disorderly manner in which he made his attack, and as it appears that on the march Cortés had spoken to the Captains of Narvaez glorifying himself on the great veneration and command that he enjoyed, and how on the road the Indians would turn out to receive him and celebrate the occasion and give him gold, and that in Mexico he ruled as absolutely over the great Montezuma as over all his Captains, and that they would give him presents of gold, as they were used to do, and when everything turned out contrary to his expectations and they did not even give us food to eat, he was greatly irritated, and haughty towards the numerous Spaniards that he was bringing with him, and very sad and fretful. At this moment the great Montezuma sent two of his chieftains to beg our Cortés to go

THE CONQUEST

rance to the Plaza we placed a cannon and with
xecution, for the enemy were so numerous that the
not hold them all. The Spaniards seeing that there
r there (which was our greatest danger) deter-
er the Plaza, and when the enemy saw this carried
d observed the multitude of our allies (although
fear of them unless they were in our company)
h our allies after them until they were shut up in
the Temple, which was enclosed with a masonry

sure would be large enough to hold a town of
houses. However, a breach was made and the
allies captured it and remained there and on the
good while. When the people of the city saw that
o horsemen with us they turned again on the
d drove them from the towers and courts, and as
e in great danger, for it was worse than a retreat,
uge in the porticoes of the courts; however, the
hastened them so severely that they abandoned
eated to the Plaza whence they were driven out
and were obliged to abandon the cannon which
ed there.
rds, unable to withstand the onset of the enemy,
reat danger and would have suffered great loss
ased God that at that moment three horsemen
who entered the Plaza, and when the enemy
hey thought that there were more of them and
and the horsemen killed some of them and we
ourts and enclosure. On the most important and
which has over a hundred steps to reach the
r twelve Indian chieftains had sheltered them-
ur or five of the Spaniards clambered up, and,
ndians fought bravely, they gained the summit
all.
nore horsemen had now arrived, and they and
nged an ambuscade by which they killed over
emy.
eady late I got the men together and ordered a
we retired such a host of the enemy fell upon
not been for the horsemen the Spaniards must
great loss. However, as I had had all the bad

The use of type as symbol is discussed to some extent under "Allusion" in CH.6. This is a particularly difficult area of symbolism because the type has not only its suggestive characteristic, but also communicates thought. It is already a symbol for the words it forms, and no other symbolic association can be free of this effect. On these pages are a few examples of type used symbolically with some success. Typographic symbolism may be valid, but it is easily overworked. Use it with care and moderation.

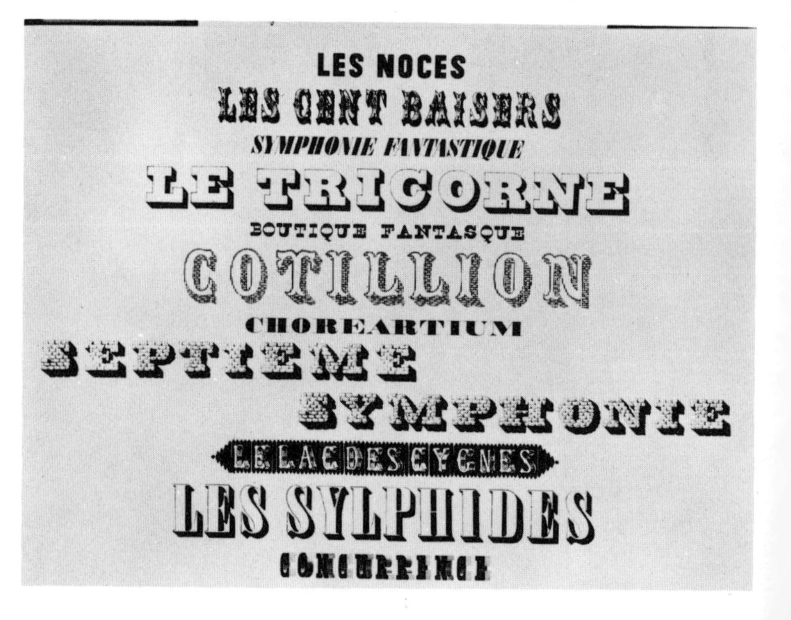

Alexey Brodovitch uses very tall, dramatic letters to suggest a line of graceful dancers and a potpourri of decorative faces to evoke the romantic and diverse world of ballet.

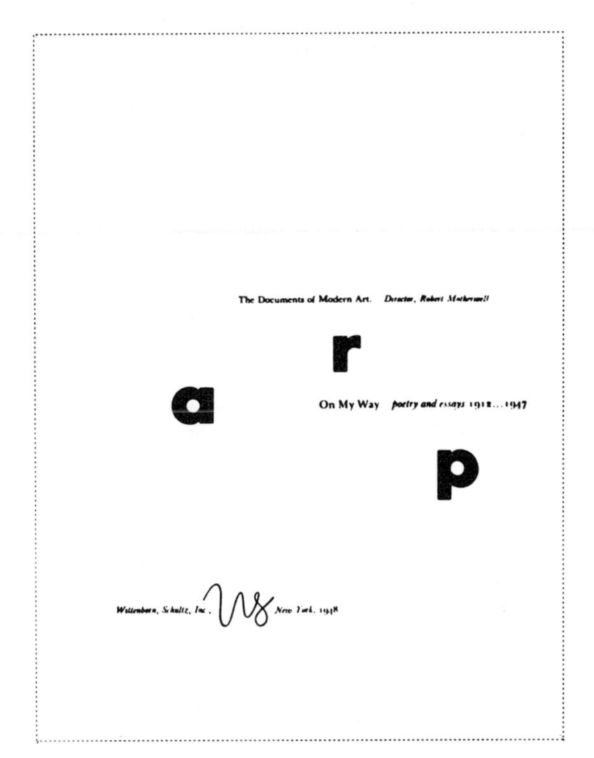

The form and feeling of the artist's work is reflected in the choice and arrangement of type for his name. Design by Paul Rand

TO
Farrar & Rinehart
Simon & Schuster
Coward-McCann
Limited Editions
Harcourt, Brace
Random House
Equinox Press
Smith & Haas
Viking Press
Knopf
Dutton
Harper's
Scribner's
Covici, Friede

S. A. Jacobs uses an ancient typographic technique to raise a cup in dedication.

COLOR

Of all the graphic elements, color has the most powerful psychological effect. Except for some specific associations (discussed below), color is almost entirely without intellectual content and speaks directly to the subconscious. Tests have definitely established a connection between color and emotions. Color is thus one of the most effective tools of communication and should be used in book design far more than it is. A knowledge of the use of color is as important to the book designer as a knowledge of typography.

Because of its psychological powers, color is particularly valuable in creating atmosphere and mood. Sometimes an author will be thinking in terms of a certain color while writing (Flaubert said that he thought of *Madame Bovary* in terms of *puce*, which is the "rich", dark red characteristic of 19th-century French bourgeois interiors) but, in any case, the Ms will have *some* character and this character will suggest a color, kind of color, or combination of colors.

Color has 3 aspects: (a) hue, (b) intensity, and (c) value.

- *Hue*—This is the "color" of the color (red, blue, yellow, green, orange-red, etc.).
- *Intensity*—This is the purity of the color (intensity is lowered as the color is grayed or "softened").
- *Value*—This is the darkness of the color (even in pure primary colors there is variation in value—yellow is lighter than blue, blue is lighter than red, etc.; however, an intense yellow may be darker than a blue whose intensity [and value] has been lowered by the addition of white).

The psychological effect of each hue changes as it is modified in hue, value, and intensity. For example, a blue that is slightly tinged with green and is high in intensity may be very gay in effect. A blue on the violet side and lowered in intensity by the addition of black can be quite somber. The same violet-blue grayed with white might be soft and romantic. The variety of colors, considering the modifications possible, is infinite.

Not only is there an infinite number of colors, but these can be used in an infinite number of combinations—each of which has its own psychological properties *entirely independent of the individual colors within it!* For example, 2 colors, each of which are quite mild by themselves may, when combined, create a clash that is anything but mild. Several intense colors can be combined to produce a feeling of subtle harmony, if they are closely related in hue. A dark color of low intensity and a light color of low intensity can be combined to produce a dramatic effect of contrasting values. The ways in which colors can be manipulated in combination is endless—as are the effects that can be created.

Some colors and combinations of colors have specific associations—school colors, national colors, company colors, club colors, etc. In an appropriate context, these colors convey meaning just as surely as do words. Don't scorn their use because they are obvious. As with graphic symbols, the pertinent questions are: Is it appropriate? Does it look good? If both answers are yes, final judgment will be based on *how* you used the colors, not *why*.

There are other, less specific, associations that can be used symbolically. Certain greens are associated with vegetation and nature in general. Some browns are conventionally connected with masculine matters because of their association with wood and leather. Some exotic combinations of violets, pinks, and greens have a tropical look, blues are used to suggest water and sky, and so on. These nonspecific color symbols can be used very effectively where they are not required to convey the meaning alone. Again, while subtlety and freshness are very desirable in design, there is no need to avoid the use of an appropriate color just because it is obvious. A slightly odd shade or an interesting combination with other colors can easily save it from banality.

Color has the potentialities of a symphony orchestra, but it is not a simple matter to use color masterfully any more than it is a simple matter to create great music with an orchestra. Much is to be learned, much experience is required—and it helps to have talent.

TEXTURE

As a device for communication with the subconscious, texture is as effective as any. It can be apprehended through two senses—sight and touch—which gives it an additional entrance to the area of response.

If texture is particularly effective, it is also relatively limited in its range of expression. However, it is an inevitable element of book design and should be utilized for positive ends.

The textural possibilities in bookmaking are not as meager as one might suppose. Printing papers are made with surfaces ranging from glassy-smooth to pebbly. Endpapers are somewhat more limited in range, but stock cover materials are reasonably varied, and a wide variety of textures can be had on special orders. Vinyl can be obtained with a surface as slick as patent leather and some of the more expensive cloths come as rough-textured as tweed.

The possibilities are greatly enlarged by the use of embossing or blank stamping (CH.10). Suppliers of binding materials have stock embossings that can be applied as ordered, but these are mostly imitation cloth and leather textures. Far more variety can be achieved by the application of texture in the stamping operation. With etched dies, this is not unduly expensive. For example, on a book about the Florida swamp country, the cover was given a texture of alligator skin by blank-stamping with a die made from an alligator-pattern wrapping paper.

Various subjects and moods suggest particular textures. Obviously, a book about machinery would suggest a smooth texture while a book on Irish farmers calls for a rough, tweedy feel. The atmosphere of a novel might be slick, soft, or bristly. One book may suggest contrasting textures, another similar ones. At the other extreme, it may be desirable to employ the literal effect of texture by using a ropelike or canvas-like material on a book about sailing, or binding a book about glass in a glasslike plastic. These would be rather special and expensive bindings, but a feasible substitute can usually be found.

As in other forms of symbolism, the esthetic and suggestive

functions of texture can be justified independently. Regardless of the psychological use (or nonuse) of texture in the design, it should be well handled for its graphic and tactile values. However, it would be as much a mistake to make a handsome combination of textures that were inappropriate to the feeling of the book as it would be to use the wrong graphic symbol or unsuitable colors.

In conclusion

The most judicious use of symbolism alone is not likely to reveal the nature of the book or establish the atmosphere. Nor are the expert handling of color or texture able to achieve the whole objective by themselves. The typography by itself can do just so much and illustration has its limitations. It may seem impractical to apply so much effort to achieve the relatively minor effect of a good textural scheme or color combination. It would indeed be a waste of time to carefully develop 1 aspect if the others were neglected. The point to remember is that *each factor contributes something* toward the desired end, and *the combination of them all* is likely to have a positive effect worth the effort.

A perfect orchestration of superbly handled elements will result in a book that greatly enriches the work it conveys. If the result falls somewhat short of this ideal, it will have value in proportion to the success of its parts—and, in design, the whole can't be any better than the poorest of its parts.

16 | The basic decisions

Having analyzed the problem and visualized an ideal solution, you are ready to begin the decision-making process. This includes the second stage of design: consideration of alternatives, and the final stage: making choices. To some extent, you went through these stages in the creative visualization, but no firm decisions were made because only 1 aspect of the problem was involved. At this point, *all* aspects of the mechanical, commercial, and editorial problems will be brought into consideration, and the decisions made now must be practical and economical, as well as creatively sound.

It may appear that the middle stage is getting little attention in proportion to the first and third. This is because it is necessary to combine the discussion of consideration and choice. Each choice entails examination of the available possibilities, so there is a constant alternation of consideration and decision as the work progresses. Nevertheless, they *are* successive processes, even if they intermingle so closely in operation that it is sometimes difficult to distinguish them as such.

There are 7 basic decisions. These must be made first because they concern the whole book and they affect all others. They relate to: (a) retail price, (b) size of first printing, (c) trim-size, (d) editorial arrangement of illustrations, (e) printing process, (f) paper, and (g) number of pages.

Retail price & first printing

Two decisions, the retail price of the book and the size of the first printing, are usually made by the editorial department before the Ms is released for design and production. These require estimating what the market will bear for a book of the kind and size. The procedure is simple enough with a tradebook; it means basing price and quantity on experience with similar books. However, estimating *correctly* is far from simple.

What seemed to have been a similar book sold 10,000 copies 2 years ago, so presumably this one will do about as well. But there are numerous reasons why this may not work out. In 2 years (or 2 weeks!) the public's interest may have shifted away from the subject, the demand for that kind of book may have been satisfied by the earlier book and others like it, or, as is often the case, what *seem* to be similar books in every significant respect may differ subtly, just enough to make one a popular success and the other a failure.

The price is a somewhat less hazardous decision, but it too has uncertain elements. A general advance in retail prices may justify adding 50¢ to the price of the earlier book for the new one, but a slightly weaker demand may not tolerate the higher price, or a general resistance to higher book prices may develop at the time of publication.

Variations in the cost of manufacture are a likely source of difficulty. Unless the second book was prepared specifically as a duplicate of the first, the chances are that the production costs will differ. Editors are not usually familiar enough with production to be able to spot the seemingly small variations that make big differences in cost. Besides, there may have been price increases in composition, printing, binding, or materials since the other book was manufactured. Whenever the Ms is complicated or unusual in any way, one should have production estimates made before the retail price of the book is decided upon. Such estimates often are the basis for deciding whether or not the book can be published at all.

The remaining basic decisions are involved with the bookmaking process, if they are not always part of it.

Trim-size

CUSTOMARY SIZES

The page size of the book is generally an arbitrary decision based primarily on custom. Economy affects the decision, but in most cases custom has been shaped by economy, so there is little conflict.

In tradebooks there are 3 sizes in common use (in America):

5⅜ x 8″
5½ x 8¼″
6⅛ x 9¼″

By custom, 5⅜ x 8″ is used for fiction and for nonfiction of minor importance, usually unillustrated. Fiction by major authors (or of unusual length) and most nonfiction call for 5½ x 8¼″. The 6⅛ x 9¼″ size is used generally for nonfiction of major importance or for books in which the illustrations suggest a larger page. These customs are by no means invariable, but they do prevail in most cases. (5 x 7⅜″ was once common but is not now.)

The mass market paperbacks are either 4⅛ x 7″ or 4⅛ x 6⅜″. The (near) standardization here is quite rigid because of the need to fit retailers' racks. A few lines have special racks for their own size. The higher-priced lines are, in many cases, produced in tradebook sizes because they are often printed simultaneously with hardbound editions.

Textbooks in elementary and high school grades vary considerably in size because they frequently have illustrations that require special treatment. Also, competition for attention has resulted in the use of odd sizes, as well as more color and illustrations. College texts are more often made in common tradebook sizes, as they are sold in stores as tradebooks also. Another determinant in textbooks is the special requirements of programmed instruction.

In children's books, particularly in picture-and-caption books for preschool children (usually called "flats"), page sizes vary considerably. Pages of 6⅝ x 10″, 8½ x 11″, and 9 x 12″ are not uncommon. Teenage books are generally made in regular adult tradebook sizes.

CHOICE FACTORS

Deviations from the above usages are usually related to the availability of paper. The price of paper being lower on larger quantities of 1 item or 1 size (CH.8), publishers tend to buy as few sizes as possible. Consequently, their paper stock may not contain the customary size and the book will be made in a size to fit the paper on hand. Another influence in the use of unconventional size is the desire to make a big "package" to appeal to the gift buyer.

Actually, books could vary in size by using less than the full dimension of standard sheets—for example, by taking 5 x 8¼″ instead of 5½ x 8¼″ out of 45 x 68″. This would waste 4″ of the sheet, or about 9%. On larger orders, the paper could be made the proper size.

Cost is a minor factor in choosing between 5⅜ x 8″ and 5½ x 8¼″. The only difference is in the amount of paper—about 5%—which usually means less than 1¢ per book. Going up to 6⅛ x 9¼″ involves not only an increase of about 30% in paper, but an increase in press cost. Whereas the smaller sizes are printed in 64-page forms, the press necessary for 64-page forms of 6⅛ x 9¼″ is economical only for long runs. If the book must be printed in 32-page forms, the number of impressions is doubled, and so is the number of sheets to be folded (CHS.7,10).

The sizes available in offset lithography are somewhat different from those in letterpress, but include those mentioned. However, it is wise to check the printer, as litho presses are made primarily for commercial, rather than book, printing and the sizes he has may not fit the stock paper size you have.

STANDARDIZATION

Complete, or nearly complete, standardization of book sizes would result in fairly substantial savings in the cost of production. Some printers have tried to lower their costs by keeping certain presses set for 1 size of sheet, plates, and margins. Books that conform to these specifications are printed at lower prices. Efforts (particularly speeches) in the direction of large-scale standardization have been part of the book industry for decades. These efforts have not been generally successful and are not likely to be, except in mass market paperback publishing, in which price is the primary element.

The possible savings in complete standardization are not, however, sufficient to sacrifice flexibility in handling diverse materials, to warrant the considerable extra work necessary to make all books fit 1 size, or to overcome the competitive urge to do the unusual or the esthetic urge to see variety, rather than uniformity, prevail. Books are not, after all, purely utilitarian objects. They have an esthetic component that justifies some expenditure of money and effort. It would be more economical, also, to make all houses exactly alike, but whenever this is done there is an outcry against "look-alikes". It is true that the houses in many parts of the world were made alike before the industrial era—the thatched stone cottages of western Europe, the tile-roofed stuccoed houses of the Mediterranean regions, the igloos of the Arctic, the buffalo-skin tepees of the Plains Indians—and we admire these structures without deploring their uniformity, but there was an identity of function, material resources, and environment that justified the similarity. In books, almost every problem is unique, so the solutions cannot properly be the same.

Illustrations

The basic decisions concerning illustrations are:

(a) where they are to occur in the book, i.e. what physical relationship to the text they will have as a whole, and

(b) how and on what they are to be printed, i.e. which printing process and which paper.

These decisions are so closely related they must treated as 1. The same considerations affect both, and each depends on the other. Where the illustrations are a major element in the book, these decisions will have a large part in determining all the specifications for composition, printing, and binding, and will influence the other basic decisions. Variations in treatment of the text are relatively limited, but there are many ways to handle illustrations, and the way chosen will have an important effect on the character of the book.

The decision on illustrations must consider 2 factors (besides time and cost):

(a) editorial requirements for relationship of illustrations to text, and

(b) the nature and purpose of the individual illustrations.

The question is: must the illustration accompany the relevant text and if so, how closely? Usually, the editor or the author can answer this but sometimes they cannot and it is up to the designer to find the answer himself.

There is no system for deciding when to place illustrations in close proximity to the text. In principle, the arrangement that is most practical is best, and it is not necessarily better to have picture and text together. Unless there is a need for the reader to see an illustration before proceeding (as in a step-by-step explanation) he might be better served by putting it elsewhere so he may read without interruption. Sometimes, an illustration is referred to several times in the text, and it is better placed where it is accessible at any time. This is frequently true of maps, which are more accessible on the endpapers or at the front or back of the text than inside. Some books are written with text and pictures closely integrated, but in many cases the best relationship is not so obvious—and must be carefully considered.

The ideal arrangement of illustrations is not always possible within budget limits. For example, it might have been better to place the illustration of 4-color process printing that is now on the front endpaper of this book opposite the explanation in CH.7. However, an additional cost in paper and binding was saved by putting it on the endpaper, where it is so accessible that inconvenience to the reader is negligible. (Also, this illustration makes an attractive and appropriate endpaper design.)

There are several possible ways of placing illustrations in a book. They may be:

(a) printed on the text paper with the text,

(b) printed on the text paper separately (by a different process),

(c) printed on different paper from the text and bound into the book in one of several ways (CH.10),

(d) printed on the endpapers, or

(e) printed on the cover (CH.10).

Any combination of these methods may be used in 1 book. Where there are many illustrations of various kinds and purposes, the best method or combination should be found for each.

Desirability and cost should be considered simultaneously, but it is quite difficult to do this effectively because of the numerous variables involved. Any change in the plan is likely to affect several other factors. The final cost of an alternative may be higher, even though the alternative itself is cheaper. A printing decision may affect paper and binding, a paper decision may affect printing, which in turn may affect binding, and so on. Where alternate plans are being considered, it is usually necessary to have actual estimates made. Particularly in complex problems, guesses are likely to be off.

In general, it is cheaper to print a book by lithography (CH.7) if there are many illustrations (particularly halftones) that must print with the text. The cost of letterpress engravings is higher than that of litho plates, and coated paper costs more than most litho papers (CH.8). However, litho paper costs a bit more than letterpress antique, so this may outweigh the cost of some line engravings.

If the illustrations may be editorially separated from the text, it might be possible to save money by printing them separately. The text can be printed on cheaper paper, and the higher cost of printing halftones will apply only to the pages on which they appear rather than to the entire book. For instance, this may make the use of sheet-fed gravure (CH.7) for the illustrations economically feasible. However, the economic advantage may be lost in the bindery, as the cost of tipping, inserting, and wrapping is high (CHS.10, 12,26). That is why publishers tend to compress illustrations into 1 or 2 sections in the book, even though flexibility of editorial arrangement is sacrificed.

Printing the illustrations separately also makes it possible to use the most suitable process for both pictures and text, and this has economic value in terms of the book's sale. This factor must be weighed with the others in making the basic decisions.

USE REQUIREMENTS

The other primary consideration, the nature and purpose of the illustrations themselves, is discussed in CH.9. There it is explained that illustrations have various uses, and each use has its own requirements. It is these requirements that are taken into account in arriving at the basic decisions.

▪ *Informative illustrations*—These must be given maximum size and clarity because their purpose is elucidation. They should not therefore:

(a) be reduced too much,

(b) be printed on too rough a paper (this reduces sharpness),

(c) be bled or cropped if significant details are lost thereby,

(d) be printed in colored inks (black or near-black ink on near-white paper gives optimum clarity),

(e) have too coarse a screen (sharpness in halftones increases as the screen becomes finer, provided the paper and presswork are suitable. See CH.7).

▪ *Suggestive illustrations*—These are concerned with effect rather than accuracy, so any treatment or means of reproduction is acceptable if it achieves the desired end. Unless accuracy happens to be the effect wanted, any amount of reduction, enlargement, cropping, bleeding, silhouetting, etc., is justified. For example, it may be desirable to enlarge the screen of a halftone or gray it down until almost all definition is lost.

- *Decorative illustration*—This is a distinctly secondary element, so the decisions on printing, paper, and binding should be based on the needs of the text, with the illustrations made suitable for reproduction within the specifications chosen.
- *Representative illustrations*—These are subject to the same general principles as the informative. All decisions must lead to the most accurate reproduction—with even higher standards required in this group. Nothing should be allowed to prevail over decisions made for the representative purpose. Here, the situation is opposite to that of decorative illustration—if necessary, the text must be treated in less than the best way. For example, if the illustrations call for coated paper, it should be used, even though the text may not then be as readable. Or, it may be necessary to print type by gravure (which is unsuitable) if the best reproduction of the pictures requires that process.

Printing process & paper

Many considerations that affect the choice of printing process and paper have been discussed already. Properly, these choices are made to accommodate the copy—text and pictures—with due respect for the commercial aspects of publishing. The sales department will certainly be happy with a book that is handsomely printed on the most suitable paper, but they will be especially anxious to have one that makes a big package. This refers not only to trim-size, but to bulk. More than once has a book been printed by lithography or gravure rather than letterpress, to benefit from the larger bulk of uncoated paper. (Provided the process used is suitable, this is a much more acceptable way of getting bulk than padding the text or using unreasonably bulky paper.)

The primary considerations, however, are the requirements of illustrations, the choice of trim-size, and the cost elements in binding. All the basic decisions are interdependent, and each must be made in the light of the others.

Behind an intelligent and perceptive choice of printing processes and papers there must be a knowledge of their characteristics. These are discussed in CHS. 7 and 8, respectively.

The number of possible combinations of copy and circumstances in book problems is infinite, and it is obviously impossible to deal with every one. We will, though, take a hypothetical situation and arrive at printing and paper decisions by the recommended procedure.

Suppose we have a nonfiction tradebook with an extensive text and a fairly large number of illustrations. The retail price will be quite high, and the sales prospects make possible a substantial first printing, so it will not be necessary to find the very cheapest way to produce the book. On the other hand, there is a lot of book to be produced, so the budget does have limits.

The mechanical analysis shows that there are 103 illustrations—of which 75 are photographs that can be called informative, and the other 28 are line drawings having a primarily suggestive purpose. A study of the Ms indicates that the photographs need not appear in a specific place in the book, but they should be fairly close to the relevant text. The line drawings are simply to enhance the atmosphere of the text, so they may be scattered at random.

With these factors to consider, we may decide to print the text and line cuts together by letterpress on an antique stock as the most effective and least expensive method (the cost of line cuts will be spread over a long run). The halftones we will print as 32 pages by offset lithography on dull-coated paper, to be inserted in the book as four 8-page wraps. The use of dull-coated stock will permit the use of a 300-line screen, which can give us quality comparable to gravure. The 4 wraps will spread the pictures fairly widely through the book, permitting us to place them reasonably close to their textual references without excessive cost. Most of the book's pages will be the antique stock, so the bulk will be adequate. The text paper need not be too smooth, as the line drawings are rather simple and do not present any difficult printing problems.

For the book you are now reading, it was decided to print the entire book by offset lithography on an off-white paper with a relatively soft surface. The illustrations should appear with the descriptive text, yet there are relatively few halftones, so it was not considered necessary to print the whole book on coated or heavily calendered paper. The text type is easier to read, the illustrations of book pages and type look better, and the halftone illustrations can be reproduced adequately for their purpose on an off-white stock without excessive smoothness or glare.

Number of pages

Given any Ms, one can make a book of relatively few pages or many. Indeed, an effective demonstration of the role of bookmaking is to place side by side 2 books of radically different appearance, pointing out that the Mss for both were almost identical. The designer has a wide range of possibilities for setting the book, and he must choose carefully.

The length of a book is determined to some extent by each of 3 main factors:

(a) the size of the Ms,
(b) the retail price of the book, and
(c) the requirements of paper and presses.

The esthetic considerations of format—whether the book should be thick or thin—may have some influence, but this is rare, and is almost never decisive.

DETERMINANTS: THE MS

In most cases, the size of the Ms is the dominant element in the decision and is modified by the other factors as necessary. A very small Ms is often padded out to justify a retail price, and a very large one is usually held in to reduce the cost, but the number of pages in the printed book is ordinarily related to the amount of material (text and illustrations) in the Ms. In any case, start with the Ms to determine the approximate length of the book as it would be normally set.

There are several methods of approaching this answer, depending upon the nature of the Ms and the nature of the problem, but the principle is always the same—you start with known elements and combine these with a hypothesis or supposition to arrive at tentative answers, which can in turn be used to find other answers. You work from the known to the unknown. The procedure used in each case depends on which elements are known. There are 2 main alternatives: (a) a specific total number of pages is required and the problem is to make the Ms fit or, (b) no specific number is required and the Ms is estimated to determine how many pages it will make.

Suppose you are told that the book should make 352 pages (perhaps because a competing book that sells for a higher price is that size). The problem is to determine if the Ms can be fitted reasonably into 352 pages of the trim-size adopted.

The first step is to make an estimate of the number of pages that would be occupied by all the material *other* than straight text.

■ *Page-for-page material*—In the breakdown (CH.14) is a list of the frontmatter copy, which can usually be counted in this way. A typical frontmatter sequence might run as follows:

1—half-title
2, 3—title
4—copyright
5—dedication
6—blank
7—preface
8—preface
9, 10—contents
11, 12, 13—introduction
14—blank

A long introduction may be lumped in with the text for this purpose. A wrong guess of 1 or 2 pages on the shorter pieces will not be serious at this point. Count other page-for-page material in backmatter, full-page tables, etc. The allowance for part-titles is discussed under "Subdivisions and units".

■ *Character-count material*—At this point, it is desirable to establish a tentative text-page size. On a sheet of tracing paper, rule a rectangle for the trim-size and place within it a rectangle for a text area (not including running heads or folios). The text area may have any size, shape, or position you desire, provided it is far enough from the gutter to avoid the curving of the page (at least ⅝″) and far enough from the outside edges to avoid being cut by the trim. Also, the folding and trimming may not be square so it is a good idea to stay *at least* 5⁄16″ away from trimmed edges, to avoid making irregularities too noticeable. Usually, an allowance should be made at the top or bottom of the text area for running heads and folios, although these may go at the side (as in this book). The most practical distance from the text is about 1 pica. The width of the text should be measured to an even pica or half-pica. In very large books, it may be desirable to set the text in 2 columns. See CHS. 5 and 6 for discussions of maximum text width.

The purpose of the tentative text-page size is to help determine an approximate number of characters per page for use in estimating the number of pages. A rough rule of thumb is: multiply the width of the text area in picas (exclusive of running heads) by the depth and double this number. For example, if the text page is 23 x 39 picas, the product is 897—so the number of characters per page would be 1794. While it is possible to have much less or much more on a page of this size, 1794 would be a reasonable starting point.

A still rougher (but even quicker) method is to use 2000 as an average number for medium-sized Mss and 3000 for large ones. While these figures are not likely to be as close to the final result, they are handy for mathematics and they obviate the need for

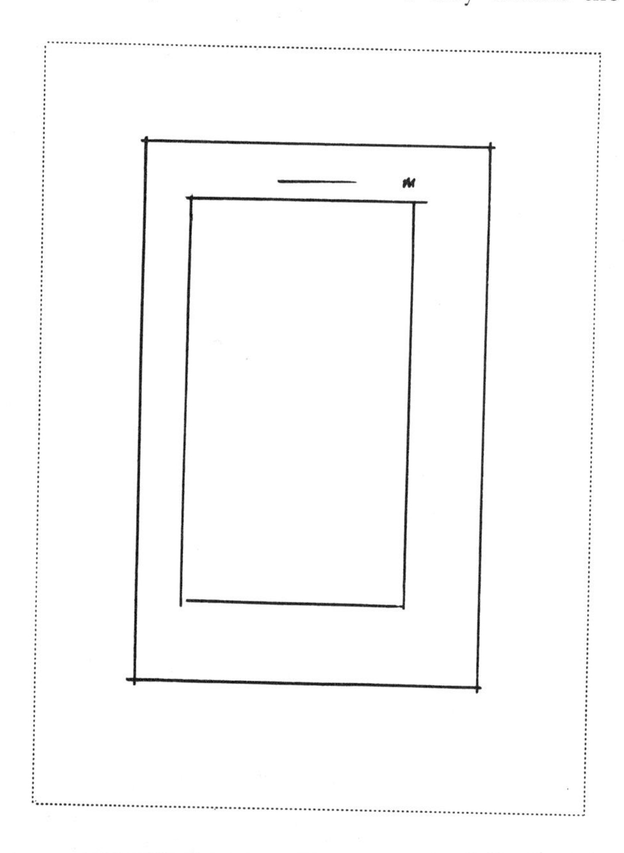

drawing a text area, etc. Since the approximate number of characters per page is only a hypothetical figure which will be corrected anyway, it doesn't really matter how wrong it is, within reasonable limits. With experience, you will be able to guess quite closely how many characters per page there will be in each book.

With an approximate number of characters per page, you can calculate the number of pages to be occupied by any item other than text, if it has been counted by characters (CH.14). Simply divide the total by your approximate number. If any of this matter should be set smaller than the text, add 20 or 25% to the per-page character number (1794 + 20% = 2152). For footnotes, which are ordinarily set *much* smaller than the text, add 50%.

▪ *Line-for-line material*—To find the number of pages, divide the counts by the text-page depth in picas if the Ms is large, or that number less 3 if the Ms is medium in size. For very small Mss, use that number less 6. In the first instance, we assume that the text will be set on a 12 pt. body, in the second, on a 13 pt. body, and in the third on a 14 pt. body. This assumes also that the text will be about 36 picas deep, so the addition of each point of leading will reduce the number of lines by 3 (1 pica = 12 pts., 1 line = 12 pts., 36 pts. = 3 picas, 3 picas = 3 lines). For example, if there are 363 lines of poetry in a medium-sized Ms, they would take 11 pages if the depth of the page were 36 picas (33 lines of 13 pts.). This method may be used for almost any size page, as the error will not be very large if there are a few picas more or less in depth.

For tabular matter and other line-for-line material which would probably set smaller than the text, *add* 3 or 6 to the number of picas of depth, depending on how many points *less* than a pica the body might be. For example, if the tables were figured for 9 on 11, and the depth of the page is 36 picas, the total number of lines of tabular copy would be divided by 39 (36 picas plus 36 points or 3 picas).

Here it is important to know that in Linotype composition the *actual* depth of the page will be somewhat more than the theoretical amount. The Linotype system is based on a point slightly larger than the standard (.014 instead of .01384). In practice, this means a gain of about 1½ point in every 10 picas. Thus, 36 lines of 12 pt. slugs will measure about 36 picas 5½ pts. Further, it is in the nature of Linotype slugs to run a little "strong", i.e. they are usually a bit thicker than they should be, because of the tendency of the trimming knives to get out of adjustment. In addition, there is the problem of *squeeze*. In galleys or page proofs the apparent depth of the page may be excessive because the slugs were not pressed together tightly enough. Occasionally there is an actual increase in the page depth when there is insufficient squeeze in lock-up.

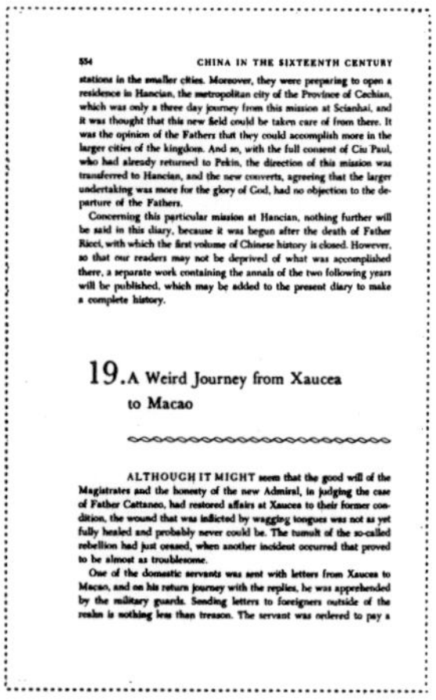

■ *Subdivisions and units*—The space allowance is figured as follows:

(a) Allow 2½ pages for each part-title—1 page for the title itself, 1 page for the blank backing it, and ½ page for blanks following parts that end on right-hand pages. (As this is likely to happen in 50% of the parts, the allowance is ½ page.)

(b) Allow 1 page for each chapter (½ for chapter sinkage and ½ for the average chapter ending) if it is to begin on a new page. If the chapters are to start on right-hand pages only, allow 1½ pages (there will be preceding blanks as with part-titles). If there are very many chapters and the Ms is large, it may be best to run-in the chapters. In this case, allow part of a page (⅓, ½, etc.) for each one, to account for the space from the end of one chapter to the first line of the next. (This space includes the chapter title, etc.)

(c) Allow a reasonable number of *lines* (text size) of space for each class of subhead—the largest number for the major subheads (perhaps 6), and progressively smaller numbers for the lesser subheads. (This allowance includes the space taken by the head itself, as well as the space above and below it.) Multiply the number of subheads of each class by the number of lines allowed for each. Then divide the product by the number of text lines per page to find how many pages each kind of subhead will occupy. Thus, if there are 150 subheads of a class for which 6 lines each are allowed, they will take 900 lines (150 x 6). If the page has 36 lines, this class of subhead will require 25 pages (900 ÷ 36).

(d) For each occurrence of extract, poetry, tabular, etc., allow some space to separate them from the text. (Make the allowance either ½ line or 1 full line above and below. A full line is best, as the half-line space often creates a problem when the unit starts on one page and ends on another.)

(e) Allow 1 line space for each occurrence of footnotes (CH.14) to separate it from the text.

(f) Allow 1 line for each spacebreak.

■ *Illustrations*—If there are illustrations that print with the text, a rough space allowance may be made for them as explained in CH.14. The space allowed should provide for captions also.

■ *Index*—Make allowance as explained in CH.14.

When everything except the actual text has been estimated, subtract the allowed number of pages from the total number required—in this case, 352. The result will be the number of pages to be occupied by the text. Divide this into the text character count to find the number of characters per page required. For example, if everything other than text adds up to 74 pages, there will be 278 pages for the text itself. Suppose that there are 538,050 characters of text. If you divide this by 278 you find that each page of text should have 1935 characters.

554 CHINA IN THE SIXTEENTH CENTURY

stations in the smaller cities. Moreover, they were preparing to open a residence in Hancian, the metropolitan city of the Province of Cechian, which was only a three day journey from this mission at Scianhai, and it was thought that this new field could be taken care of from there. It was the opinion of the Fathers that they could accomplish more in the larger cities of the kingdom. And so, with the full consent of Ciu Paul, who had already returned to Pekin, the direction of this mission was transferred to Hancian, and the new converts, agreeing that the larger undertaking was more for the glory of God, had no objection to the departure of the Fathers.

Concerning this particular mission at Hancian, nothing further will be said in this diary, because it was begun after the death of Father Ricci, with which the first volume of Chinese history is closed. However, so that our readers may not be deprived of what was accomplished there, a separate work containing the annals of the two following years will be published, which may be added to the present diary to make a complete history.

19. A Weird Journey from Xaucea to Macao

ALTHOUGH IT MIGHT seem that the good will of the Magistrates and the honesty of the new Admiral, in judging the case of Father Cattaneo, had restored affairs at Xaucea to their former condition, the wound that was inflicted by wagging tongues was not as yet fully healed and probably never could be. The tumult of the so-called rebellion had just ceased, when another incident occurred that proved to be almost as troublesome.

One of the domestic servants was sent with letters from Xaucea to Macao, and on his return journey with the replies, he was apprehended by the military guards. Sending letters to foreigners outside of the realm is nothing less than treason. The servant was ordered to pay a

run-in chapter opening

TITLE: *Example*
Ms pp: 339

DATE: *12/2/81*

FRONTMATTER	
half title *1* pp, title *2* pp, cpyrt *1* pp, ded *1* pp	*6*
preface 2762 c	*2*
contents 44 L	*2*
introduction 5250 c	*4*
TEXT:	
538,050 c	
103 L	*3*
EXTRACT: (p.67)	
5892 c	*3*
POETRY: (p.29)	
129 L	*4*
14 units	*1*
PLAYSTYLE: (p.162)	
1264 c	*1*
10 L	*–*
4 units	*–*
TABULAR: (p.212)	
42 L	*1*
12 units	*1*
BIBLIOGRAPHY: (p.318)	
4922 c	*2*
53 L	*2*
INDEX:	
allow *8* pp	*8*
FOOTNOTES:	
1640 c	*1*
14 units	*–*
ILLUSTRATIONS:	
halftone:75	*–*
line:28	*10*
SUBDIVISIONS:	
part titles:3	*8*
chapters:8	*8*
A heads:18 *@ 6L*	*3*
B heads:41 *@ 3L*	*3*
spacebreaks:19 *@ 1L*	*1*
	74

352
74
278

1935
278 ⟌ 538,050

The breakdown with a rough calculation of length. When entering the figures for each item, leave room for later columns.

If this figure roughly equals the approximate number of characters per page used for your estimate, you may assume that the book will make 352 pages. If the figure varies substantially from your tentative number, you will have to make some changes in your specifications, such as enlarging or reducing the text-page area, changing the space allowance for subheads, modifying the allocation of space for illustrations, etc. If this cannot be done, abandon the idea of making 352 pages and aim for a more realistic figure, either more or less.

When there is no specific total number of pages required, the procedure is somewhat different. First, ideal specifications for text and illustrations are selected, and calculations are made to determine how long the book will run using these specs. The quickest method is to adopt a round number of characters per page as suggested previously and divide this into the character count for text and other character-counted matter, then divide the line-for-line counts by an estimated number of lines per page, and continue to estimate the length of each kind of material as described above. However, a better result is obtained if the characters per page is determined by making a page layout, and even selecting type face, size, and leading (CH.17).

The results of this procedure will represent the "normal" (or ideal) length of the book. This number of pages may be impractical for one reason or another, but you will have, at least, a reasonable figure which can be modified as necessary.

At times, the designer begins with other definite factors which influence the number of pages. The illustrations may be planned for a specific size, the type page may be required to match that of another book, or the type size may be prescribed for editorial reasons. The principle is always: work from the known to the unknown. Use whatever figures or decisions are provided to determine other answers. For example, if you are told that the illustrations must occupy 16 pages, this figure can be subtracted from a total number of pages at the start—or it can be used to arrive at a normal length.

When the second procedure is used, and a normal number of pages is established, a final decision on number of pages is reached by considering the 2 other main factors involved—retail price and the requirements of paper and presses.

DETERMINANTS: RETAIL PRICE

Let us say that the normal number estimated from the Ms is 359 pages. Presumably, it is possible to reduce or increase this by about 10% without serious effect. The retail price that seems to be right for the book's potential market is $7.95. In any case, this is what has been decided. It is determined that this price won't support a book of more than about 350 pages, considering the illustrations, length of run, etc., but there should be that many pages to make the book seem worth the price.

DETERMINANTS: PRESSES & PAPER

Now we know that the normal length is 359 pages, and the optimum length from the commercial standpoint is 350 pages. What about presses and paper?

The trim-size has been determined as 5½ x 8¼″. This cuts out of a sheet 45 x 68″ (CH.8) which permits printing 64-page forms, so there is obviously an advantage in having a total number of pages that is a multiple of 64. The nearest multiple of 64 to 359 is 384 and to 350 it is 320, but these are not very close. If no multiple of 64 comes close to the other figures, a multiple of 32 (a half-form) is almost as satisfactory. (A multiple of 16 can be used, but the printing becomes progressively less economical as the units become smaller [CHS.7,12].) In this case, eleven 32s, or 352 pages, would seem to be the best number.

In conclusion

The problem has been analyzed and studied in its mechanical, commercial, and editorial aspects. The creative concept of the book is established. The basic decisions have now been made. We know the trim-size, the arrangement of illustrations, the printing processes, the papers, and the number of pages—as well as the retail price and the size of the first run. At this point, it is possible to begin detailed planning of the various parts of the book, in accordance with our overall design.

17 | The text plan

People outside of bookmaking—and some in it—love to say, "A book is to be read", implying that designers are unaware of, or even opposed to, this truism. They seem to assume that the designer is concerned with graphic effects that are unrelated to the process of reading, if not actually obstacles to it. Nothing could (or should) be further from the truth.

The text *is* the book. It is the source of the designer's inspiration and the object of his efforts. Except in some picture-text books, in which the text is hardly more than captions for the illustrations, the text is the primary consideration in all bookmaking decisions. The object is to make it supremely *readable*—which means that it must be extremely legible, inviting, pleasing, and appropriate to its subject (CH.6).

Planning the text is a complex process, despite the often simple appearance of the result. The interaction of esthetic and practical factors must be kept in constant balance during the planning stage, so that conflicts may be resolved without vital damage to either. The demands of readability and economy are dealt with alternately in the following discussion, but they are considered simultaneously in practice.

Copyfitting (I)

In the previous chapter, rough calculations were made to determine the number of pages the book will have. Now refine the calculations to be certain that you do indeed get that number.

The example used gave us 359 pages as the normal number and we decided that we would aim for 352. However, there are several factors that could cause a miss—even though the mathematics may be perfect. The character count might be inaccurate, the author might make changes in galleys, the machine operator might set unusually loose or tight, or there might be an unusual number of bad breaks in chapter endings, subheads, widows, etc. An error of 2% in either direction could easily result from any one of these factors. It would not matter much if we came out 7 or 8 pages short, but it would be quite embarrassing to run 7 pages over. So, instead of aiming directly for 352 pages, we will aim for 344 to get some leeway. This means that we must come down 15 pages from the normal length of 359.

If the space allowances for chapter openings, subheads, etc. were generous, it may be possible to pull in enough pages by reducing these. Usually (not always) chapters can begin on left *or* right rather than right-hand pages, or even run in without seriously hurting the design concept. If it is not possible to reduce these spaces, it is usually possible to save pages by combining frontmatter or reducing illustrations, but it is best to leave such measures for emergencies. Even with the best planning it may be necessary to make a last-minute effort to save space (CH.20). A sounder policy at this point is to increase the number of characters in the text page—which may not be possible at a later stage.

To find out how much the characters per page must be increased, subtract from 344 the total number of pages of other-than-text (74) as determined in the rough estimate. This will give the number of pages of text you must have (270) which, divided into the text character count, will give the number of characters per page required. Using 538,050 as the text count, the answer is 1992, as compared to the 1935 of our preliminary estimate. Granted that this figure depends on some rough guesses in the calculation of other-than-text matter, it is not likely to be very far off, especially if there is a relatively small amount of other-than-text. However it is subject to further correction after all other calculations are made.

If the alternate method of computing the length was used, i.e. the copy was fitted into a required total number of pages (352), simply reduce the number of text pages (278) by about 2% of the *total* pages (8) and divide the reduced number (270) into the text character count (538,050). This will give the characters per page (1992) needed for 344, the safer objective.

With the basic arithmetic tentatively established, some typographic decisions are in order.

The text

In making choices concerning the text, all the factors of readability should be considered. In CH.6, these factors are listed and the principles of readability discussed in detail. Since all decisions cannot be made simultaneously, the presently required ones:

(a) text typeface,
(b) text type size,
(c) text measure,
(d) text leading, and

(e) number of text lines per page,

must be made in the context of earlier visualizations and general plans. Each subsequent decision is made in the light of the previous ones plus approximations based on the original conception.

Thus, while some of the text-page specifications are not needed until later (CH.18), some broad plans are necessary now in order to properly develop those required. With the basic decisions (trim-size, paper, etc.) made (CH.16) and the editorial problem analyzed, what remains is to determine a tentative page pattern comprising the text and whatever other elements occur with it.

The unit used for copyfitting purposes is the single page, but in planning a page pattern, the *double spread* [facing pages] should be considered as a unit. An effective method (but not the only one) of developing the visual arrangement is: (1) on tracing paper, rule the outlines of 2 facing pages in actual size, (2) on separate sheets, rule the outlines of 2 text areas as conceived, (3) move the 2 text areas around under the page outline until the positions seem best, and (4) sketch in a tentative indication of running heads and folios, moving the text areas again if necessary. When the arrangement is decided, draw all elements on the 1 sheet. The pattern arrived at in this way is not necessarily final, but it represents thinking that should precede decisions on the text typography.

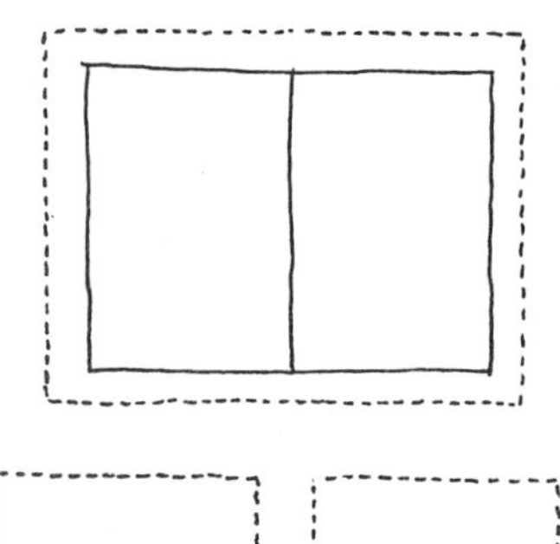

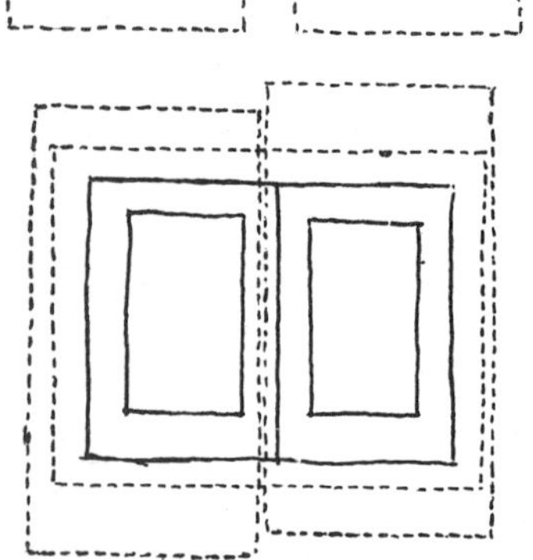

In this book, the pattern was determined by the following rationale: the reader would frequently want to find other parts of the text because there are numerous referrals and the factual and procedural discussions are separated. So, it would be useful to have easy-to-find marginal heads on the outsides of the pages. The ideal width of (10 pt.) text, considering the need to fit in as much as possible, is about 24 picas. To have marginal heads with this measure requires a page at least 6¾″ wide. Since there would be a large amount of space not occupied by the heads, it was possible to put many small illustrations on the side, thereby saving space in the text. The running heads and folios could also be placed at the outside without using more space, and they would be very accessible for reference. To avoid cramping the pictures, the page was made 7″ wide. Standard paper and press dimensions suggested a height of 10″. For economy of space, the text area utilizes as much of this height as is visually and practically desirable.

The text type, Electra, was chosen because it is economical of space due to its narrow width (CH.5), has a clean look suited to the didactic nature of the book, and its tall, narrow shape is harmonious with the shape of the text area. The 10 pt. size is satisfactory for general adult readers, and 3 pts. of leading seems optimum for the length of line.

layout of facing text pages

For the example being used, suppose that all considerations led to a choice of 11/13 Linotype Baskerville x 23, with 36 lines per page.

Copyfitting (II)

Having made the text-type decisions, it is necessary to calculate their effect on the number of pages. If the result is substantially different from the number needed (270), changes in the specifications must be made. However, these modifications will be final. Note that this concerns the basic text only—refinement of specifications for illustrations and other matter comes later—but, in each case, the procedure is the same: (1) preliminary calculation is followed by (2) detailed specifications, which are then (3) modified to accord with decisions resulting from the preliminary calculation.

To calculate how many pages of text will result from the specs chosen: (a) find out the characters per pica (CHS. 5, 6, Part D) of the text type and size (11 pt. Baskerville = 2.4*), (b) multiply this figure by the measure (23 picas) to get the number of characters per line (2.4 x 23 = 55.2), (c) multiply that by the number of

* This is the figure generally used, but for more accuracy it may be carried to the next digit—2.43 (see Type width table in Part D).

lines per page to get the number of characters per page (55.2 x 36 = 1987), and (d) divide that into the total number of characters of text (538,050) to get the number of pages of text (271). This is close enough to the number needed (270) so that no changes in specs are required.

There are tables for finding the characters per *page* if the typeface, type size, measure, and page depth are known. While these tables are not completely accurate for all combinations, they are accurate enough for quick answers in preliminary calculations. It is possible, also, to use these tables for finding other answers when the characters per page is known. For example, if you know that you must have 1992 characters, and you want to set the text in 11/13 Baskerville x 23, the table will show how many lines per page you need. There are some copyfitting tables (such as *Haberule*) that give the number of characters for each measure for various type faces and sizes.

A copyfitting table for fonts of about 2.4 characters per pica

	16	18	20	21	22	23	24	25	26	27	28	29	30
29	1216	1376	1536	1600	1696	1760	1856	1920	1984	2048	2144	2208	2304
	1102	*1247*	*1392*	*1450*	*1537*	*1595*	*1682*	*1740*	*1798*	*1856*	*1943*	*2001*	*2088*
	1026	**1161**	**1296**	**1350**	**1431**	**1485**	**1566**	**1620**	**1674**	**1728**	**1809**	**1863**	**1944**
30	1254	1419	1584	1650	1749	1815	1914	1980	2046	2112	2211	2277	2376
	1140	*1290*	*1440*	*1500*	*1590*	*1650*	*1740*	*1800*	*1860*	*1920*	*2010*	*2070*	*2160*
	1064	**1204**	**1344**	**1400**	**1484**	**1540**	**1624**	**1680**	**1736**	**1792**	**1876**	**1932**	**2016**
31	1292	1462	1632	1700	1802	1870	1972	2040	2108	2176	2278	2346	2448
	1178	*1333*	*1488*	*1550*	*1643*	*1705*	*1798*	*1860*	*1922*	*1984*	*2077*	*2139*	*2232*
	1102	**1247**	**1392**	**1450**	**1537**	**1595**	**1682**	**1740**	**1798**	**1856**	**1943**	**2001**	**2088**
32	1330	1505	1680	1750	1855	1925	2030	2100	2170	2240	2345	2415	2520
	1216	*1376*	*1536*	*1600*	*1696*	*1760*	*1856*	*1920*	*1984*	*2048*	*2144*	*2208*	*2304*
	1140	**1290**	**1440**	**1500**	**1590**	**1650**	**1740**	**1800**	**1860**	**1920**	**2010**	**2070**	**2160**
33	1368	1548	1728	1800	1908	1980	2088	2160	2232	2304	2412	2484	2592
	1254	*1419*	*1584*	*1650*	*1749*	*1815*	*1914*	*1980*	*2046*	*2112*	*2211*	*2277*	*2376*
	1140	**1290**	**1440**	**1500**	**1590**	**1650**	**1740**	**1800**	**1860**	**1920**	**2010**	**2070**	**2160**
34	1406	1591	1776	1850	1961	2035	2146	2220	2294	2368	2479	2553	2664
	1292	*1462*	*1632*	*1700*	*1802*	*1870*	*1972*	*2040*	*2108*	*2176*	*2278*	*2346*	*2448*
	1178	**1333**	**1488**	**1550**	**1643**	**1705**	**1798**	**1860**	**1922**	**1984**	**2077**	**2139**	**2232**
35	1444	1634	1824	1900	2014	2090	2204	2280	2356	2432	2546	2622	2736
	1330	*1505*	*1680*	*1750*	*1855*	*1925*	*2030*	*2100*	*2170*	*2240*	*2345*	*2415*	*2520*
	1216	**1376**	**1536**	**1600**	**1696**	**1760**	**1856**	**1920**	**1984**	**2048**	**2144**	**2208**	**2304**
36	1482	1677	1872	1950	2067	2145	2262	2340	2418	2496	2613	2691	2808
	1368	*1548*	*1728*	*1800*	*1908*	*1980*	*2088*	*2160*	*2232*	*2304*	*2412*	*2484*	*2592*
	1254	**1419**	**1584**	**1650**	**1749**	**1815**	**1914**	**1980**	**2046**	**2112**	**2211**	**2277**	**2376**
37	1520	1720	1920	2000	2120	2200	2320	2400	2480	2560	2680	2760	2880
	1406	*1591*	*1776*	*1850*	*1961*	*2035*	*2146*	*2220*	*2294*	*2368*	*2479*	*2553*	*2664*
	1292	**1462**	**1632**	**1700**	**1802**	**1870**	**1972**	**2040**	**2108**	**2176**	**2278**	**2346**	**2448**
38	1558	1763	1968	2050	2173	2255	2378	2460	2542	2624	2747	2829	2952
	1444	*1634*	*1824*	*1900*	*2014*	*2090*	*2204*	*2280*	*2356*	*2432*	*2546*	*2622*	*2736*
	1330	**1505**	**1680**	**1750**	**1855**	**1925**	**2030**	**2100**	**2170**	**2240**	**2345**	**2415**	**2520**
39	1634	1849	2064	2150	2279	2365	2494	2580	2666	2752	2881	2967	3096
	1482	*1677*	*1872*	*1950*	*2067*	*2145*	*2262*	*2340*	*2418*	*2496*	*2613*	*2691*	*2808*
	1368	**1548**	**1728**	**1800**	**1908**	**1980**	**2088**	**2160**	**2232**	**2304**	**2412**	**2484**	**2592**
40	1672	1892	2112	2200	2332	2420	2552	2640	2728	2816	2948	3036	3168
	1520	*1720*	*1920*	*2000*	*2120*	*2200*	*2320*	*2400*	*2480*	*2560*	*2680*	*2760*	*2880*
	1406	**1591**	**1776**	**1850**	**1961**	**2035**	**2146**	**2220**	**2294**	**2368**	**2479**	**2553**	**2664**
41	1710	1935	2160	2250	2385	2475	2610	2700	2790	2880	3015	3105	3240
	1558	*1763*	*1968*	*2050*	*2173*	*2255*	*2378*	*2460*	*2542*	*2624*	*2747*	*2829*	*2952*
	1444	**1634**	**1824**	**1900**	**2014**	**2090**	**2204**	**2280**	**2356**	**2432**	**2546**	**2622**	**2736**
42	1748	1978	2208	2300	2438	2530	2668	2760	2852	2944	3082	3174	3312
	1596	*1806*	*2016*	*2100*	*2226*	*2310*	*2436*	*2520*	*2604*	*2688*	*2814*	*2898*	*3024*
	1482	**1677**	**1872**	**1950**	**2067**	**2145**	**2262**	**2340**	**2418**	**2496**	**2613**	**2691**	**2808**

Horizontal and vertical figures represent pica widths and depths of type pages.
Roman indicates solid, *Italic* 1 point, **Bold** 2 point leading.

In cases where the number of pages must be changed—unless the difference can be made up by manipulating illustrations or other-than-text matter—the text will have to be modified by changing 1 or more of the following:

(a) the typeface (to one that is narrower or wider),
(b) the type size,
(c) the measure, and/or
(d) the number of lines per page.

Changes in lines per page are usually accompanied by an addition or deletion of leading in order to maintain the page depth when more than 1 or 2 lines are involved. However, if the preliminary calculations of length were done properly, there should be no need to make such extensive corrections. Addition or subtraction of a pica or half-pica in the measure, or a line in the page, should suffice. A change of type face or size is undesirable, if these were carefully chosen for suitability. If a change is made in the dimensions of the text area, its position on the page should be reconsidered. In making *any* adjustments, all of the considerations that went into the original choices should be reexamined.

Special matter

The various kinds of matter other than text must now be specified in detail so that the amount of each can be calculated. While there are many special problems involved in this material, the same principles of readability that apply to the text are relevant here.

LINE-FOR-LINE

There is usually no special treatment of line-for-line matter in text or within extract, appendixes, etc., unless it is one of the separate categories of copy that are counted by lines in their entirety, such as poetry. Sometimes there is miscellaneous line-for-line matter which is neither part of the text nor a separate category, but each such case must be dealt with individually. These items may be telegrams, signs, newspaper headlines, etc.

POETRY

The most frequently encountered line-for-line matter is poetry. In CH.28, the treatment of poetry books is covered in detail. Verse appearing in prose text is a somewhat different problem because it is usually in small amounts and is subordinate to the text.

As with all brief passages of copy, poetry within text can be set smaller and still be readable. This is good, because it looks best when well differentiated, and it really should be. Poetry in prose usually presents a distinct change in style of expression, especially when quoted from another author. Indeed, it may be set entirely in italic, which has a somewhat more lyrical quality than roman.

It is conventional to center poetry in books having a centered plan, but this rarely works well (CH.28).

a seed of endless discontent. It is because of men's dissatisfaction with the customs, sanctions and modes of behavior of their age and race that moral progress is possible. New insight begins when satisfaction comes to an end, when all that has been seen or said looks like a distortion to him who sees the world for the first time.

Self-contentment is the brink of the abyss, from which the prophets try to keep us away. Even while the people of Israel were still in the desert, before entering the Promised Land, they were warned to brave the perils of contentment. "When I bring them into the land which I swore to their fathers to give them, a land abounding in milk and honey, and they eat their fill and wax fat, and turn to alien gods, and serve them, despising Me, breaking My covenant . . ." (Deuteronomy 31:20). For this is the way of languid downfall:

Jeshurun grew fat, and kicked—
Thou didst grow fat, thick, gorged.
(Deuteronomy 32:15)

If we should try to portray the soul of a prophet by the emotions that had no place in it, contentment would be mentioned first. The prophets of Israel were like geysers of disgust, disturbing our conscience till this day, urging us to be heartsick for the hurt of others.

Woe to them that are at ease in Zion,
And trust in the mountain of Samaria . . .
That lie upon beds of ivory,
And stretch themselves upon their couches,
And eat the lambs out of the flock,
And the calves out of the midst of the stall;
That chant to the sound of the viol,
And invent to themselves instruments of music, like David;

258

116) ANDRÉ CHÉNIER

familiar with as many words chosen from what I aspire to write for all the world!

With the "rhapsody" carefully folded and safe in his pocket, André Chénier met his appointment. It might have been with certain English acquaintances whom he occasionally joined at a club where men of such eminence as Richard Price and William Wilberforce were wont to lead discussions of social problems, or it could have been with a group of artists in Mrs. Cosway's drawing room. But Chénier's inability to converse with ease in the English language would have made him all the more depressed at either a club or at Mrs. Cosway's. So it is more likely that on this day of dejection, when he wanted above all else to forget the "sad circumstance" responsible for his dining in solitude at Hood's Tavern, he had arranged for a rendezvous with a group in whose orgies he participated from time to time, a company of devotees of Bacchus and Venus dominated by Aglaé, Byblis, and other daughters of joy.

City of marble colonnades,
Of sculptured images, of trees!

Late that night, or possibly not until the next morning, he returned to his apartment at the French embassy and filed the "rhapsody" in one of the many portfolios in which he kept his manuscripts. Recently added to the collection, or to be placed in a portfolio within a few days, was an elegy which surpasses the "rhapsody" in showing the depth of the despair in which Chénier found himself at this particular period. The verse pattern he adopted for the piece is that of all his elegies, alexandrines rhyming in couplets.[22]

Oh, hard necessity! Oh, heavy slavery!
Oh, destiny! Must I then see, while yet in youth,
My days adrift in this mad flow and counterflow
Of hope and pain—my days, tissues of wants and tears?
Wearied of servitude, of drinking to the lees
This woeful cup called life, of hearing in my heart
The scorn with which the doltish rich burden the poor,
I often summon up an image of the grave.
Desired retreat! I smile at Death, willing and near!
In tears I dare to pray for strength to break my chains.

Examples of poetry in text; centered and indented.

TABULAR Tables vary greatly in their nature and their relationship to the text, and the ways of setting them vary accordingly. In general, they are set 2 or 3 sizes smaller than the text. When tables are set on slug machines, the use of horizontal rules usually presents no problems, but vertical rules may be very expensive if it is necessary to cut slugs. In simple tables, each column can be set on its own measure, with vertical rules dropped in between. Complicated tables which require both horizontal and vertical rules might be more economically set by Monotype or photocomposition. It may be necessary to turn tables the other way of the page (*side turn*) if there are too many columns for the width.

LISTING Lists are usually set in the same size as the text, except where 2 or more columns are required and it becomes necessary to reduce it. Ordinarily, lists can be reduced to 8 or 9 pt. without adversely affecting readability. Under some circumstances (such as a list of ingredients in a recipe) it may be desirable to use a larger size—or even a contrasting face—for emphasis or clarity.

OUTLINE The outline form itself normally provides the distinctions required to clarify this kind of material, so there is no need to make any typographic change. Sometimes, however, the outline is so complex

SPENCER, D. M. *Disease, Religion and Society in the Fiji Islands.* American Ethnological Society, Monograph 2, New York, 1941.

FIJIAN PHARMACOLOGICAL THERAPY

Plant Drug Employed as Abortifacients		*Part of Plant Used and Method of Preparation and Use*	*Source*	*Remarks*
SCIENTIFIC NAME	FIJI NAME			
Cerbera manglias Linn.	rewa	Inner bark of root is soaked in cold water; drink liquid until desired results are obtained	Field notes	This turns foetus to liquid which is passed out as blood, according to native theory
Hibiscus (Abelmoschus) diversifolius	kalani soni	Juice of leaves used	Seeman [1]	
Hibiscus (Abelmoschus) Abelmoschus	waki waki	Juice of leaves used	" "	

[1] Seemann, Berthold. *Flora Vitiensis.* London, 1865–73.

side turn table

that the customary devices (*indention*, numbered paragraphs, etc.) are not sufficient. In such cases, italics, boldface, or variation of size can help.

EXTRACT

Extract is quoted material within, but set apart from, the text, as opposed to that which runs in the text line, preceded and followed by quotation marks. It is important to make clear typographically that such material is from another source, especially if it is by another author. The need for such distinctions becomes greater as speed-reading techniques make it easy to miss a brief attribution preceding an extract.

There are several ways of making distinctions. The use of 1 may suffice if it is drastic enough, but more likely 2 or more of these devices will be required:

■ *Indention*—The extract may be indented 1, 2, or more ems from right or left, or both.

■ *Size*—The size may be larger or smaller than text, although it is almost always smaller.

■ *Leading*—An increase or decrease of leading is usual, particularly the latter. (It is conventional to type extract single-spaced in double-spaced typescript.)

■ *Face*—Italic, boldface, or even an entirely different classification of type may be used.

■ *Space*—A line or half-line space above and below each item of extract may be used to separate it from the text.

Two ways of setting extract.

[184] CYNTHIA

ity Co-ordination, which its chief directed from the thirty-sixth floor of a New York skyscraper.

It is as Cynthia that I knew her and remember her, and it is under that name that she mostly appears in this book, although her baptismal names were Amy Elizabeth and she was known as Betty to her family and friends. Born an American citizen, she twice in her life changed her nationality as well as her surname, first when she took a British husband and later when she married a Frenchman, both of whom were in the diplomatic service of their respective countries.

> But whatever we talked about, it would be a great pleasure to see you again. You belong to that happy period that even in wartime exists for those who have a common cause and are especially united where there is a "Quiet Canadian." Long life to him, and to you!

She was brought up and educated in the most conventional, upper-middle-class way, by late-Edwardian standards, with a tiger lurking in her blood, and, unfortunately for her, but fortunately for British intelligence, a cool objective mind. She grew up a passionate, lonely girl, and a far-gone addict of excitement, always set in the most protocol environments. It took a war to stop the war between her two natures. Only as a spy, with a noble cause (essential, with her Edwardian standards) was the pace fast, dangerous and exciting enough to use her total energy and to give her surcease and tranquility. When life was acute, her mind was firm and precise, her aim implacable, her actions swift and exact.

She knew languages, enough about art to enjoy it; she

formed by a network of burlap-covered panels could have had any inkling of the impact that this event would have upon the future of American art. But everyone who wandered about in the din compounded of excited talk, laughter and the strains of Baines 69th Regiment Band ensconsed in the balcony, and loked at the pictures on the walls and the sculptures spotted around the floor, must have felt the electric excitement of that moment. The partitions festooned with greenery, the pine trees, the flags and bunting, the yellow-hued streamers that formed a tent-like cap to the exhibition space, the richly dressed and gay crowd, the bright floodlights and the brassy blare of the band, all helped create a festive air. Congratulations were in order. The AAPS had done the impossible. They had, all on their own, collected and exhibited more than 1200 American and foreign works of art for the edification and education of the American art world and public. The exhibition had been calculated from the beginning as a mental jolt to stir America out of its long esthetic complacency. So it was with an air of exultation that, after a fanfare of trumpets and a few modest words of introduction by the Association's president and the exhibition's guiding genius, Arthur B. Davies, John Quinn formally opened the exhibition.

> The members of this association have shown you that American artists—young American artists, that is—do not dread, and have no need to dread, the ideas or the culture of Europe. They believe that in the domain of art only the best should rule. This exhibition will be epoch making in the history of American art. Tonight will be the red letter night in the history not only of American but of all modern art.

It is difficult to be certain whether the Armory Show was the largest exhibition of art held in the last quarter century here or in any other country, and one can pardon Quinn's sweeping assertion, but it was beyond question the most important ever held in the United States to that date and, one might add, to the present. It presented in its over-

184 THE AMORY SHOW

While making extract distinct from text, remember that it also is meant to be read. It can be reduced in size, leading, etc., without serious loss when it occurs in brief passages, but when it is extensive, the solution might be to use a different but equally readable type face and size. Note that indention becomes ineffective, unless very pronounced, when the extract occupies full pages, because there is no full-width text for contrast.

PLAY STYLE

Not all playstyle is dramatic script. Any material which is a succession of statements by identified speakers is playstyle. This includes interviews, courtroom examinations, hearing records, etc.

The problem is mainly how to handle the speakers' names. This is discussed in detail in CH.28 for the design of plays, but the technique is the same for all playstyle. There is usually no reason to set playstyle within text in another size, unless it has the character of extract, but it is a good idea to separate each passage from the text with a line space before and after—particularly if there is no difference in size.

FOOTNOTES

There are 2 kinds of footnotes: (a) references and (b) explanations. Their treatment depends on their nature.

■ *Reference notes*—These are references to sources and other bibliographical information intended for the scholar and researcher rather than the reader. They constitute a distraction at the bottom of the page and are comparatively difficult to reach at the end of each chapter. The most practical location for them is at the back of the book, where they are most accessible to students and out of the way of the reader. The treatment of reference notes is covered in CH.23.

■ *Explanatory notes*—These must be read at the appropriate time if they are to be useful at all, and so should appear on the page where the reference occurs. It is an imposition to ask the reader to search for notes at the back of the book (and a felony to make him find them at the end of each chapter). Many, if not most, readers don't bother to read them under these conditions, so the notes are a waste of time and space for part of the audience and a source of irritation for the remainder who do take the trouble to find them.

There is a feeling among publishers, editors, reviewers, and a great many readers that the appearance of footnotes in a book is somehow repellent. The book that is "cluttered" with footnotes is disparaged as a forbidding chore for the reader. This attitude is probably justified, but for the wrong reasons.

After all, if the text is interesting and well written, the addition of useful footnotes should increase, rather than lessen, the pleasure of reading. However, the mingling of bibliographical references with explanatory notes is a real nuisance. At each reference mark the reader must go to the bottom of the page to find out whether the note is of interest or not. If not, he must travel back up the page and find his place—probably in the middle of a sentence that must be reread. Where the note *is* pertinent to the text he may properly wonder why it wasn't incorporated in the narrative. (Very often he will be correct in assuming that it was an afterthought which the author found easier to insert as a footnote than to rewrite the text.) Yes, footnotes are to be avoided, but only when they are misplaced or unnecessary. Those that *are* necessary should be placed where they are most useful.

Footnotes may be set in very small sizes, but they must be readable. Very brief notes—a line or two—can be readable in most 8 pt. type with 1 or 2 points of leading. Longer notes should be set larger. In some books, the footnotes are a major part—perhaps 25 or 30%. If these notes are essential, they should be as readable as the text and probably the same size or only 1 size smaller. They can be distinguished from text by using a contrasting face or a particularly readable italic or oblique.

Footnotes can be separated from the text by a line space when there is a sharp contrast in size. Where sizes are closer, a small typographic device such as a dash, asterisk, colon, or suitable ornament may be set in the space. In some cases, a rule of full measure or nearly so may be required. This must be kept distinct, however, from the full-measure rule ordinarily used above footnote material that has run over from the previous page.

Reference marks may be handled in several ways, and the choice can substantially affect composition costs. The highest expense comes from resetting lines (after page makeup) to insert references that begin a new sequence on each page. This can be avoided by commencing a sequence in each chapter or, if there are not too many notes, continuing one sequence through the entire book.

The reference marks may be symbols, such as asterisks (*), daggers (†), section marks (§), etc., and the doubling and tripling of these. If numbers are used, they may be *superior figures* [small numerals above the x line²], which are an extra expense in slug machines because they do not run in the magazines, or the regular text-type figures enclosed in parens (2).

The corresponding reference marks in the notes may be either regular or superior figures, although it is preferable to use the same kind as used in the text. In the notes, the use of parens around regular figures is not essential, as these numbers occur only at the beginnings.

The first line of each note may be indented as a paragraph; it may be flush, with the turnovers indented (*hanging indent*); or all lines may be flush. In the latter case, it may be best to separate the notes from each other by some space. Whatever style is used, consider the probability that 2 or more 1-line notes will occur successively on the same page.

When there are many short footnotes, it is often possible to set 2 or 3 on each line with a few ems between, rather than waste space by placing one beneath the other.

* This question is discussed on page 273, but in any event *all copy* be typed in lower case with caps only at the beginning of sentences and on proper nouns. When setting type, if the specifications call for a

* This question is discussed on page 273, but in any event *all copy* sh be typed in lower case with caps only at the beginning of sentence. and on proper nouns. When setting type, if the specifications call for

* This question is discussed on page 273, but in any event *all copy* sh be typed in lower case with caps only at the beginning of sentences and on proper nouns. When setting type, if the specifications call for a

[7] ***Ps.*** **lxvii, 2.** [8] ***Titus*** **i, 10.** [9] **The Manichaeans.** [10] ***Ephes.*** **v, 8**
[11] ***Jo.*** **i, 9.** [12] ***Ps.*** **xxxiii, 6.**

SUBDIVISIONS

It is not necessary to decide on specifications for chapter heads or subheads at this time, as they will be contained within the spaces allowed for them. Their treatment is covered in the next chapter.

Copyfitting (III)

Each kind of special matter can now be calculated for length according to the specifications adopted.

To calculate the number of pages of line-for-line material being set on slugs of the same size as the text, divide the number of lines of such matter by the number of lines per page of text. To calculate copy which will be set on a different-sized slug, first multiply the number of text lines per page (36) by the size of the text slug (13 pts.) to find the depth of the text page in points (36 x 13 = 468). Then you can find the number of lines per page for any slug size by dividing 468 by that size. So, if poetry is being set 9/11, divide 468 by 11 to get 42 lines. (Drop the odd points left over. These will be absorbed in the space around each item.) Dividing 42 into the total number of lines of poetry will give you the number of pages of poetry.

Prose copy (extract, outline, etc.) should be calculated as though each kind was the text of a separate book. The only figure carried over from the text is the depth of the page in points. For example, suppose the extract is set 10/12 Baskerville and is indented 2½ ems on the left in the 23-pica measure. This gives it a measure of 21 picas (approximately). The 10 pt. Baskerville has 2.6 characters per pica which, multiplied by 21, gives 54.6 characters per line.

Divide 468 by the 12 pt. slug size to get 39 lines per page. A full page of extract will have 2129 characters (54.6 x 39). Divide this into the total number of characters of extract to find out how many pages there will be.

The calculation of footnotes is always inexact, even knowing how they are to be set. It is almost impossible to determine how many pages will have footnotes, which, if any, will run over to another page, or how many short ones can be combined. Nevertheless, the best figures possible must be obtained. The usual procedures in calculating line-for-line and prose copy are followed, with some generous allowances made for combining, frequency of occurrence, runovers, etc.

On the appropriate lines on the breakdown sheet, enter in a column the number of pages calculated for text, each kind of special matter, space allowances, illustrations, page-for-page material, and, if there is one, the index. The total should come close to your objective (344 in the example). If not, carefully examine each item before deciding where to make the changes necessary.

In conclusion

In all estimating, it is better to figure a little on the high side than too low. If, after composition, the book should turn out to have fewer pages than estimated, there are usually some easy solutions available. Should the number of pages turn out to be *more* than estimated, there may be serious difficulty. There are several ways of shortening the book, but their use may not be possible in all circumstances (CH.20).

TITLE: Example DATE: 12/2/[illegible]
Ms pp: 339

FRONTMATTER		
half title 1 pp, title 2 pp, cpyrt 1 pp, ded 1 pp	6	6
preface 2762 c	2	2
contents 44 L	2	2
introduction 5250 c	4	4
TEXT:		
538,050 c		271
103 L	3	3
EXTRACT: (p.67)		
5892 c	3	3
POETRY: (p.29)		
129 L	4	4
14 units	1	1
PLAYSTYLE: (p.162)		
1264 c	1	1
10 L	—	—
4 units	—	—
TABULAR: (p.212)		
42 L	1	1
12 units	1	1
BIBLIOGRAPHY: (p.318)		
4922 c	2	3
53 L	2	1
INDEX:		
allow 8 pp	8	8
FOOTNOTES:		
1640 c	1	1
14 units	—	—
ILLUSTRATIONS:		
halftone:75	—	—
line:28	10	10
SUBDIVISIONS:		
part titles:3	8	8
chapters:8	8	8
A heads:18 @ ~~6L~~ 4L	3	2
B heads:41 @ 3L	3	3
spacebreaks:19 @ 1L	1	1
	74	(344) / 352

352
74
278

1935
278 ⟌ 538,050

344
74
270

1.992
270 ⟌ 538,050

2.4 ch/pica
x 23
55.2 ch/line
36
1987.2 ch/page

270+
1987 ⟌ 538,050

The breakdown with final calculations.

18 | Sample pages

With basic decisions and text specifications settled, the design process goes into a largely graphic stage. However, while the details of the book's visual aspect are considered one by one, they are parts of the overall conception visualized earlier, and each choice—no matter how small—should relate to the analysis and must be based on a real consideration of alternatives.

The way to proceed is to have set and printed a sample showing at least 1 example of each kind of material in the book. This gives everyone, including the designer, a chance to see how the problems have been solved and how the pages will look. Changes made at this stage cost nothing—later on they can be very expensive.

For an average book, 2 or 3 sample pages are sufficient. A complex work may require 6 or 8 pages to include all the problems. The object is to make the sample pages as useful as possible in minimizing the number of questions that need to be asked by the printer. This means a careful selection of specimens with typical and extra-difficult problems. You fool no one but yourself by using relatively easy material.

At a minimum, sample pages should show the following: (if any exists)

(a) some text—preferably two full facing pages,
(b) an example of each kind of special matter,
(c) running heads and folios on facing pages,
(d) a chapter opening, and
(e) subheads.

It is useful to show a part-title, but this is not absolutely necessary. A careful sketch will usually suffice. To avoid overloading the sample, omit examples of material of which there is very little.

Chapter openings

With the text already planned, it would seem logical to design next the running heads and folios, so as to complete the text page.

However, the chapter openings set the typographic style of the book, particularly in the choice of display type, and so they should determine how the text page will look, rather than vice versa.

Because the chapter openings are repeated (with variations) throughout the book, their design should be very carefully considered so that *all* of them will look well, not just the one used for the sample. This is sometimes difficult because of wide variations in the copy. There seems to be a conspiracy among authors to make 1 chapter title so different from all the others as to frustrate any successful design. When most titles have 1 or 2 words, 1 will almost surely have 12 or 14, or vice versa. So, if small type is chosen to accommodate the very long title, the short ones look weak. If the short titles are set larger, the long one looks enormous.

Chapter openings need to be kept subordinate to the title page and part-titles. They should not reach, or even approach, the limits of emphasis or graphic interest. Remember also that the impact of a single chapter opening in a sample page is one thing, but the effect of, say, 54 of the same may be too much.

The design of chapter openings depends to a considerable extent on 2 factors: (a) the number of chapters in the book and (b) the size of the run. In both cases the consideration is financial. If a chapter opening costs $5 to set and make up, the total cost is not so important if there are only 6 chapters, but it *might* be important if there are 60. The significance of the total amount is relative to the number of books being printed. For example, $300 means 10¢ per copy (about 50¢ of retail price) in an edition of 3000, but only 1¢ per copy in a run of 30,000. The variation in cost of a chapter opening can be substantial, depending on the kind of type used and its arrangement (CH.12).

CHAPTER OPENING SPACE

Before the choice and arrangement of display type is considered, decide on the exact amount of space in which it is to appear. If chapters run-in, this space will have been allocated when the length of the book was calculated (CHS.16,17). For chapters beginning on a new page, an allowance of 1 page was made for each—assuming that the opening would take half. Some change in this is usually possible, so that the space may be more or less than a half page if desired. If there are only a few chapters, the addition or subtraction of some lines of text on opening pages will not ordinarily matter. If the book has very many chapters, variations in the number of lines *may* make a serious difference. To know what, if any, effect such changes will have, it is necessary to calculate the length of each chapter separately (this is fairly simple when the text has no extract, etc., but may be tedious otherwise) to find how many lines will be on the last page of each, and therefore, which will gain or lose a page when the number of lines at the beginning is changed.

There are several reasons for varying the number of chapter opening lines. You may want to reduce them to make room for illustrations, or there may be a suggestive purpose in changing the relationship of type and space. Also, don't overlook the fact that this is one of the few opportunities in most books—sometimes the only one—to introduce some space (light and air) into the text.

The Demands of Civilization

FREUD WAS turning into an adjective and an ism. He who had been disclosing the commonplaces of the home was becoming a household word. Noisily aware and showily advanced circles delighted in finding that they dreamed Freudian dreams and let Freudian lapses slip from their tongues. The sluggard mass before long found themselves buried under mountains of plays, novels, and manuals about child care which reflected someone's view of what Freudianism supposedly was.

Fame shook Freud's balance almost as little as abuse had

215

the moon is born

When and how the moon was born is one of the great mysteries of science. For more than three hundred years astronomers have studied the moon through telescopes. They have measured the heights of its steepest mountains, finding that many of them stretch higher than the mighty Everest, earth's loftiest peak. They have studied the hundreds upon hundreds of strange circular forms called craters and have given names to many of them—names such as Tycho, Aristarchus, and Herodotus. Every night in nearly every country of the world, men are photographing and making diagrams of small sections of the moon, each hoping that he may discover something new about it. Yet all of their work, which could fill the shelves of a small library, still leaves one of the most tantalizing questions unanswered.

Where did the moon come from?

If you ever ask an astronomer this question, he would most likely say, "We aren't sure. All we can do is guess." But then he would probably tell you about scientists like Sir George Darwin and Von Weizsäcker, who advanced explanations of how the moon was born.

The picture George Darwin (son of the great naturalist, Charles Darwin) painted of the birth of the moon is perhaps the most dramatic

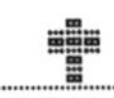

CHAPTER 13

CONQUERORS EAST AND WEST

THE BEGINNING of the new year saw Žižka return from his excursion into politics to his own sphere: the waging of the war. It was one of the unusual features of this new campaign that he began it when the worst of the winter was still imminent. But his peasants were hardy men and by attacking at such time he was most likely to surprise his enemies.

With Chval of Machovice and his friend Peter Zmrzlík as lieutenants, Žižka set out on a long march which took him into the region dominated by the Landfrieden of Pilsen. This powerful alliance of Royalist lords, squires, and towns was the strongest force inside Bohemia with which now, after the armistice with Rosenberg, the country's Hussite forces were still in open warfare.

Žižka attacked the Pilsen region not in its eastern part where his enemies would be most likely to expect him but in the west where he could threaten its connections with Germany.[1] The first gains of the campaign were the fortified monastery and small town of Chotěšov, some twelve miles southwest of the city of Pilsen which he had quietly by-passed on his way. Farther northwest he then took the monastery of Kladruby. Both monasteries had been abandoned in time by their monastic inhabitants. Kladruby was a strong fortress and was now used as such by the Taborite army. As commander of the new garrison Žižka left his friend Zmrzlík. He then tried to go one step further in cutting the main lines of communication between Pilsen and the Empire by investing Stříbro, a town of considerable size and strength, on the main route from Pilsen to Cheb and to German Franconia. At the same time a harrowing war was waged against the outlying possessions of the city of Pilsen.

The people of Pilsen, in a somewhat hypocritical fashion, lodged a written complaint about this treatment. Žižka answered in a letter

[1] Main sources for this campaign: Březová, p. 469, Old Annalists, p. 44, *Chronicon veteris Collegiati*, Höfler, I, 82.

· 199 ·

STYLE & FEELING The general style of the chapter-opening pages will follow the conception developed in working out the creative solution (CH.15). If you did not actually visualize the appearance of the chapter openings at that time, you at least conceived of them as being formal or informal, dynamic or placid, masculine or feminine, etc. Now you can interpret these characteristics in terms of the arrangement of the type and illustrations on the chapter openings (CH.6).

Discussing the characteristics of books in terms of opposites does not mean that there are no gradations or subtle variations. On the contrary, most books will not fall into simple categories. The important thing is to impart to the chapter-opening design the true essence of the book, because this must pervade every aspect large or small, and the chapter opening is the first opportunity to create the proper feeling.

ROUGH LAYOUT When the chapter-opening space has been decided upon, make an outline of the page (on tracing paper) with the text lines indicated

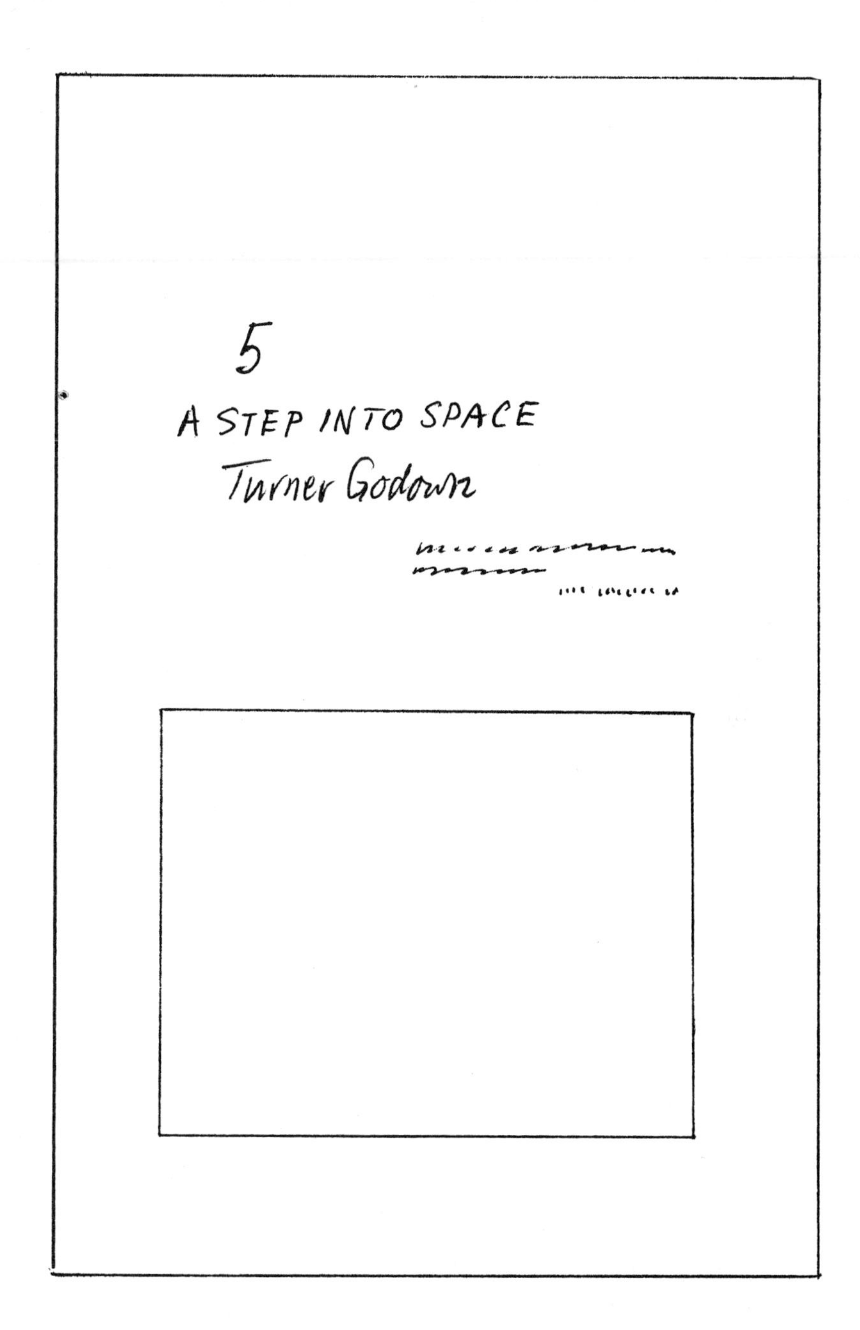

on it, and very roughly sketch in the approximate size and position of the heads, titles, etc. There is no need, at this point, to decide on typefaces. The general arrangement should be settled first, with 2 main purposes:

(a) to reflect the relative importance of each element, and

(b) to establish the basic style of the layout.

There are many ways of achieving emphasis (CH.6), so the designer can maintain a specific order of importance among several elements without sacrificing esthetic or other values. In anthologies and other books in which an author's name and other copy appear on the chapter-opening pages, the problem of creating a proper order of relationships is the same as in designing a title page (CH.22).

CHAPTER HEADS

Chapter heads [the *number* of the chapter is the head, not the title] are usually the least important elements and are best subordinated unless (a) the numerical sequence has a special significance (as it might in a novel of suspense or a series of lessons) or (b) the head is used as an important graphic element, either because there is no other copy or to emphasize a chapter title by contrast. The word "chapter" usually serves no purpose at all unless it is used as a graphic device, and it is best omitted.

Roman numerals beyond 10 should be avoided in any case where the reader is expected to use them. As the age of the Caesars recedes further into the past, fewer people are able to translate CXLVI or LXIV fast enough for practical use. This archaic form is useful for period flavor or when a decorative purpose is served, otherwise nothing but confusion and irritation result.

CHAPTER TITLES

Very long titles are better set in lower case than caps. Lower case takes less space and is easier to read. (Large amounts of capitals are less readable mainly because we are unaccustomed to them.)

When breaking chapter titles into more than 1 line, break for sense, i.e. at logical places. Also, avoid excessive breaking. Don't make it too difficult to read the title just to achieve a graphic effect.

poor

SHADOWS IN MODERN
PHOTOGRAPHY

better

SHADOWS
IN MODERN PHOTOGRAPHY

Chapter titles are sometimes set like book titles, with all words beginning with a cap except articles, conjunctions, etc. This is impractical, as it deprives the author of the use of capitals for their proper functions—designating proper nouns and the beginnings of sentences. In some books, a lack of distinction between proper nouns and others creates confusion, so it is best to capitalize according to normal grammatical usage. There are adequate typographic means of indicating the special value of chapter titles without limiting their ability to communicate.

INITIALS

Initials [the decorative first letters of chapters or parts] are usually expensive and rarely serve a practical purpose. They originated as a means of indicating the beginning of new chapters in medieval Mss, when there was very little use of punctuation and space was too precious to waste on chapter breaks. This solution is still applicable to very crowded books in which there is little room for space around chapter openings. Initials are useful, too, where there are no chapter titles or heads for display. In most situations they are superfluous.

When initials *are* used, they may be either (a) set into the text (*dropped*) 2, 3, or more lines deep; or (b) projected above the text (*stickup*).

DROPPED INITIALS should align with the base of the text line at bottom, and with the top of the x line at the top if the following letters are lower case or small caps, and with the top of the line if followed by caps. The alignment at the top is not vital, but at the bottom, a sloppy appearance results if the initial sinks below the baseline or fails to reach it. Very often it is impossible to find a size of the preferred face that properly fits the desired number of lines. In such cases, the alternatives are to choose a different number of lines or to use another face—or both. In photocomposition no such problem exists, as the initial can be enlarged or reduced. In any case, be careful of "J"s and "Q"s that descend below the baseline.

STICKUP INITIALS should align with the base of the first text line. They, like the dropped initials, may be followed by lower case, small caps, or full caps for the remainder of the first word, the first phrase, or the whole line. Either kind of initial may be indented or flush. It is possible to use a machine-face initial in Linotype (and a sharply contrasting face can be quite effective) but remember that the initial will align at the *top* of the slug, so it cannot stick up.

If no special initial is used, the text may begin in one of several ways: (a) the first word, phrase, or line may be set in small caps or caps with various amounts of letterspacing or (b) it may start with a cap and continue in lower case without any special treatment.

A variant of the display initial idea is to set the first word or phrase in display size, rather than just the first letter. This is effective graphically, but thought must be given to the editorial effect of so much emphasis on these words. There are probably some very special books in which such a device is appropriate, but generally it is unduly distracting.

To some extent, the same thing is true of the use of small caps or caps. In the work of a fine writer, each sentence is carefully designed and the use of capitals where they were not intended does violence to the delicate balance he creates. It can be argued that this affects only a few of the thousands of sentences in the book. It can also be argued that most books are not that well written nor that important. Some writers on book design tend to assume that every book is a classic, but among the thousands of titles published each year, some are fine, some are mediocre, some are hardly more than trash—and each should be designed according to its kind. A classical treatment for a frivolous text is just as wrong as the opposite. However, any typographic device that radically alters the emphasis of words must be carefully weighed.

Indentions of various amounts may be used with any initial style, but it is unwise to indent so far that there is not enough width left to avoid bad breaks. Enough means about 35 characters—and even this may not be sufficient with a particularly awkward combination of words. If the first line consists of letterspaced caps or small caps, the problem is worse.

CHOICE OF TYPE

The choice of typefaces for display can now be made. Again, this is a matter of fulfilling a visualization which may or may not have included this detail. In any case, the choices will be based on the considerations discussed in CHS. 6 and 15.

The type size in each case is determined by comparing your rough layout with specimens of the face chosen. It may turn out that there is no size exactly like your sketch. Unless you are prepared to change the face to one that has such a size, the nearest size available will have to be used. Whether it should be smaller or larger than your sketch will depend on the effect of each size on the other elements of the page. *Every time one element is changed, all the relationships in the design must be reconsidered.*

THE FINISHED LAYOUT

When the type faces and sizes have been selected, the layout can be completed. This means tracing the display type in its exact position and indicating the position and general characteristics of the text sizes. The finished layout should be as much like a printed page as you can make it, within reason. It is much cheaper and faster to make changes on the layout than in type, so, the more accurate the layout, the better you will be able to visualize what the proof will look like.

There are 2 faults that commonly spoil layouts: (a) the presence of guidelines and (b) failure to catch the true character and weight of the typefaces.

■ *Guidelines*—These are necessary to insure the straightness and squareness of lines of type, but they need not show on the finished sketch. Draw them on the *back* of the tracing paper, then they can be erased easily after the tracing is finished. Also, there is no need to draw guidelines on both top and bottom when type is being traced. The bottom line is sufficient. No guidelines or outlines, except the outline of the trim-size, should show on the finished layout, because no such lines will appear on the printed page, so they would be misleading.

■ *Tracing type*—Doing this well requires some practice and a bit of a knack. Laborious effort will help to some extent, but it is not enough. Each typeface has certain features that give it its special look, and you must be familiar with these in order to capture the right feeling. This cannot be done, ordinarily, by tracing the outlines of the letter and filling them in. Try to rough in the *masses* of the lines in their proper weight, and observe the essential forms and details. If the transition from thick to thin is abrupt, be sure you make it so; if gradual, make it so. If the serifs have no brackets, make none; if the ends are square, make them square. Not every detail need be drawn fully and perfectly, but draw enough to convey the feeling of the face. You must learn to put down a minimum of rapid strokes that accurately catch the salient features—not to produce a masterpiece worthy of the Louvre but in order to properly evaluate the effect of the type as it will look on a proof.

Doubt

poor

Doubt

good

For convenience, we have spoken in terms of making all your type selections first, and then completing the layout. In practice, it is better to make the choice of each face and size after having traced the one before. Thus you can *see* what the effect of a particular line of type will be, rather than just visualizing it. Actually, the processes of visualization, consideration, and choice are usually intermingled and will vary in relationship according to the particular problem and the individual designer.

Indicating illustrations is discussed in CH.20.

LAYOUT TOOLS

Choice of tools is as important here as it is in any craft. A certain amount of personal preference is involved, but the necessities largely decide the matter. The drawing tool must be capable of making very fine and very heavy lines. It must be suitable for making straight lines and curves, large forms and very small ones. It must make a reasonably dark mark that is erasable, but should not smear easily. It must move smoothly and be suited to the surface of tracing paper. All these requirements add up to a graphite pencil of medium hardness. An HB or H is about right.

Besides a drawing tool, you need a ruler for pica and inch measurement, and a right-angle triangle. A T square is essential for finished mechanicals, but is not needed for making layouts. It is handier to have a printed grid (with lines ruled every 1/8″) to put under the tracing paper when drawing rectangles or parallel lines. Grids of this kind on 8 x 10″ plastic sheets are available in art supply stores.* They are calibrated in inches or picas. If you make mistakes, buy a kneaded eraser. They make no crumbs.

Subheads

Subheads are chapter openings on a lower scale of value, so the problems of design are basically the same: (a) How much space shall each be allocated? (b) How is the first line of text to be treated? (c) What type face and size? (d) What shall be the position? In each case, the decision should be related to the chapter opening, with a descending order of emphasis (chapter title, first order of subhead, second order, and so on).

▪ *Space*—The allocation of space was decided in determining the length of the book (CH.17). If a closer examination of the problem suggests a change in this allocation, some compensating change must be made so as to retain the same total number of pages.

▪ *First line*—The first line of text following subheads usually calls for some special treatment, but unless the subdivision is of major importance, beginning flush or setting the first word in small caps is the maximum distinction appropriate. For lesser subheads, the regular paragraph indent is sufficient. In no case should the treatment of a subhead be more distinctive than that of a superior subhead or a chapter opening, as the primary purpose is to clarify the book's organization by indicating the relative value of headings.

▪ *Type face and size*—The typographic treatment of the headings themselves should reflect their relationship to each other. A number 2 subhead does not merely *follow* a number 1 head, it is a subdivision of it, and this should be made clear. Remember, though, the average reader is not as sensitive to typographic distinctions as you are, so the differences among classes of headings must be quite pronounced or they may be overlooked.

For economy, it is best to use variations of the text font for subheadings—caps, small caps, caps and small caps, or italics. However, in a complex book it may not be possible to get enough contrast and variety from these alone. The cost of a change of type face or size varies according to the typesetting method and the bill-

* *or from the John Warner Company, Box 595, Ithaca, N.Y.*

ing practices of the individual compositor, but it is not a large enough amount (CH.12) to deter such a change if it is needed.

One of the values of subheads is the graphic interest they add. Many subheads are inserted in books simply to break up the large blocks of text that seem to discourage some readers, especially children and those who do not ordinarily read books. But even where the subheads have a real textual function, they offer opportunities to add variety and visual interest. Contrast with the text is useful not only to enliven the page, but to help the reader find the subheads. The amount of contrast should be adjusted to the importance of the subhead and the frequency of its occurrence. A degree of visual excitement which is desirable in a few places can be irritating when repeated too often.

■ *Position*—The arrangement of subheads within the spaces allowed should be consistent with the style established for the chapter opening. (From here on, the need for consistency must be considered in connection with every choice or decision.) Consistency in this sense does not mean necessarily *the same in form*, but it does mean *the same in spirit*. Achieving a finished book that has unity—the visual integration that conveys a sense of "rightness"—is much more difficult than it may seem. It is possible to have the outward forms entirely consistent but the total will not hang together or have the inner harmony that is essential. It is somewhat like trying to make a man by putting all the right parts together in the right way. You will get the form, but you won't get a living thing unless there is something more than that.

Subheads may be centered, set flush left or right, indented from left or right, or centered on some point other than the center of measure. They may be set on a separate line or run-in on the first text line. In a book with several classes of subheads, a combination of these positions will probably be necessary. Be sure to provide for those occasions where 2 or more classes of subhead occur together. The combination of centered and off-centered arrangements should be avoided as much as possible (CH.6) but the needs of editorial sense must be met, even at the expense of harmonious design.

Run-in subheads should contrast sufficiently with the text type to stand out. The use of italics is usually inadequate, although the addition of a substantial space (at least 1 em) after the subhead may make enough difference. Attention can be drawn to a run-in subhead by using a strong typographic device at the beginning such as a paragraph mark, bullet, star, etc.

The style and position of subheads must be considered in relation to the running heads as well as to the text. Any subhead may break just beneath a running head, so they should not be too similar. If possible, no subheads should be set in the same size and face as any running head, unless one is italic and the other roman, or one is in small caps and the other italic, etc. Where running heads and subheads are only slightly dissimilar, it helps to set one flush left and the other flush right. Subheads that are numbered, or contain numbers, should be considered in relation to folios. Usually, the subheads take precedence over running heads where there is a conflict. Especially in complex books, it is easier to change the running heads.

The subheads in this book, being outside the text, did not require size or weight to stand out. They are set in small size because of the narrow measure and are in a contrasting class of typeface (CH.6) to make them distinct from the text and running heads.

Running heads & folios

RUNNING HEADS

Running heads may serve as practical guides, as in reference books, textbooks, etc., or they may have a purely decorative function. In books with no part or chapter titles, the book title may be used as a running head, not only to add graphic interest to the spread, but to heighten a psychological effect. (An example might be a book entitled *Pressure,* about tunneling under a river. Repetition of the word "pressure" would give an appropriately insistent quality to an ever-present menace in the text.) On the other hand, repetition of a title of no evocative value is pointless and irritating, unless it can be justified typographically. There is almost never any excuse for repeating the book title twice on one spread (i.e. once on each page).

Conventional practice is to use the left-hand page for a book or part-title and the right for the next smaller subdivision (left, book; right, part—left, part; right, chapter—left, chapter; right, subhead, etc.). However, the arrangement should be based on the usefulness of the various heads.

Sometimes book, part, and chapter titles are very similar in wording. It is particularly important in those cases, but useful in all books, to make a typographic distinction between the left- and right-hand running heads if they are different titles. This helps clarify the book's organization, permits distinctions in emphasis, and provides graphic interest. The typographic difference should be sufficiently pronounced to avoid vagueness, and thus confusion. A frequently used combination is small caps on one side and italics on the other. Entirely different typefaces can be used, but this may involve extra expense.

If the titles being used for copy are very long, don't specify widely spaced caps or deep indentions. Sometimes, the titles are so long that cutting is unavoidable, but don't pick a style that will just miss fitting in short or medium-length titles.

The simplest and cheapest way to set running heads is to use the book title only and set it in the text type and size (CH.5). In general, as composition and makeup increase in complexity, the cost goes up (CH.12), so the fewer changes of running-head wording there are, the less the cost. If the book title is used, it is set only once (presuming it is set by machine) and sufficient duplicates are made. If subheads are used, there may be dozens (or even hundreds) of changes. This can be quite significant, especially if letter-spacing is used. Even in Linotype, handspacing a book title is no problem, but handspacing 153 different running heads will result in some very sore fingers and a whopping bill.

FOLIOS

Folios vary in importance, as do running heads. In some reference books they are vital and should be prominent in style and position. Other reference books, particularly those with alphabetical-order running heads (directories, etc.), need no folios at all. In any book with an index, the folios should be very accessible. In fiction, folios are helpful to some readers, but most use the jacket flap or a library card to mark their place. (We can ignore those who turn down the corner of the page.)

The most effective position for folios is the upper outside corner of the right-hand page, the closer to the edge the better. The lower outside corner is only a little less practical. The folio becomes less readily found as it moves further in toward the gutter. For books in which the folio has no practical value to the reader, the inside corner, top or bottom, is a satisfactory position.

There is some difference of opinion as to the need for folios on chapter opening pages. They have no value in locating the chapter, because the opening page is identified by the title once it is seen. Indexes do refer to page numbers, but there is usually a folioed page facing the chapter opening. If chapter opening folios *are* used, it is probably best to place them in the same position as on the other pages. If this is not possible, they should still be treated as a respectable part of the page. Too often, these numbers are simply tacked on to the bottom of the page in reduced size without regard for their appearance.

From the reader's standpoint, a good case can be made for the elimination of left-hand folios on many books and the omission of all page numbers on some. Certainly, it should be sufficient in most cases to number the spread rather than each half of it. However, folios are helpful to the compositor, printer, and binder, and it is worth retaining them just to prevent a mixup of pages that might tell us whodunit in the middle of the story.

RELATING RUNNING HEADS & FOLIOS

The relationship of folios to running heads is not too significant, except where having them together enables the reader to use either one for reference. Otherwise, they may be: (a) on the same line, either close together or at opposite ends, (b) on separate lines, one above the other, or (c) on separate lines with one at the top of the page and the other at the bottom. If they are on the same line, it is usually desirable to have at least a pica space between, or some typographic device to separate them.

When folios and running heads are set on the same line by Linotype, remember that all alignment is at the top, regardless of the sizes used (CH.5). In general, bear in mind that each folio means an individually set line. Even if the running heads are simple, if they are to be set on the same line as the folio, they become individual lines rather than duplicates. In Linotype, there are tricks by which the operator can avoid resetting each line entirely, but these may be thwarted if the arrangement is too complicated. The additional charges involved in setting difficult running head lines can be substantial (sometimes hundreds of dollars), so it is best to check with the compositor.

POSITION & LAYOUT

If the price of composition is based on emage (CH.12) there is an advantage in having the running head and folio on 1 line rather than 2. However, if the book is being stretched out to a larger number of pages by using a small text area, placing one at top and the other at bottom tends to fill the page more.

Except where the demands of easy reference dictate a particular position, there is no reason why the running head or folio must be at top or bottom. The conventional position for running heads is at the top of the text area, but they might just as well be at the bottom or the sides. When they are not being used for reference, they are actually less obtrusive at the bottom left corner than anywhere else. A running head that is flush left at the top has a tendency to read as the first line of the page, particularly if it is similar to the text type and when the space underneath is not much more than the text leading. Compositors are inclined to place running heads close to the text for economy, but there should be enough distance between to avoid difficulty for the reader. An optical space (CH.5) of about a pica is the minimum needed with normal text sizes and leading. This space should be increased if there is more than 2 pts. of leading in the text.

When the running heads and folios have been designed they should be carefully sketched on the sample-page layouts. With experience, it is possible to visualize these elements well enough to dispense with tracing the type, but it is better at first—and where there is any doubt as to the visual effect—to treat running heads and folios as you would display type.

184 « FATHER OF PREHISTORY

"It is a portion of a stag's antler. It was, when still fresh, exposed to fire and it was worked with a crude stone implement, probably not a flint; some sort of primitive chopping tool."

"But that's impossible. It comes from Choukoutien."

"I don't care where it comes from; it was fashioned by a man and by a man who knew the use of fire."

The bit of horn came, in fact, from a site in the Western Hills, some thirty-five miles southwest of Peking where had been found, during the preceding three years, portions of the skulls and other bones of a sort of Man that had not been quite satisfactorily classified, but who obviously lived a very long time ago. It was, in fact, some 400,000 years ago. No one in 1930 suspected that this "Peking Man" had used fire. Man's mastery of fire was thought to have been achieved much later on in our history. Indeed, until comparatively recently, some held that fire did not enter into men's lives—at least as a servant—until the time of pots and pans, earthenware; that is to say, in New Stone Age or neolithic cultures which even in the Near East did not begin until some 10,000 years ago at the most, and not until very much later (about 2500 B.C.) in Britain.

A fortunate meeting, then, between two priests in Paris, led to one of them radically changing our ideas about Man's past. Although it was known by some in 1930 that the Neanderthaloids used fire maybe a hundred centuries ago, no one had supposed that the much more primitive "Peking Man" had been a fire maker. Since learning to control fire was the first great step towards Man's mastery of his surroundings—for such control enabled him to see in the darkness and to penetrate into new areas—obviously men, a very long time ago, were more advanced in com-

185 « *The Fires of Choukoutien*

ing to terms with their environment than had been thought probable. This identification of the Choukoutien implement as having been fired was but one of the many discoveries we owe to the Abbé Henri Breuil who, during his long lifetime, was to revolutionize prehistory—that is to say, mankind's history before the invention of writing —and consequently our views of Man's past.

On the matter of the Choukoutien bone, he was proved to be absolutely right. His deduction of a great fact from a tiny bit of bone was indeed one of his more spectacular achievements. For the proof he gave that hominids (a less question-begging term than "men") hundreds of thousands of years ago used fire gave us new concepts of the life of our remote ancestors and threw light on one of the most puzzling problems in our whole history.

There is evidence that men occupied caves from very early on in their careers. Yet it is fairly clear that man could not occupy caves until he knew the use of fire and could light a blaze to keep off prowling beasts attracted by those rattling grunts he makes while he sleeps (further proof of our kinship with gorillas, chimpanzees and orang-utans). The great apes and ourselves are the only mammals to snore, emitting a buzz-saw noise while sleeping.

In Europe, in fact, there is little evidence that our ancestors used caves as homes before possibly 150,000 years ago, during the last Interglacial, or warm, Period between two Ice Ages. But then, until the last Ice Age (or Würm, beginning some 70,000 years ago) men probably did not live in Europe at all during the great cold.

However, in other parts of the earth, sparks from flint chipping, lightning, volcanic eruptions, all offered Man flames very early on in his story. Maybe men played with

has contributed so much to the vocabulary and syntax of other modern western languages, particularly English, that it is almost impossible to gain an intelligent control of any of those languages without it. Greek, on the other hand, supplies major portions of our scientific and technical vocabulary. Often scientific terms which are puzzling in their English form become crystal-clear when they are analyzed into their Greek components. ("Microscope," for example, is "small-see," while "telescope" is "distance-see.") This situation is not at all peculiar to English but applies to all western languages. So widespread is Latin and Greek participation in the terminology of the more scientific, literary, and intellectual segment of European vocabularies that many people think this Graeco-Latin complex will form the nucleus of the international language of the future.

The Latin-Greek role in the formation of modern languages is not, however, merely a matter of vocabulary contributions. The civilization of the Greeks and Romans forms the basis of our common western culture. Views of life and habits of thought that Westerners today hold in common have been inherited from Greece and Rome, having been blended with a new religious element stemming from the Hebraic culture of the Jews and early Christians. Our philosophy of religion, government, human relations, science, and progress rests firmly upon this classical foundation, which has a continuous history extending from antiquity to our own day.

During the Middle Ages and the Renaissance, Latin was the common language of scholarship and international intercourse in western Europe, while Greek performed a similar function in the Balkans and Asia Minor. With the fall of Constantinople to the Turks in 1453, Greek was

44

reintroduced by refugee scholars to western Europe, and the two languages were used side by side until the final emergence of the modern tongues as languages of written and official as well as spoken communication relegated them to the position of cultural tongues.

Today, Latin is fully available in the American educational system, and it is the language selected by many as their first choice when they venture outside the field of their native English. Greek, once widespread, is now less generally available. The study of Hebrew, once the pursuit of Biblical scholars, has a new vogue in connection with the rebirth of a national Jewish state in Israel.

From the point of view of the individual seeking to expand his knowledge of languages, the claims of the classical tongues deserve serious consideration.

The practical, spoken-language use of Hebrew is limited to the relatively small population of Israel, which is less than two million. The classical Greek taught in the schools has strong points of contact with the modern Greek used by about eight million inhabitants of Greece, and a transfer from the one to the other is not too difficult. Latin, outside of its use in the Catholic Church, has no immediate speaking population.

There is, however, a powerful transfer value that attaches to each of these tongues. Hebrew unlocks the gates to the Semitic languages, and one who knows Hebrew finds Arabic relatively easy. A good foundation in Latin acts as a key to the entire Romance group of modern languages and gives us a sharper understanding of English. Both Latin and Greek give an insight into the basic structure and vocabulary of the entire Indo-European language family (see page 254), of which they are typical. Since some of the languages of the family, notably Russian and the other

45 LANGUAGE IN YOUR DAILY LIFE

Text pages with running heads at top and at bottom.

In this book, it was decided to use the chapter title at right, where it is most easily found when going through the book from front to back (as one would do after using the contents page), and place the chapter number on the left—where it is most accessible to a reader referring *back* from one of the many chapter references in the text. Both running heads and folios are in the upper outside corners for maximum convenience. The line underneath prevents any confusion resulting from the occurrence of a subhead directly underneath.

Margins

It is true that the designer should think rather of relating graphic elements on a page (page pattern) than in terms of margins (CH.6), but, having done so, one must specify margin dimensions in order to indicate the position of the type area on the paper for printing purposes (CHS.11,25).

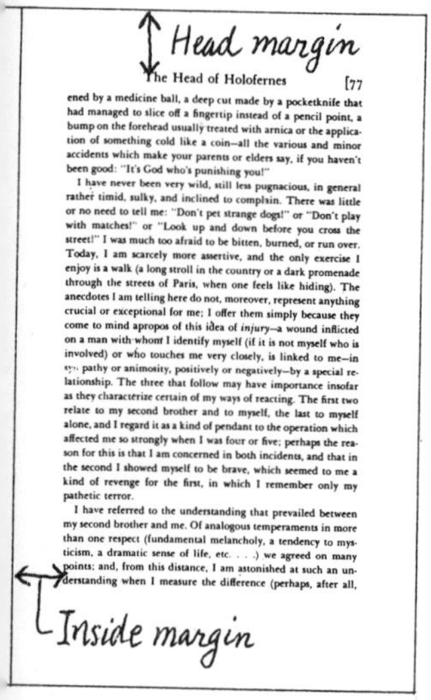

Head margin

The Head of Holofernes [77

ened by a medicine ball, a deep cut made by a pocketknife that had managed to slice off a fingertip instead of a pencil point, a bump on the forehead usually treated with arnica or the application of something cold like a coin—all the various and minor accidents which make your parents or elders say, if you haven't been good: "It's God who's punishing you!"

I have never been very wild, still less pugnacious, in general rather timid, sulky, and inclined to complain. There was little or no need to tell me: "Don't pet strange dogs!" or "Don't play with matches!" or "Look up and down before you cross the street!" I was much too afraid to be bitten, burned, or run over. Today, I am scarcely more assertive, and the only exercise I enjoy is a walk (a long stroll in the country or a dark promenade through the streets of Paris, when one feels like hiding). The anecdotes I am telling here do not, moreover, represent anything crucial or exceptional for me; I offer them simply because they come to mind apropos of this idea of *injury*—a wound inflicted on a man with whom I identify myself (if it is not myself who is involved) or who touches me very closely, is linked to me—in sympathy or animosity, positively or negatively—by a special relationship. The three that follow may have importance insofar as they characterize certain of my ways of reacting. The first two relate to my second brother and to myself, the last to myself alone, and I regard it as a kind of pendant to the operation which affected me so strongly when I was four or five; perhaps the reason for this is that I am concerned in both incidents, and that in the second I showed myself to be brave, which seemed to me a kind of revenge for the first, in which I remember only my pathetic terror.

I have referred to the understanding that prevailed between my second brother and me. Of analogous temperaments in more than one respect (fundamental melancholy, a tendency to mysticism, a dramatic sense of life, etc. . . .) we agreed on many points; and, from this distance, I am astonished at such an understanding when I measure the difference (perhaps, after all,

Inside margin

With the sample page layouts completed, the basic text margins are determined by measuring the distance from the top edge of the (paper) page down to the topmost element of the type area (*head margin*), and measuring the distance from the gutter to the nearest element of the type area (*inside margin*). No other margins should be given. The width and height of both text area and paper page are fixed, so that establishment of the head and inside margins automatically determines the other two.

Be sure to allow for the requirements of perfect binding, side stitching, and mechanical binding when planning inside margins of books to be bound by such methods (CH.10).

Margins are given in inches, because they relate to paper dimensions which are measured in inches. Measurements *within* the text area are given in picas and points, because they relate to type—which is measured that way (CH.5).

Specifications

The requirements of type specification are described in CH.5. The sample page layouts should contain such specifications in full in addition to the title of the book, the trim-size, and the text margins. The trim-size and margins are not composition instructions but are necessary for printing the sample pages.

If the text type has both lining and old style figures, indicate which are to be used. The choice is purely esthetic. Old style figures look well in text because they have more space around them, but for some kinds of tables they can be confusing.

19 | Ordering composition

Estimates

The sample pages usually contain enough information to enable an estimate of the cost of composition to be made and, with a few additional specifications, an estimate of the printing and binding costs. In most cases, such estimates are required before production of the book may begin.

It is good practice to have a printed form on which the essential specifications can be tabulated for the estimator's use. This provides a record of the specifications and enables the estimator to work while the layouts are being used for composition of the sample pages. It also serves as a check list. On the following page is a typical specification form. (With a few modifications, the composition order form may be used for this purpose.) When the sample pages are unusually complex, the estimator may need the layouts, or a copy of them, in addition to the specifications.

For a discussion of cost estimating, see CH.12.

Copy editing & keying

When the sample pages have been approved by all concerned, the Ms is, presumably, ready for composition. It is *not* ready for composition if it has not been completely *copy edited* to correct errors of fact, grammar, and spelling. Such corrections are just as easy to make in the Ms as in proof, and are an expensive matter after the type is set (CHS.5,12).

The copy editor should also *key* the Ms to the sample pages where this is necessary. The sample will indicate *how* a number 2 subhead is to be set, but it cannot tell the compositor *which* heads are number 2, which are number 1, etc. Sometimes the Ms is typed so well that these distinctions are perfectly clear, but this is rare. The best practice is to have every subhead keyed with a number (or letter) in a circle. Extract should be indicated by a vertical line in the margin, and any other special material should be identified

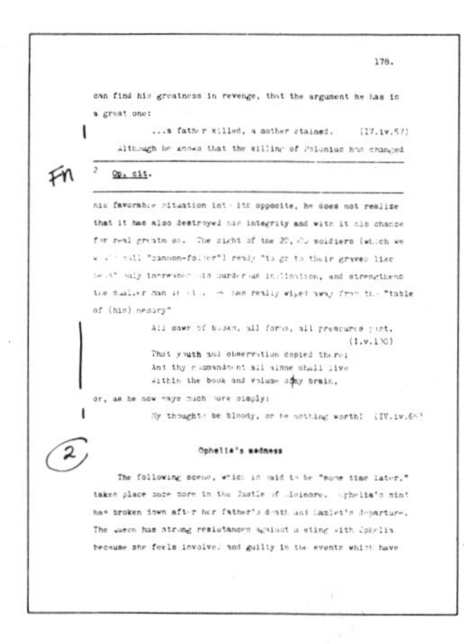
178.

can find his greatness in revenge, that the argument he has is a great one:

...a father killed, a mother stained. (IV.iv.57)

although he knows that the killing of Polonius has changed

Fn

[2] *Op. cit.*

his favorable situation into its opposite, he does not realize that it has also destroyed his integrity and with it his chance for real greatness. The sight of the 20,[illegible] soldiers (which we [illegible] "cannon-fodder") ready "to go to their graves like [illegible]" only increases his murderous inclination, and strengthens the [illegible] "table of (his) memory"

All saws of books, all forms, all pressures past, (I.v.100)

That youth and observation copied there;
And thy commandment all alone shall live
Within the book and volume of my brain,

or, as he now says much more simply:

My thoughts be bloody, or be nothing worth! (IV.iv.65)

2

Ophelia's madness

The following scene, which is said to be "some time later," takes place once more in the Castle of Elsinore. Ophelia's mind has broken down after her father's death and Hamlet's departure. The queen has strong resistances against [illegible] with Ophelia because she feels involved and guilty in the events which have

SPECIFICATIONS FOR ESTIMATING

title date

type face

text page x picas overall lines picas rh picas folio

sizes of type

text

extract

poetry

outline

playstyle

tabular

bibliography

appendix

index d.c. pages

footnotes

spacebreaks

pages of front matter

display

part number

part title

chapter number

chapter title

initial

subheads (1) (2)

(3) (4)

running head left

running head right

folio

chapters start: left or right run-in lines right

illustrations: line @ page each halftone @ page each

presswork

quantity trim size x edges

text: plates/type illustrations: plates/originals margins: head inside

binding

quantity

insert

headbands stain

back board

ends

jacket

cover material

back ext. in. on side

sides

stamping imp. foil sq. in.

imp. ink

in the margin by some clearly understood symbol. All such markings should be made with a colored pencil. When the copy is very complex, several colors may be used.

Composition orders

No matter how complete the sample-page specifications, no matter how well edited and keyed the Ms, a written and signed composition order is essential. One reason is that the compositor is entitled to a formal set of instructions to use as a basis for *his* instructions to the plant, and to use in the event there is any misunderstanding —although a misunderstanding is far less likely to occur when there *is* a formal order. Also, neither the sample-page specifications nor the estimate form answer all the questions.

The composition order will vary according to the process by which the text is to be printed, as well as the method of setting. If the printing is to be letterpress, the order must indicate whether or not plates will be made, and if so, what kind of plates, as there are differences in the composition and makeup (CH.7). If offset lithography or gravure printing is involved, this must be indicated so that the type and makeup will be suitable for reproduction proofs—unless the type is to be set by photocomposition, in which reproduction copy or film is the normal product. In this case, the kind of product wanted should be specified (after checking with the printer).

Proof requirements, at least for galley proofs, should be noted on the composition order (CHS.5,20). It should name the authority to be consulted on questions of style, grammar, and spelling—usually one of the major dictionaries (CH.5)—although a properly edited Ms will not raise any questions other than the manner of breaking words at the end of a line. The proper instruction for punctuation, spelling, and other matters of style should be: Follow copy.

The other information required should appear in the specifications set with the sample pages. There are certain questions of choice in connection with page makeup which are not included in the composition order, because they are subject to change *after* the galleys are cast off (CH.5). These are discussed in CHS. 20 and 24.

In most Mss, particularly nonfiction, there are minor problems of composition which are not covered by the sample pages, nor is it practicable to give such detailed instructions in the composition order. Also, some points may escape an inexperienced designer on initial examination. Therefore, the designer should go through the Ms thoroughly before sending it for setting, to find and dispose of any typographic problems not covered by the sample page or general instructions. Each instance should be marked for style where it occurs. Even where the general style has been established and shown in the sample—say, for tables—there may be unique headings or other material within some of the tables and these must be marked. No detail may be omitted, because *some* style must be used, and there may be a delay if you have not made a decision before composition begins. Unfortunately, the rapid pace of most modern book publishing provides too little time for such careful attention, but the best effort must be made.

Below is a typical composition order form.

COMPOSITION ORDER

To ______________________________ Date ______________
Title ______________________________
Author ______________________________ Order number ______________
Trim size ______________ Overall type page _____x_____picas
Type face ________ point ______________on ________ point body
Cast off from galleys at __________ lines per page overall length wanted __________ pages
Running heads ______________________________
Folios ______________________________ Lining__________ Old Style
Chapt. nos. ______________________________ sink ________ picas
Chapt. titles ______________________________ sink ________ picas
Initials ______________________________
__________lines of text on chapter opening pages
Heads ( ) ______________________________ ________ pts. above, ________ pts. below
( ) ______________________________ ________ pts. above, ________ pts. below
( ) ______________________________ ________ pts. above, ________ pts. below
( ) ______________________________ ________ pts. above, ________ pts. below
( ) ______________________________ ________ pts. above, ________ pts. below
( ) ______________________________ ________ pts. above, ________ pts. below
Tables ______________________________
Back matter ______________________________
Extracts ______________________________space above and below
Footnotes ______________________________
Index ______________________________
Illustrations ______________________________
Captions ______________________________

Galley proof ______________, plus ______________ spiral bound,
Page proof ______________________________ Foundry proof Plate proof
Reproduction proofs, 3 sets ______________ Film ______________

Send forms to your pressroom your foundry
prints from slugs cast plastic plates electros
ship plates to ______________________________

With this order is copy for sample pages
manuscript complete
to come front matter index
" " ______________________________

Remarks ______________________________
____

By ______________________________

MARGINS: __________gutter
__________head after trim

20 | Galley proofs & castoff

Procedure at this point varies with the kind of book, the schedule, and circumstances. It is certainly most desirable to design the entire book together and have the maximum opportunity to achieve unity—which means planning the title page, frontmatter, backmatter, binding, etc. at the same time as the sample pages. However, this is not always practically possible. Very often the title is not yet definite or some part of the copy is incomplete. Pressures from several directions may require turning attention to other urgent work. Also, where there are many illustrations in text it is often better to first determine the exact length of the text—because this will strongly affect the treatment of illustrations and perhaps front and backmatter as well. This requires waiting until complete galley proofs (CH.5) are delivered so that corrections and a castoff can be made. (When the design *must* be interrupted for any reason, the value of a strong and complete initial visualization becomes apparent.)

A minimum of 3 sets of galleys are pulled: the Author's Proof, 1 set for the editor, and 1 (retained by the compositor) for the castoff. If a dummy is to be made (CH.21), an extra set should be pulled. In addition to these, other sets are usually required for promotion purposes. These may range in number from just a few BOM sets (CH.5) to dozens for advance reading by prospective endorsers of the book.

Galley proof corrections

The methods and practices of proofreading are covered in CH.5. Here we are concerned with design rather than editorial corrections and changes.

Design corrections in galleys (other than changes needed to adjust length) should involve no more than minor adjustments of space, improvements in letterspacing of display lines, and occasional refinement of layout. The cost of *re*setting type is much higher than original composition, so any major changes should have been made in sample pages. One of the marks of a competent designer is the ability to achieve his objective in 1 try. Extensive and/or numerous changes in proof indicate that the designer is unable to visualize clearly or is unable to translate his visualization into effective specifications. The economics of book publishing are not suited to such deficiencies. It is true that first-rate work usually requires more care and effort than the ordinary product, and truly great work often needs to be fussed over and refined repeatedly, but few of the books that are published can support this kind of treatment. Generally, the designer must utilize the available time and energy to develop his conception of the book and improve his preparation. Once production is under way it must continue without major change, or the book will suffer serious, perhaps fatal, consequences in cost and schedule.

It is a good idea for the designer to go through the galleys to check on the appearance of unique items of special matter that were not shown on the sample. Designers' corrections should be made on the Author's Proof, in a color different from any other markings.

The castoff

With the galleys, it is possible to determine within a page or two (usually) the actual length of the text, and therefore to make the adjustments required, if any, to reach the number of pages desired. To accomplish this, it is necessary to make a castoff—which involves measuring-off the number of pages in the galleys.

HOW TO MAKE ONE

To make a castoff, cut a strip of tough paper about 1″ wide and a little deeper than the full text page. Lay it down on a galley proof or sample page and make a mark along one edge at the base of each text line, for the number of lines on the text page as estimated. Number each mark consecutively, from 1 at the top. (It is useful to make a special mark indicating the number of lines on chapter opening pages or any other frequently used measurement.) Using this scale, measure off the number of lines on each page, making a mark on the galley where each page ends. At the end of each galley, simply note how many lines remain from the end of the last full page and carry this number over to the next galley. When finished, go back to the first galley and number the pages straight through to the end. (Recheck this numbering carefully, it is the most frequent cause of castoff error.)

Casting-off a book of straight narrative text is fairly simple. Making an accurate castoff of a book containing many subheads, special matter, and illustrations is not very different in procedure, but requires a great deal of care and good judgment. The simple job may page and carry this number over to the next galley. When finished, go back to the first galley and number the pages straight through to the end. (Recheck this numbering carefully, it is the most frequent cause of castoff error.)

Casting-off a book of straight narrative text is fairly simple. Making an accurate castoff of a book containing many subheads, special matter, and illustrations is not very different in procedure, but requires a great deal of care and good judgment. The simple job may eft to a reasonably intelligent clerk, but a difficult one is best e by the designer, as many decisions are involved which affect layout of pages and other significant matters. With a particu- complicated book, it may be necessary to make a dummy 21) since a castoff would be too difficult.

re are 2 kinds of castoff: justified and unjustified.

ijustified castoff—This is simply a linear measurement without vance for alignment of short or long pages due to widows 5) or other makeup problems. However, an unlucky sequence idows can throw a chapter over to another page by adding al lines and, if there are part-titles or chapters beginning on -hand pages, this can materially affect the overall length. For eason, an unjustified castoff has limited value.

stified castoff—To make a justified castoff, use revised galley fs if possible. Unrevised proofs may be used if the corrections ninor and the Author's Proofs are at hand, so that the effect of hanges can be taken into account. A difference of a line or two ome cases a word or two!) may have a serious effect when the ber of pages is very close to the limit.

a justified castoff, the pages should come out exactly as in eup, which means that all problems must be solved in detail. e include: (a) final determination of the space to be used for rations, (b) disposition of odd amounts of space resulting from er set in lines of various depths, (c) provisions for widows), and (d) disposition of the various problems caused by run- eaks that fall at the ends of pages.

treatment of spacebreaks, run-in chapter titles, and subheads fall at the bottoms of pages is a major problem of the castoff. osing, for example, that a number 1 subhead is normally in a space, but the preceding text ends only 4 lines from the m of the page. There are 2 alternatives: either the space d the subhead is reduced so that it, and a minimum number t lines below it, will fit, or the page will be kept short (like nd of a chapter) and the subhead will go at the top of the page. This choice requires policy decisions as to:

How many lines of space may be "stolen" from around the (The space may be reduced to the minimum acceptable visu- out not less than that of an inferior class of head.)

What is the minimum acceptable number of text lines be- he head? (For most subheads, 2 lines are sufficient, for major ads or chapter openings 3 or 4 may be appropriate.)

If the head goes to the next page, how many lines of space d be left above it? (This is measured in *lines of text*, exclusive running head.)

e same procedure is followed whether the break is a minor ad or a run-in chapter. In all cases, the relative value of the must be preserved.

One-line spacebreaks present a special problem when they fall at the bottom or top of the page. Some people prefer simply to omit the space. This solution does eliminate the graphic problem, but it is editorially unsound. The author puts in the line space because he *wants* a break in the text—inferior to a chapter or subhead to be sure, but presumably of some editorial value—and it should be maintained in all cases.

None of the alternate solutions is ideal, and each should be considered in relation to the running heads, if any. The simplest practice is to retain the 1 line space at bottom or top as it falls, but be left to a reasonably intelligent clerk, but a difficult one is best done by the designer, as many decisions are involved which affect the layout of pages and other significant matters. With a particularly complicated book, it may be necessary to make a dummy (CH.21) since a castoff would be too difficult.

KINDS OF CASTOFFS

There are 2 kinds of castoff: justified and unjustified.

▪ *Unjustified castoff*—This is simply a linear measurement without allowance for alignment of short or long pages due to widows (CH.5) or other makeup problems. However, an unlucky sequence of widows can throw a chapter over to another page by adding several lines and, if there are part-titles or chapters beginning on right-hand pages, this can materially affect the overall length. For this reason, an unjustified castoff has limited value.

▪ *Justified castoff*—To make a justified castoff, use revised galley proofs if possible. Unrevised proofs may be used if the corrections are minor and the Author's Proofs are at hand, so that the effect of the changes can be taken into account. A difference of a line or two (in some cases a word or two!) may have a serious effect when the number of pages is very close to the limit.

In a justified castoff, the pages should come out exactly as in makeup, which means that all problems must be solved in detail. These include: (a) final determination of the space to be used for illustrations, (b) disposition of odd amounts of space resulting from matter set in lines of various depths, (c) provisions for widows (CH.5), and (d) disposition of the various problems caused by run-in breaks that fall at the ends of pages.

CASTOFF PROBLEMS

The treatment of spacebreaks, run-in chapter titles, and subheads that fall at the bottoms of pages is a major problem of the castoff. Supposing, for example, that a number 1 subhead is normally in a 5-line space, but the preceding text ends only 4 lines from the bottom of the page. There are 2 alternatives: either the space around the subhead is reduced so that it, and a minimum number of text lines below it, will fit, or the page will be kept short (like the end of a chapter) and the subhead will go at the top of the next page. This choice requires policy decisions as to:

(a) How many lines of space may be "stolen" from around the head? (The space may be reduced to the minimum acceptable visually, but not less than that of an inferior class of head.)

(b) What is the minimum acceptable number of text lines below the head? (For most subheads, 2 lines are sufficient, for major subheads or chapter openings 3 or 4 may be appropriate.)

(c) If the head goes to the next page, how many lines of space should be left above it? (This is measured in *lines of text*, exclusive of the running head.)

The same procedure is followed whether the break is a minor subhead or a run-in chapter. In all cases, the relative value of the heads must be preserved.

One-line spacebreaks present a special problem when they fall at the bottom or top of the page. Some people prefer simply to omit the space. This solution does eliminate the graphic problem, but it is editorially unsound. The author puts in the line space because he *wants* a break in the text—inferior to a chapter or subhead to be sure, but presumably of some editorial value—and it should be maintained in all cases.

None of the alternate solutions is ideal, and each should be considered in relation to the running heads, if any. The simplest practice is to retain the 1-line space at bottom or top as it falls, but this creates an ambiguous effect. The reader is usually less aware of a line space than that the text is not aligned on the facing pages. When the space falls at the top, it is apparent enough only when there is a substantial running head on both pages. A 2-line space may be used at the top, but when there is no running head even this is not really enough, particularly if the folding is inaccurate. One solution is to make top or bottom breaks more definite by introducing into the line space some unobtrusive typographic device such as an asterisk, colon, dash, or elipse. Although this makes these breaks a little more prominent than the others, it is probably better to emphasize them somewhat than to omit them entirely. It might be even better to use a device in *all* spacebreaks, and thus eliminate the problem.

Where illustrations in the text are involved, the allowance of space must include the picture itself, the caption (if any), the space between picture and caption, and the space separating the illustration from the text.

Adjustments for length

When the castoff is completed, you will know whether there are too few pages, too many, or—with luck—exactly the right number. There are many possible ways of coping with the problems.

- *Too few pages*—If circumstances permit, pages can be added by stretching out the front and/or backmatter, by starting chapters on right-hand pages if they were left or right, or by making full page titles (backed blank or not) of the chapter breaks. (The latter means upgrading the chapter break value, and should have the editor's approval.) None of these measures requires a new castoff. Simply renumber the pages.

When none of the foregoing solutions is feasible, it may be possible to: (a) reduce the number of lines on the text page, (b) increase the amount of space around heads, illustrations, etc., or (c) if no engravings have yet been made, increase the size of the illustrations themselves. In such cases, a new castoff should be made.

If only a few pages are left over, there is no harm in having a blank leaf or two at the front and/or back of the book. Where the number of blanks is large—say 8 or more—it is usually better to *cancel* them [cut them off the sheet].

■ *Too many pages*—The reverse of most of the above measures may be applied. In some cases, frontmatter can be telescoped by combining copyright notice and dedication, starting a foreword on the back of the contents instead of on the next right-hand page, etc. If chapters begin on right-hand pages, save the preceding blank pages (CH.16) by making all chapters begin left or right. Blanks backing part-titles can be saved by beginning the text on those pages. The entire 2 pages for each part-title can be saved by putting the part-title on the opening of the first chapter. Again, no new castoff is needed.

If these measures are not sufficient or practicable, it may be necessary to: (a) *add* 1 or more lines to the text page (if space permits), (b) *decrease* the space around heads (or even run-in the chapters), or (c) decrease the size of illustrations. In most cases, it would be desirable to make a new castoff.

If all the available measures are used and there are still too many pages, it may be necessary to print an additional 4, 8, or 16 pages—a rather expensive matter, to be avoided if at all possible.

21 | Layout of illustrations

In CH.9, illustrations were discussed from the standpoint of their origin, nature, and function. The relationship of illustrations to text, printing press, paper, and binding were covered in CH.16 in connection with the basic decisions. From the standpoint of layout, there are 3 basic kinds of situation, with several variations and combinations possible. The illustrations are:

(a) scattered through the text,
(b) accompanied by some text, and/or
(c) printed separately without text.

General principles

SIZE

The sizes of the illustrations were determined roughly in calculating the length of the book.

In making the castoff, the space allowances were further refined and perhaps, where there are relatively few illustrations scattered through the text, a specific page was assigned to each one. In books containing a very high percentage of illustrations, the castoff generally determines only the total space to be allotted to them, modifying the rough calculation as necessary. Where the illustrations are printed separately, the castoff has no bearing. In all cases, there is no need to use the sizes originally chosen, but there should be compensatory changes whenever a size is radically changed.

In crowded books, there is a tendency to make all the illustrations medium in size to save space. A better solution, in most cases, is to make some large and some small. This has the editorial virtue of reflecting the relative importance of the pictures (they are rarely of equal interest), it gives the designer an opportunity to cope with variations in quality of copy, and it introduces contrast and variety into the layout.

SHAPE

The sizes of pictures are related primarily to their importance and purpose, but their shape is largely an esthetic matter, provided their content is not sacrificed. Make an effort to create interesting and varied shapes. A book full of similar rectangles can be very dull. Most photographs can stand much more cropping than is done, so it is usually possible to vary the golden rectangles with some narrow ones and some squares. A sprinkling of silhouettes helps greatly.

CONTRAST & VARIETY

In general, contrast is preferable to insufficient variety. While a majestic effect can be achieved by skillful repetition of identical elements, a profusion of similar elements is likely to become boring, unless broken occasionally by a sharp change. Contrast is accentuated variety, it can be used to enliven the page and create a distinct rhythm.

There are many ways to achieve variety and contrast in illustration layout—not only in size and shape, but in value, pattern, style, scale, subject, period, atmosphere, etc. The problem is rather to orchestrate the complex elements into a unified whole than to find means of achieving effects.

Some of the (obvious) ways of producing variety and contrast are to use:

(a) large pictures with small ones,
(b) square pictures with silhouettes,
(c) long oblongs with square oblongs,
(d) photographs with line drawings or engravings,
(e) dark pictures with light ones,
(f) close-ups with panoramas,
(g) curving subjects with angular subjects,
(h) crowded areas with blank areas,
(i) old subjects with new subjects,
(j) quiet pictures with active ones,
(k) color with monochrome, and
(l) formal with informal arrangements.

Pages with uninteresting shapes.

Pages with contrast and variety.

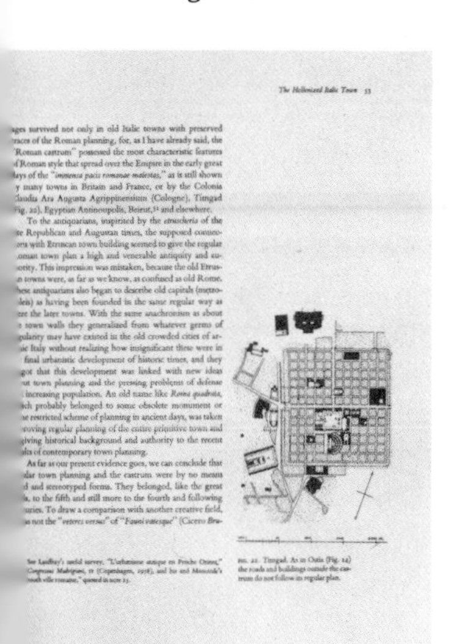

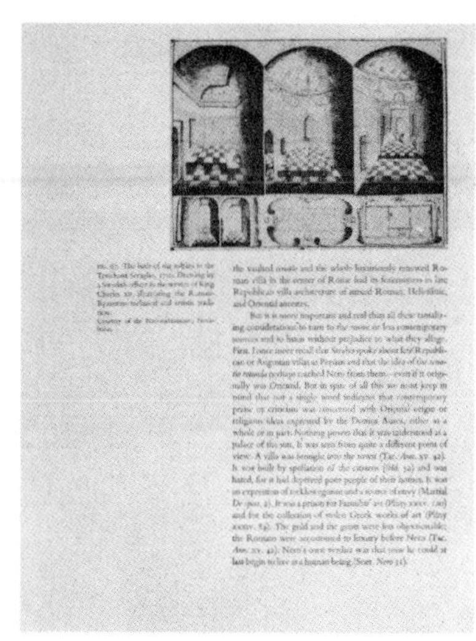

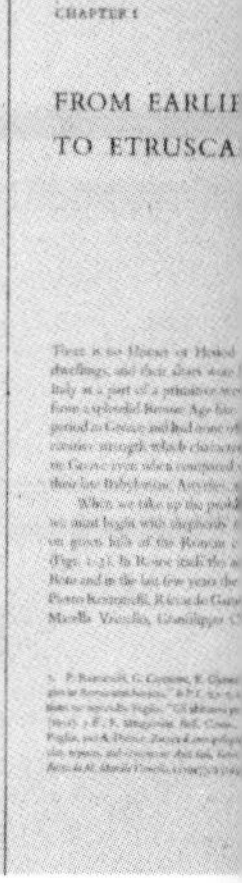

This is the story of a new line of *classroom furniture*. The manufacturer, Brunswick-Balke-Callender Co., enlisted the aid of a consulting industrial design office, *Dave Chapman*, to add to its own design and engineering staff. The industrial design office was involved in every phase of the development story from its very inception to the market presentation, working constantly with the various departments of the client's staff.

April, 1951 First meeting of Design Committee, which included representatives of management, sales, plant design engineering, and the consulting design office, was held.

May, 1952 Orthopedic research statistics were compiled in chart form for visual study.

Competitive lines were studied, evaluated, and charted. Renderings made, establishing direction of design considering both stamped and rod construction for chairs. Cost estimates proved that either technique was feasible.

July, 1952 Research reports from abroad were correlated with reports from the States. Results from 1,125 questionnaires sent to school administrators across the country were analyzed. First rough model started as a result of analysis of materials, standards, engineering and production methods. Decision was made to use tapered tubular steel for legs rather than stamped forms.

August, 1952 Development of first design prototypes with handmade tapered legs. Several assembly techniques and support constructions were considered.

October, 1952 Revised model drawings were prepared for second set of prototypes based upon available production equipment. Further design refinements were made, emphasis was placed upon the function of the units with respect to the needs of the educational system. Children were brought into the plant to make a "live test" of their reaction to the furniture.

November, 1952 The prototypes of the line were presented to the management. Shortly thereafter followed a showing to sales personnel.

December, 1952 Based on comments of management and sales, further refinements were made and the concept of the entire line as to range and size of units was established.

January, 1953 The Chapman office was asked to prepare design and production detailing of an industrial space for the first trade showing of the line in Atlantic City in February, 1953.

In creating dynamic layouts, it is necessary not only to maintain a sense of unity and order, but to be consistent with the nature of the text. It is quite possible to have a beautiful and very dramatic illustration layout that is wrong because the text is low in key or vice versa. The intensity of contrast and the extent of variety must accord with the book's character.

CONSISTENCY

Regardless of how simple an illustration layout may be, it should be considered as a double spread. It will be *seen* as a spread, so it should be planned as one. There must be an effective balance of all

PROCEDURE

elements on the facing pages—text, illustrations, captions, space, and, if any, running heads and folios.

Layouts should be made the actual size of the book. It is difficult enough to visualize the final effect without confusing matters by using a different size. Thumbnail sketches are useful for preliminary planning, but the effect of small layouts is quite misleading. The best practice is to make a dummy, whether a small signature or an entire book is involved. In this way, the layouts can be related to each other and to the whole. In general, the closer you can approximate the end result in your planning, the less you have to imagine.

Illustrations scattered through text

In books that have occasional illustrations appearing in the text, it is necessary to determine:

(a) their size and shape,

(b) their vertical position—whether they are to be placed at the top, bottom, or middle of the page,

(c) their horizontal position—centered, indented, flush left or right,

(d) how much space will separate them from the text, and

(e) the style and position of captions.

Four kinds of development in sequence.

Visually, there is no reason to treat pictures in a letterpress book differently from those in a text printed by litho or gravure. In letterpress, however, the mechanical difficulties—and costs—increase considerably when the picture extends beyond the basic type page (CHS.5,7,12). Having taken these factors into consideration, the vertical and horizontal position of the illustrations may be based on esthetic factors, unless there is some special requirement of the text.

Thought must be given to the *sequence* of illustration position and size, as well as to the layout of each spread. Variety, rhythm, and order should be planned in terms of the whole book—which has a consecutive order more like a motion picture than a series of separate frames. For example, illustrations might be placed alternately at top and bottom, or they might repeat a sequence of bottom, middle, top, etc. Sizes and shapes should develop in an interesting pattern from first page to last. A haphazard sequence will result in confusion and lack of unity. This is one of the more subtle aspects of book design, but it is real. The book exists in time as well as space—which is one of the features that distinguishes it from other graphic forms.

Runarounds [narrow cuts with text alongside] are to be avoided for both practical and esthetic reasons: (a) they are costly and inefficient because the text around them must be reset when the pages are made up, and (b) when the lines alongside are short, they usually look poor because of the awkwardness of wordspacing and breaking in a narrow column.

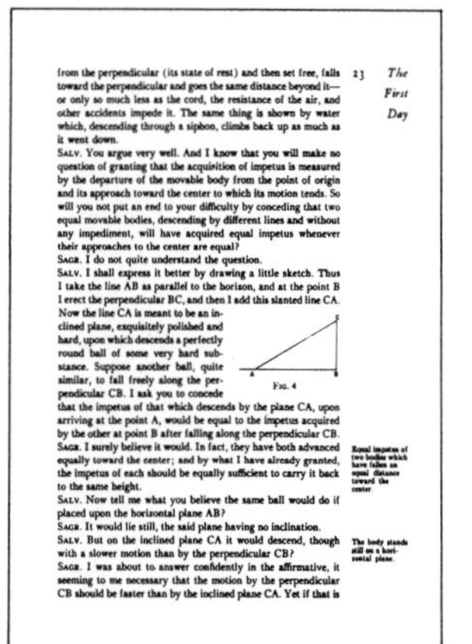

23 *The First Day*

from the perpendicular (its state of rest) and then set free, falls toward the perpendicular and goes the same distance beyond it—or only so much less as the cord, the resistance of the air, and other accidents impede it. The same thing is shown by water which, descending through a siphon, climbs back up as much as it went down.

SALV. You argue very well. And I know that you will make no question of granting that the acquisition of impetus is measured by the departure of the movable body from the point of origin and its approach toward the center to which its motion tends. So will you not put an end to your difficulty by conceding that two equal movable bodies, descending by different lines and without any impediment, will have acquired equal impetus whenever their approaches to the center are equal?

SAGR. I do not quite understand the question.

SALV. I shall express it better by drawing a little sketch. Thus I take the line AB as parallel to the horizon, and at the point B I erect the perpendicular BC, and then I add this slanted line CA. Now the line CA is meant to be an inclined plane, exquisitely polished and hard, upon which descends a perfectly round ball of some very hard substance. Suppose another ball, quite similar, to fall freely along the perpendicular CB. I ask you to concede that the impetus of that which descends by the plane CA, upon arriving at the point A, would be equal to the impetus acquired by the other at point B after falling along the perpendicular CB.

FIG. 4

SAGR. I surely believe it would. In fact, they have both advanced equally toward the center; and by what I have already granted, the impetus of each should be equally sufficient to carry it back to the same height.

Equal impetus of two bodies which have fallen an equal distance toward the center.

SALV. Now tell me what you believe the same ball would do if placed upon the horizontal plane AB?

SAGR. It would lie still, the said plane having no inclination.

SALV. But on the inclined plane CA it would descend, though with a slower motion than by the perpendicular CB?

The body stands still on a horizontal plane.

SAGR. I was about to answer confidently in the affirmative, it seeming to me necessary that the motion by the perpendicular CB should be faster than by the inclined plane CA. Yet if that is

mortals have the power to destroy much of mankind. We may be used to the fear, but it does not go away. We may shrink from thinking about the unthinkable, but there is no topic that requires better thought. To make us think about it is the purpose of many novelists whose books would like implausible tall stories if they did not dramatize possibilities that be probable. One specialist in lit

Peter G

If the book has just a few small pictures, it is better to place them in the full width of the text and avoid runarounds. When there are a great many, they may be combined so that 2, 3, or more fit on 1 page, or it may be possible to place them in the margins (as in this book). The latter solution depends on editorial requirements and relative costs (CHS.16,17).

Pictures that occur at the tops of pages or occupy a full page may or may not have running heads and folios. If there are a great many such, the advisability of omitting that many folios is involved. Otherwise, it is simply an esthetic matter. Usually, illustrations look better without running heads at the top.

Illustrations accompanied by text

The space occupied by text can be adjusted with considerable accuracy and little trouble. When only a few illustrations are involved, a miscalculation of the space they will take is not likely to cause a serious error. But, where the proportion of pictures and text is heavily weighted toward pictures, the problem is more complicated, particularly if there is to be a close relationship of illustration and relevant text. Not only is it more difficult to achieve a specific number of pages, but very often the size of pictures must be changed in order to keep them on the same spread as the text to which they refer.

First, the text is set according to the text plan (CH.17). A castoff (CH.20) will show whether or not the space allowed for illustrations should be changed. If a drastic change is called for, the illustrations should be reviewed and re-sized accordingly. Small variations can be managed in the course of making the final layout. For books of this kind, a dummy is essential.

DUMMY

A blank dummy is made, and the pages numbered. The most practical dummy is a Smyth-sewed, unbacked, uncovered book of about 70 lb. litho-sized paper. This will open flat, yet stay together, and the paper is tough enough to take a lot of handling, erasures, repastings, etc. Regular endpaper stock is suitable also.

An allowance is made for the estimated number of pages of frontmatter and backmatter, and those pages are clipped together. The text and illustrations must fit into the pages remaining. The galleys (a duplicate set) are cut into pieces of the proper number of lines and pasted down. The illustrations are sketched in to complete the layout.

Exactly how the layout is made depends on the nature of the book. If it is editorially sufficient that the illustrations appear within a few pages of the text reference, the problem is fairly simple. Examining a galley or two at a time, the designer can see how many of what size pictures will be needed, and the layouts may be made according to the general scheme visualized at the beginning.

It is better to have pictures occur *after* the reference rather than before it but, except for this requirement, it should be possible to make each illustration about the size allocated.

Rather than cut up all the galleys in advance, first mark them off with the appropriate page numbers written in the margin. In this way you can go through the entire dummy, indicating the amount of text, and roughly sketching in the size, shape, and position of each illustration. If at the end you find that you have pages left over, or not enough pages, it may be possible to change the front and/or backmatter specs enough but, if not, you can make changes in the text more easily than if the galleys had been cut up.

It is useful to check your calculations at intervals (every 2 or 3 chapters) to see if text and illustrations are being used in correct proportion to the number of pages laid out. This practice reveals tendencies before they go too far and when adjustments are less painful.

The same procedure may be used when the illustrations and references must appear on the same spread, but only if there are not too many pictures in proportion to text. When there are 3 or 4 illustrations for each page, the problem of layout becomes so complex, it is just about necessary to proceed spread by spread—working out each one in considerable detail. In some books (particularly textbooks) where this situation prevails, there is no anticipation of a definite total number of pages. The layout is completed as editorially required, and the front and back matter are adjusted (sometimes by adding or deleting copy) to make an even form—even if it is a small one.

There are several ways of proceeding with a dummy once the preliminary layout is made. With the galley proofs pasted in: (a) the pictures may be sketched in, (b) photostats may be made to the proposed size and pasted in position, or (c) the illustrations may be sized, negatives made by the engraver or printer, and blueprints pasted in (CHS.5,7,11).

These methods involve an increasing degree of commitment from first to third, so the choice will depend mainly on your confidence and skill, although there is not as much difference in cost between positive stats and blueprints as one might suppose (especially when you consider that the blueprints are not wasted, except for the few that may be changed, while the stats are entirely an extra expense). Comprehensive sketches take time to make, and are not nearly as close to the final result as either stats or prints, although they can be changed without any cost (except your time). So, unless it is necessary to obtain approval in the sketch stage, it is just as well to go from rough sketches to blues.

Making good sketches of illustrations is a special technique re-

quiring some ability and practice. The first problem is to define the function of the sketches. Generally, they must give a reasonably accurate impression of the distribution of light and dark masses, dynamic lines, details, and other prominent features. Also, they are usually expected to be clear enough for identification of the picture.

To achieve the necessary effects quickly, it is worth spending a few seconds studying each picture before beginning to sketch, in order to fix the salient points in your mind. Then sketch rapidly with a soft pencil, and the main features will tend to come through automatically. Don't begin in one corner and work your way across, but make broad strokes fairly lightly all over. This produces a basic pattern which can be refined as needed. Then use the side of the pencil point to lay in the heavier masses of dark tones. Finish by using the point to make a few outlines and details to provide definition and indentification. One or two minutes should be sufficient for a half-page illustration. If the proportions and relationships are correct, there is little need for time-consuming details or refinements.

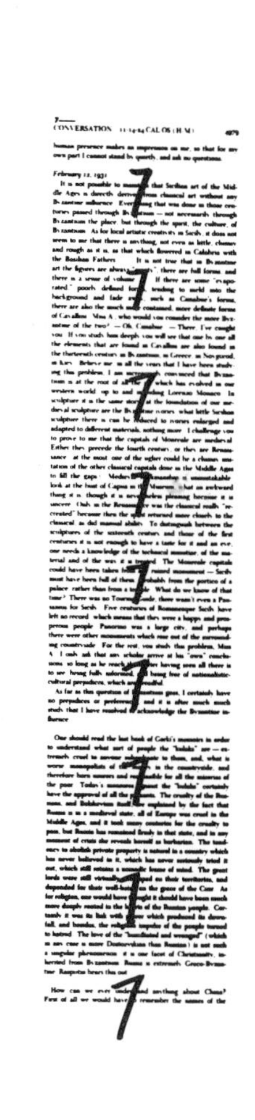

When pasting in galley proofs, wait, if possible, until the corrected galleys have been returned by the author. If the corrections are extensive, have revised proofs pulled. The need for revised proofs will depend on how complex is the problem of fitting pictures to text. In some books, a change of a few lines will be serious, in others, not.

Be sure that each piece of galley proof has the galley number written on it. An unidentified strip of proof might mean searching through a hundred galleys to find 3 or 4 lines of type. The safest practice is to write or stamp the galley number 6 or 8 times on each galley *before* it is cut apart. Even then, watch for strips cut out between the numbers.

The proofs, blueprints, etc. may be pasted in the dummy with rubber cement but it is quicker to use "magic mending" tape—the clear plastic tape which is easy to tear off and has a matte finish that will accept pencil or ink. Changes are easier and there is less mess.

LAYOUT

The *principles* of layout for picture-text books are not different from those for books with only occasional illustrations, but the *practice* is more complex. Pictures are more flexible to arrange than lines of type, but they require more imagination and ability to organize. Thus, the possibility of making a stunning layout with pictures is greater, but so is the possibility of making a mess. Not only must each spread be appropriate, interesting, and handsome, but it must remain an integral part of the whole book, having a well-balanced relationship to the other spreads and to the basic pattern and spirit of the design.

A sense of order and continuity can sometimes be created amid a profusion of varied layouts by repeated use of a prominent element (such as a running head or folio) that recurs in the same position on all or most spreads. Another effective measure is to repeat the layout pattern of a particular spread. When such devices are employed, they should be pronounced enough to impinge themselves on the reader's awareness.

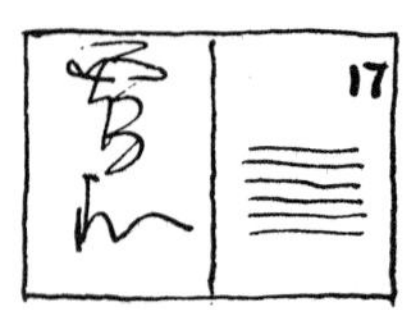

If the demands of picture-text relationship are not too confining, try to vary the amount of text on each page. This adds variety and provides another opportunity to create an orderly pattern.

Illustrations separate from text

When illustrations are to be printed separately and inserted as a tip, wrap, insert, or signature in the text, the problems of layout are somewhat simpler, although (again) the principles remain the same. Everything said about illustration layout applies here, excepting comments on the relationship of pictures to text on the page.

Of course, the first and last pages of such inserts will face pages of text or blanks, or perhaps the endpapers, and these too must be treated as parts of spreads. Sometimes it is impossible to know what the facing page will be like, but an attempt must be made to find out as soon as possible, and the illustration page should be adjusted accordingly.

While the absence of text (except for captions) on such pages relieves the designer of the problem of editorial accommodation, he acquires the responsibility for making a sensible, as well as an esthetically satisfactory, arrangement of pictures. The sequence of pictures is usually decided by the editorial department, but there is often considerable variation in the way they may be combined and arranged. The designer must plan each spread so that it makes sense and must arrange the sequence of spreads so that the whole section tells a coherent story.

Sometimes the editor (or author) has no idea in mind other than to include all the illustrations provided; sometimes he suggests a sequence which can be changed to a more effective order. Even when the editor's sequence is followed strictly, there is need for intelligent thought in layout. For example, if pictures 6, 7, 8, and 9 are related in subject, while 10 and 11 belong to another category, it would be more reasonable to place the first 4 on 2 facing pages and the other 2 on the next page together, than to put 6, 7, and 8 on one spread and 9 on the next page with 10. This seems obvious enough when put this way, but designers sometimes neglect consideration of the subject altogether.

The problem is further complicated by the various *kinds* of subject relationship that could be the basis for an arrangement. The same group of pictures might be arranged chronologically, geographically, or by subject development in a number of different ways. A perfectly good arrangement could be made on each basis, but one may be better than the others.

Captions & credits

■ *Captions*—These are elements of the page design just as much as pictures or text. If they consist of just a line or two, they may be used to contrast with a large block of text or a picture. When they are extensive, they become blocks of type to be given graphic consideration of the same kind as the text.

Captions must be readable but must contrast with the text sufficiently to avoid confusion. They are usually brief, so they may be set 1, 2, or even 3 sizes smaller than text and still be readable. It helps to set them in italics or in another face. In crowded layouts, there is often a need to set captions in narrow measures, but there is a limit to how short the line can become without the usual trouble in wordspacing (CH.6).

When placing captions above and below illustrations, particularly square halftones, remember that there are usually more ascenders and caps than descenders. This means that there is optically more space below a line than above, so it is necessary to specify a little more space (perhaps 2 pts.) between pictures and captions placed below than those placed above. The closer the captions to the illustrations and the larger the type, the more significant this factor becomes.

■ *Credit lines*—Especially where the acknowledgment is to an institution, it suffices if credits are legible. This satisfies any requirement that the source of a picture be identified. There is no reason why obtaining this information should be made especially easy or pleasant. In most cases, the credit line is an advertisement for the supplier of the picture and is disproportionate to the picture's contribution to the book—particularly when a fee has been paid. For such pictures, the credit should be made as inconspicuous as feasible; 4 or 5 pt. type is sufficient. Any position that is visible, clearly associated with the relevant picture, and graphically useful is valid.

Where an individual artist or photographer is credited for a substantial contribution, it is customary to include the credit in the frontmatter.

Illustration proofs

BLUEPRINTS

Whenever a photomechanical plate is made (CH.7), it is possible to have a blueprint or one of its variants (CH.5).

Prints of this kind are no certain indication of the quality of a negative and should not be taken as such. The appearance of a spot or other unwanted mark on a blueprint should be brought to the attention of the printer or engraver, as the defect *might* be in the film, but such marks are usually in the print only. And remember that most of them shrink irregularly.

Printers and engravers charge extra for the blueprints, so their usefulness must be weighed against their cost. In letterpress, where the engraver's proof is available, blueprints are not usually ordered. For litho and gravure, *loose blues* [blueprints of individual illustrations] are usually ordered for dummying. Page blueprints are standard for checking makeup (CH.24).

PROOFS OF PLATES

On halftones, the first things to check are size and squareness (if it is a square halftone). Check silhouetting to be sure that it follows the edges of the subject exactly, and that the edges are soft and natural. Watch out for inside silhouetting (such as the space between legs) where the background should be dropped out.

Look for a good range of tones. There should be definition of form in the lights and shadows, and a nice spread of middle values between. Watch out for either a flat, lifeless proof of *all* middle tones or an excessively contrasty one with washed-out highlights, solid shadows, and *no* middle tones.

Remember that the plate cannot (normally) be expected to be better than the original, and don't assume that it will be as good. The percentage of failures and mistakes by even the best platemakers is high enough to warrant a close examination of *all* proofs.

On letterpress halftones and line cuts (CH.7), compare the proof against the original to see that the engraving is neither heavier nor lighter. Object to heaviness particularly, as there will be a tendency for the illustration to become still darker when it is printed on a high-speed press on paper rougher than the engraver's proofs. Excessive lightness is to be avoided too, since it means a loss of fine lines, details, etc.

The general practice of photoengravers is to provide 2 proofs on coated paper. Additional proofs are subject to a charge. It is useful to get a proof of line cuts on antique paper (CH.8), but few engravers keep such stock on hand, although they do have newsprint.

One coated proof should be kept as a model for the printer and another should be kept in the file. When proofs are required for dummy or promotion purposes, they should be ordered in advance.

Ordinarily, the plate has not been blocked when the proof is sent for approval, as most corrections are made on unblocked cuts. Unless there is a specific understanding that engravings are to be blocked without approval, the proofs should be returned with corrections, or the engraver should be notified that the cuts are O.K. for blocking and delivery.

COLOR PROOFS

For a discussion of checking color proofs, see CH.7.

The engraver furnishes 2 sets of progressives, and one of them must go to the printer. One complete proof goes in the file and another may be used for a dummy. 6 should be provided.

For jackets, covers, illustrations, etc., there is often a demand for additional proofs for promotion. These are charged at about $1 per color for each proof in addition to the regular proofs—which usually cost about $12 per color. On very simple jobs, involving only 2 or 3 colors and no process work, it is sometimes possible to dispense with color proofs entirely.

22 | Title page & part titles

The frontmatter is the entrance to the book and so it should be revealing and interesting. It should invite the reader and give him confidence that the book will be esthetically and practically satisfying. The front pages should be at least as excellent in every way as any part of the book. In books that have no illustrations or chapter display type, the frontmatter will be the only place to provide interest and variety. This opportunity should not be lost.

Title page

The dominant feature of the frontmatter is the title page. To express its relationship to the book we might compare a book to the human body, and say that the text is the torso, the frontmatter the head, and the title page the face.

It is best to design the title page before the rest of the frontmatter. There should be perfect harmony among all the front pages, and it is better to coordinate the other pages with the title than to compromise the design of this key element to fit them.

However, *the title page must be in complete harmony with the text that is already designed.* The title page provides an outstanding opportunity to express the book's character and make an effective display, but it must never fail to be an integral part of the whole book—no matter how excellent it may be as an individual unit. It is sad to see a well-designed text and a superb title page that don't go together. Although the parts are good, the total is a failure.

The tendency to produce unrelated title pages is very common. Designers frequently become engrossed in these attractive creations and begin moving things about without regard for what already exists. To avoid this, it is a good idea to work on the title page with a sample page in full view—to fill the eye with the spirit and character of the text.

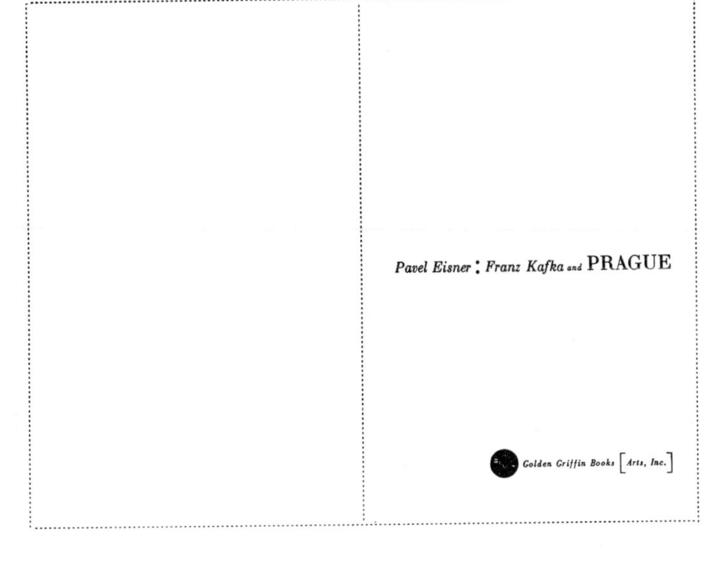

Pavel Eisner : Franz Kafka and PRAGUE

Golden Griffin Books [Arts, Inc.]

A title spread with all type on 1 side.

POSITION

The title page is conventionally thought of as a right-hand page but, as elsewhere, both sides of the spread are visible and thus both are part of the title-page design. This does not mean that type or illustration must appear on both sides. It does mean that the design must reckon with the whole spread—even if there is nothing but space on half of it. Space is as much part of a design as the type and illustrations that form and divide it (CH.6).

There is no question but that the right side of the spread is the more prominent one. Where a conventional arrangement is in order, and there is no special consideration to indicate otherwise, the title-page type is just as well placed on the right-hand page—and so it is in most books. However, once the type or illustration reaches across the spread it may be assumed that the reader will perceive all of it. The title page is not a poster which must catch the eye of a passing shopper—that is the role of the jacket or cover—it is for the use of one who is already aware of the title and is interested enough in it to have opened the book.

It has been customary, also, to confine the title-page type to the text-page area. This practice tends, as does any uniformity, toward simplicity and unity—2 highly desirable attributes—but there is no reason to be limited to it if your design objective can be realized in other ways. From an economic standpoint there is a slight advantage in keeping the title page within the type-page area in letterpress—in litho or gravure, none at all.

Indeed, not only need the title not be confined to the text area or the right-hand page, it does not necessarily have to appear entirely on 1 spread. If the problem calls for such treatment, the copy and illustrations may be extended over 4, 6, or more pages. Just as in a movie—which exists through successive frames as the book exists through successive pages—the title and credits may appear in

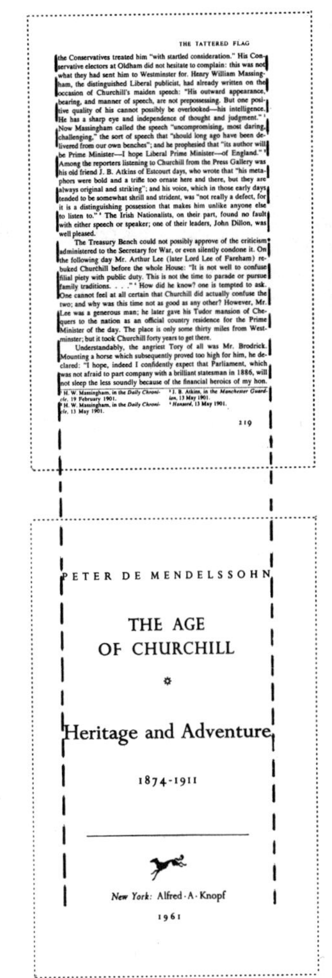

THE TATTERED FLAG

the Conservatives treated him "with startled consideration." His Conservative electors at Oldham did not hesitate to complain: this was not what they had sent him to Westminster for. Henry William Massingham, the distinguished Liberal publicist, had already written on the occasion of Churchill's maiden speech: "His outward appearance, bearing, and manner of speech, are not prepossessing. But one positive quality of his cannot possibly be overlooked—his intelligence. He has a sharp eye and independence of thought and judgment."[1] Now Massingham called the speech "uncompromising, most daring, challenging," the sort of speech that "should long ago have been delivered from our own benches"; and he prophesied that "its author will be Prime Minister—I hope Liberal Prime Minister—of England."[2] Among the reporters listening to Churchill from the Press Gallery was his old friend J. B. Atkins of Estcourt days, who wrote that "his metaphors were bold and a trifle too ornate here and there, but they are always original and striking"; and his voice, which in those early days tended to be somewhat shrill and strident, was "not really a defect, for it is a distinguishing possession that makes him unlike anyone else to listen to."[3] The Irish Nationalists, on their part, found no fault with either speech or speaker; one of their leaders, John Dillon, was well pleased.

The Treasury Bench could not possibly approve of the criticism administered to the Secretary for War, or even silently condone it. On the following day Mr. Arthur Lee (later Lord Lee of Fareham) rebuked Churchill before the whole House: "It is not well to confuse filial piety with public duty. This is not the time to parade or pursue family traditions. . . ."[4] How did he know? one is tempted to ask. One cannot feel at all certain that Churchill did actually confuse the two; and why was this time not as good as any other? However, Mr. Lee was a generous man; he later gave his Tudor mansion of Chequers to the nation as an official country residence for the Prime Minister of the day. The place is only some thirty miles from Westminster; but it took Churchill forty years to get there.

Understandably, the angriest Tory of all was Mr. Brodrick. Mounting a horse which subsequently proved too high for him, he declared: "I hope, indeed I confidently expect that Parliament, which was not afraid to part company with a brilliant statesman in 1886, will not sleep the less soundly because of the financial heroics of my hon.

[1] H. W. Massingham, in the *Daily Chronicle*, 19 February 1901.
[2] H. W. Massingham, in the *Daily Chronicle*, 13 May 1901.
[3] J. B. Atkins, in the *Manchester Guardian*, 13 May 1901.
[4] *Hansard*, 13 May 1901.

219

PETER DE MENDELSSOHN

THE AGE OF CHURCHILL

Heritage and Adventure

1874-1911

New York: Alfred·A·Knopf

1961

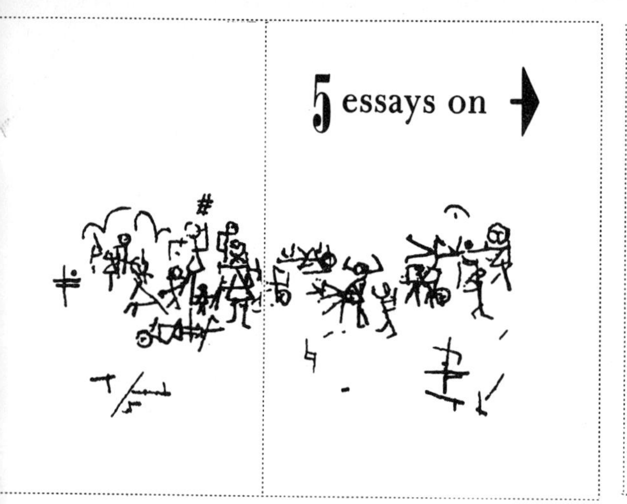

A successful use of 6 pages for the title, by Merle Armitage.

sequence rather than at once. Used inappropriately or ineptly this device could be extremely irritating. Well-handled, it can serve several useful purposes: (a) it may be used to build suspense, (b) it can be an effective way to deal with complicated and/or extensive copy, (c) it can be a means of creating atmosphere, and (d) it can help fill out a short book, provided that the device is justified by a valid editorial purpose.

ELEMENTS The title page may contain all or some of the following elements:

title
author
subtitle
credits (translator, editor, illustrator, author of introduction)
imprint (the publisher's name)
colophon (the publisher's trademark)
date
copyright notice
quotation
illustration
ad card (a list of other books by the author)

The designer's first obligation is to establish and maintain the proper relationship of emphasis among these elements. Ordinarily, the order of importance would be roughly as listed above, but circumstances might suggest an entirely different one. A well-known author's name might be more important than the title. Where the title is "literary" and the subtitle descriptive, it might be best to emphasize the latter. In books that are extensively illustrated it may be appropriate to give the illustrator billing equal to the au-

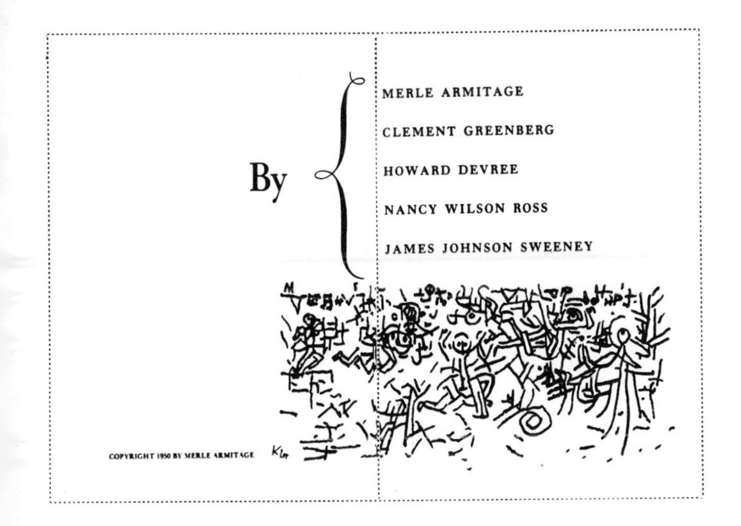

thor's, and so on. The editor will have views on this matter so it might be best to discuss the problem before making a design.

ILLUSTRATION

If illustration is desirable at all, some should appear on the title page, where it is likely to be most effective. Especially in books with titles that neglect to reveal the nature of the text, illustration can serve an important function in suggesting the subject matter. It is almost always possible to manage *something*, even on a very small budget (CH.9).

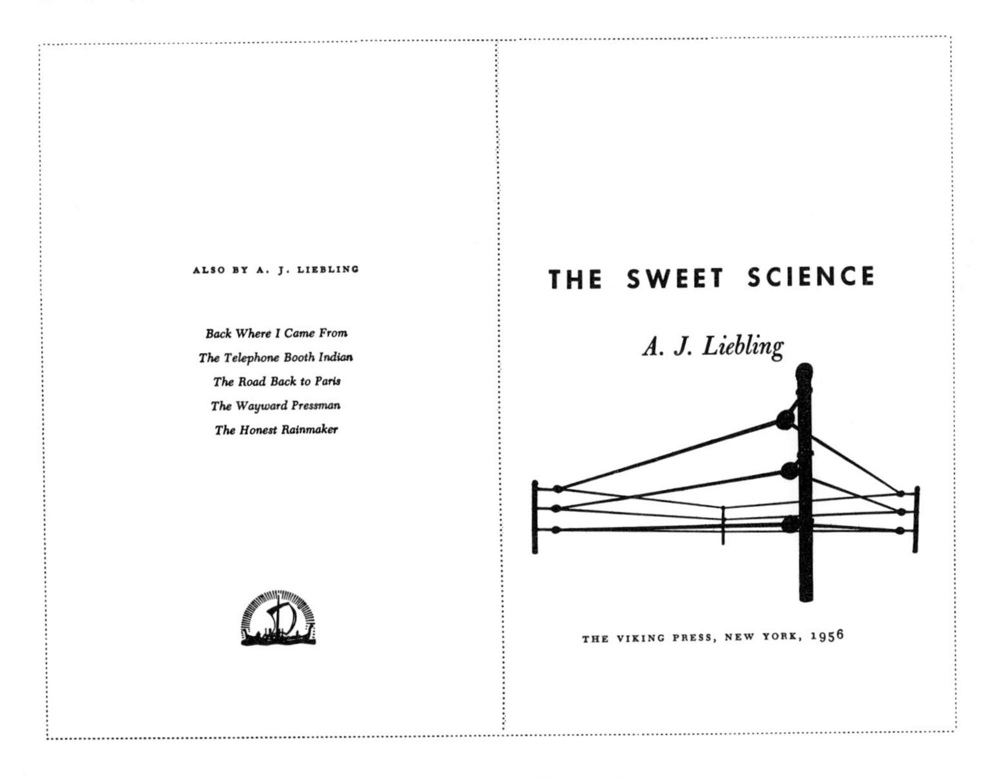

The title page of a book on boxing, with an illuminating illustration by the designer.

Sometimes a "*frontispiece*" is supplied with the Ms. The term is misleading because it implies that this picture is something separate from the rest of the book, and in practice it is often so treated. But the "frontispiece" is actually an illustration meant to appear on the title-page spread, and it should be treated as an element of the title page. This is true even if the illustration is printed on different paper from the text—as in the familiar case of a halftone on coated stock tipped into a book printed on antique paper. The variation in paper then becomes an element in the design and should be used to good effect.

LAYOUT & TYPOGRAPHY

The popular concept of a "frontispiece" is that of a picture alone on the left-hand page (perhaps with a caption) and all type on the right. Regarding it as a title-page illustration, don't hesitate to move it to the right side of the spread, or to place some of the type on the left with the picture. It is most important to integrate the picture into the spread. To this end, it is sometimes useful to silhouette the picture or, if possible, to separate it into parts and distribute them over the spread.

Two spreads in which a "frontispiece" (not an illustration made for the title page) becomes an integral part of the design. The one at left is by Alvin Lustig, the one below is by Albert Cetta.

A BESTIARY

COMPILED BY RICHARD WILBUR

ILLUSTRATED BY ALEXANDER CALDER

PRINTED AT THE SPIRAL PRESS FOR Pantheon Books
NEW YORK

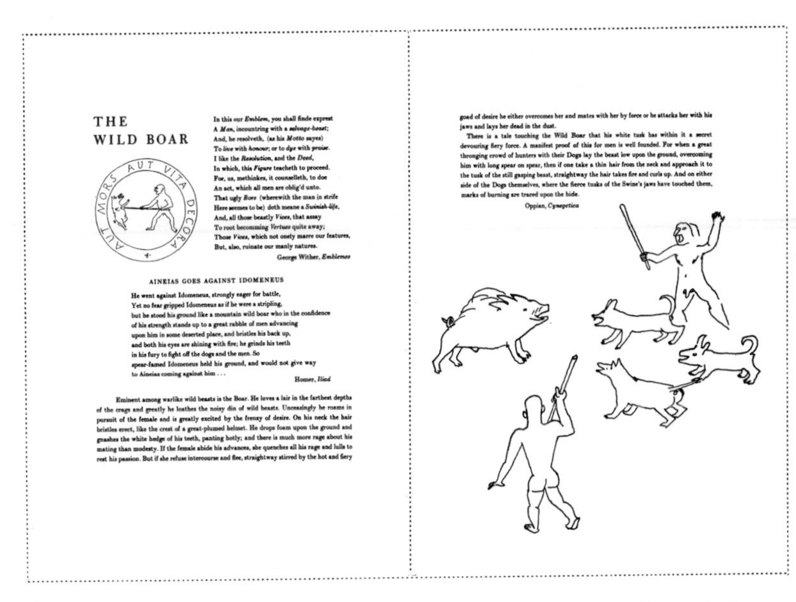

THE
WILD BOAR

In this our *Emblem*, you shall finde exprest
A *Man*, incountring with a *salvage-beast*;
And, he resolveth, (as his *Motto* sayes)
To *live* with *honour*; or to *dye* with *praise*.
I like the *Resolution*, and the *Deed*,
In which, this *Figure* teacheth to proceed.
For, us, methinkes, it counselleth, to doe
An act, which all men are oblig'd unto.
That ugly *Bore* (wherewith the man in strife
Here seemes to be) doth meane a *Swinish-life*,
And, all those beastly *Vices*, that assay
To root becomming *Vertues* quite away;
Those *Vices*, which not onely marre our features,
But, also, ruinate our manly natures.

George Wither, *Emblemes*

AINEIAS GOES AGAINST IDOMENEUS

He went against Idomeneus, strongly eager for battle,
Yet no fear gripped Idomeneus as if he were a stripling,
but he stood his ground like a mountain wild boar who in the confidence
of his strength stands up to a great rabble of men advancing
upon him in some deserted place, and bristles his back up,
and both his eyes are shining with fire; he grinds his teeth
in his fury to fight off the dogs and the men. So
spear-famed Idomeneus held his ground, and would not give way
to Aineias coming against him . . .

Homer, *Iliad*

Eminent among warlike wild beasts is the Boar. He loves a lair in the farthest depths of the crags and greatly he loathes the noisy din of wild beasts. Unceasingly he roams in pursuit of the female and is greatly excited by the frenzy of desire. On his neck the hair bristles erect, like the crest of a great-plumed helmet. He drops foam upon the ground and gnashes the white hedge of his teeth, panting hotly; and there is much more rage about his mating than modesty. If the female abide his advances, she quenches all his rage and lulls to rest his passion. But if she refuse intercourse and flee, straightway stirred by the hot and fiery goad of desire he either overcomes her and mates with her by force or he attacks her with his jaws and lays her dead in the dust.

There is a tale touching the Wild Boar that his white tusk has within it a secret devouring fiery force. A manifest proof of this for men is well founded. For when a great thronging crowd of hunters with their Dogs lay the beast low upon the ground, overcoming him with long spear on spear, then if one take a thin hair from the neck and approach it to the tusk of the still gasping beast, straightway the hair takes fire and curls up. And on either side of the Dogs themselves, where the fierce tusks of the Swine's jaws have touched them, marks of burning are traced upon the hide.

Oppian, *Cynegetica*

A title page in complete harmony with the text. Design by Joseph Blumenthal.

The title-page arrangement—whether symmetrical or asymmetrical—should be consistent with the design of the text (CH.18). Not that blind consistency is necessary, but the Ms characteristics that suggested the chapter-opening arrangement would also indicate how to handle the title page. In both (and all) cases, the nature of the text is the key.

Nor is it necessary that the same type be used for the title page as for the other parts of the book. What *is* essential is unity and harmony. It does not matter whether these are achieved by using a close match or strong contrast. Sometimes a combination of both is most effective. Quite often, a good result is achieved by setting everything on the title page in the same face as the other type, except for the title itself—which may be set in a distinctly contrasting face. The same principles apply to the other aspects of typography (CH.6).

Where type runs across the spread, it is important to recognize that the gutter does exist and is a substantial obstacle. Not only does it create a physical break in which a certain space is lost, it is a psychological barrier. Further, unless the title spread is in the middle of a signature, irregular folding may cause a misalignment of the two sides (CH.10).

To avoid the worst effects of crossing the gutter, use a fairly large size of type. The gutter in a Smyth-sewed book requires that about 2½ picas of space be kept clear, to be sure that nothing gets caught in the fold. In order that this space does not make too noticeable a break in the line of type, it should be not very much greater than the normal space between words or letters—whichever falls at the gutter. For example, if the normal word-spacing is 1½ picas, a space of 2½ picas between words at the gutter will not be too disturbing, because almost 1 pica will disappear into the fold, so the optical space will be just about 1½ picas. However, a word-space of 1½ picas would be normal for quite a large size of type—perhaps 36 pt.—or for a letterspaced line of somewhat smaller type. Since the space needed at the gutter is constant, it is obvious that the smaller the type, the more excessive that space will seem. Also, if the pages don't align, the fault is less noticeable when the type is larger.

In both examples the space between BOOK and MAKING is the same. In both, also, the pages are ⅛" out of alignment (in original size).

B O O K M A K I N G

In a perfect-bound book, add 1½ picas (before trim) to the gutter space, and in side-stitched books, add 3 picas. In both cases, the optical space remaining will be about 1½ picas, as in Smyth-sewed books (CH.10).

COLOR

When a second color is used on a title page, it should be used as part of the design. Rather than merely adding an element of gaud to the page, it should serve an editorial and graphic purpose (CH.15).

Color can be used to establish emphasis, to create atmosphere, or to make graphic distinctions not otherwise possible. The conventional use of a second color is to print the title or a small illustration, but there are many other possibilities. Graphic elements in color may overprint the type successfully if they are light enough. Print a pattern or a solid panel with some or all elements dropped out. Color borders have always been used, but there are certainly new ways to use them. When appropriate, a ghost effect may be obtained.

When using color on the title page, consider using it also on other pages on the same side of the sheet, as virtually no additional cost is involved. Be sure, though, that the color makes sense wherever used. It is better not to use it at all than to throw it in simply because it is available.

The effect of a second color may be lost to a large degree if it is too dark. Particularly where it appears in small areas, the color is affected by its contrast in value with the paper. When this contrast is almost as great as that of the black, the color (hue) itself becomes relatively unnoticeable. Second colors that are not more than 50% of the value of the black ink are most effective. The intensity of the color has some effect here, but not as much as the value, except in extreme cases.

In choosing a swatch of color to be matched, remember that color looks lighter in value and more intense in large areas than in small ones. This is especially significant when the color will be used for type or fairly narrow lines, where the printed color will look considerably darker than on the swatch, even if the ink is an exact match (also due to the effect of contrast with the white background). To avoid this difficulty, choose a swatch somewhat lighter than you want the color to look. And remember that type printed in color will not look as heavy as when black. It may be necessary to compensate by using a larger or heavier face.

Part-titles

Part-titles fall between chapter opening and title page in emphasis. As there is this order of interest and value among these elements of the book, it is important to keep all of them in mind while working on each one. You may find it more satisfactory to design the part-titles before the title page, but don't make them so much more dramatic than the chapter openings that there is no room for a still more important treatment of the title. If the title page is done first, it should be enough stronger than the chapters to allow for the part-titles to fall in between.

The part-titles may include echoes or reiterations of a title-page motif. This tends to unify the design and enhance the effect of the title page.

When appropriate, part-titles may vary considerably to reflect the nature of differing parts. For example, if the parts each deal with a different era, the titles might be designed in the styles of each period. With such an arrangement, although the part-titles are entirely unlike each other, they must nevertheless preserve the unity and identity of the book. (This sounds like a tall order, but it is possible.)

Don't overlook the value of part-titles as opportunities to inject space into a book. When the text is crowded and there is not much space around chapter openings and subheads, it may be best to hold down the size of part-title type to get the relief of white space.

There are usually few practical demands on part-title pages, so there is a large opportunity to use imagination in their treatment. In general, the considerations of typography, layout, illustration, etc. that apply to title pages are valid for part-titles as well.

This design by John Begg carries the title page feeling through the book by using the same typeface and size for the title and part titles, varying only the position on the page.

23 | Frontmatter & backmatter

Frontmatter

The treatment of frontmatter pages is determined mainly by the design of the rest of the book, where a pattern of layout, typography, and feeling has been established. The problem is to design the frontmatter pages so that each will be entirely suited to its purpose and yet fit into the established patterns. Each page must be given careful consideration, no matter how unimportant it may seem to be.

Generally, the display type and layout on frontmatter pages is the same as that of chapter openings, but not always. Items of lesser importance may be given subordinate headings, which may or may not appear elsewhere in the book, or it may even be desirable to use entirely different display type.

The sequence of frontmatter is a subject of some dispute. There are various arrangements suggested by different authorities, and a good case can be made for an order different from any of those. Below is a sequence widely accepted as proper:

(1) half-title
(2) ad card
(3) title
(4) copyright
(5) dedication
(6) acknowledgments
(7) preface (or foreword)
(8) contents
(9) list of illustrations
(10) introduction
(11) second half-title (or first part-title)

These elements will be discussed in the order given above.

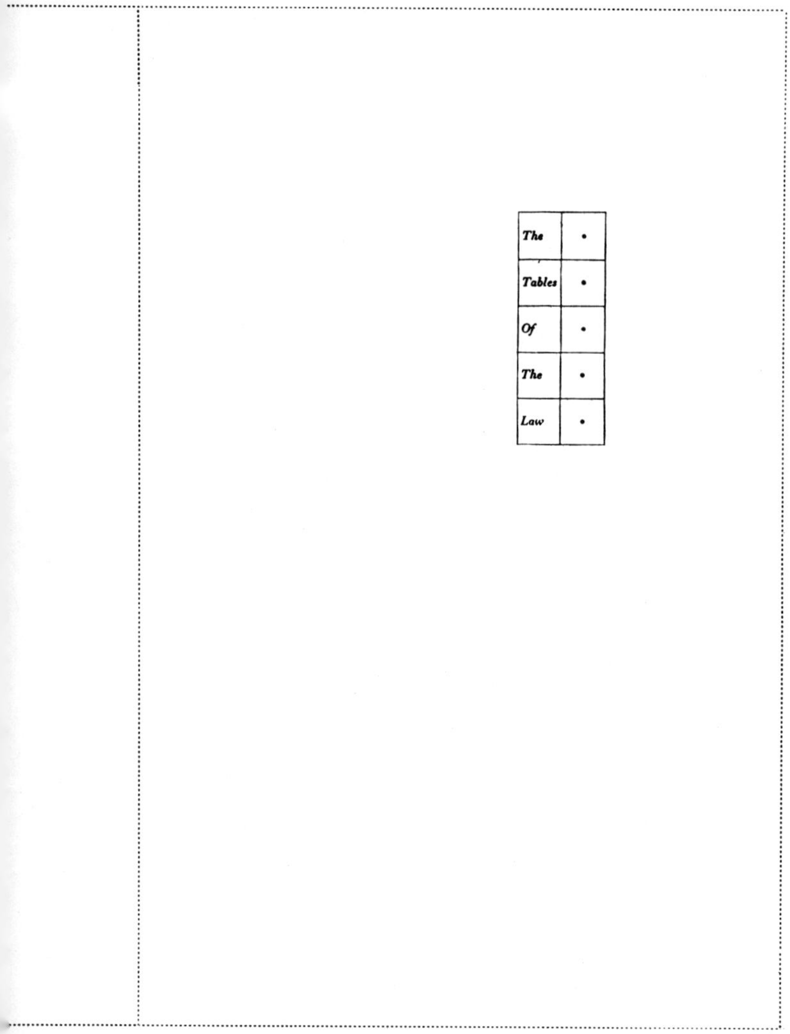

The	•
Tables	•
Of	•
The	•
Law	•

Although Paul Rand used the half- title , it is incorporated in a strongly suggestive design element.

HALF-TITLE

The half-title before the title is a superfluous anachronism. It originated when books were stored and sold without covers, to be bound individually for the purchaser. For protection, the title page was printed on p.3, so p.1 needed the title for outer identification of the volume. This requirement has not existed on any large scale for generations, but the practice hangs on.

The first half-title may be eliminated entirely and the page left blank, or the page may be used for some other purpose. Much can be said for placing the dedication there. An inscription and/or autograph by the author is ordinarily written on this page (or the flyleaf of the endpaper), so it seems reasonable that his dedication should appear at the very beginning of the book rather than several pages back.

Page 1 may be used for a symbol or other element that sets the tone of the book or that builds up to the title page. This might be a quotation supplied by the author, it might be an illustration suggestive of the whole book, it might be an element of the title page

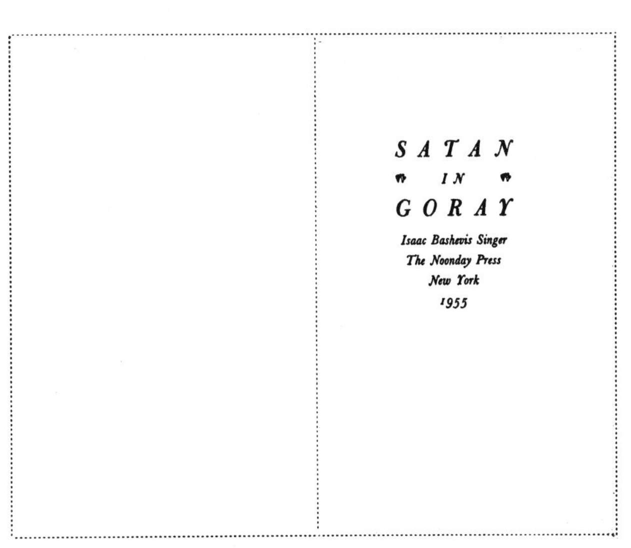

In this book designed by the author, a pattern of type ornaments is used on page 1 to introduce the title page.

(such as a subtitle or a series title), or it could be the author's initials. This is a wonderful opportunity to set the stage or play an overture.

An increasing practice is to use p.1 for a blurb about the book. This is a logical substitute for the jacket flap copy when there is to be no jacket (CH.26).

If the title *must* be repeated here, it should be made as inconspicuous as possible. Bear in mind that it appears on the jacket, binding, title page, and (sometimes) second half-title as well. The repetition is particularly irritating if there is little frontmatter, when the title page is preceded and followed by half-titles in rapid succession.

In designing p.1, remember that it is part of a spread, of which the other part is the endpaper. Also, consider what will happen to p.2 when the material on p.1 shows through, especially when 2 is part of the title spread. Try to back up all elements, particularly in books using lightweight paper.

AD CARD

The ad card is generally on the title page, but it is just as effective on another except, perhaps, where it is desirable to call attention to a successful previous work by a little-known author. In this case, the older form of ad is sometimes used, i.e. "author of . . ." is placed beneath the author's name. Usually, however, there is a separate heading ("other books by . . .", etc.) under which the titles are listed. Wherever it appears, this type may be quite small.

When it is not on the title spread, the ad card is usually placed ahead of it—which requires at least 2 additional pages. The usual practice is to put the ad on p.3, making the title spread 4 and 5.

TITLE PAGE

See CH.22.

COPYRIGHT

The copyright notice customarily appears on the page backing the right side of the title spread or, occasionally, on the title page itself.*

Other material than the notice usually appears with it. The Library of Congress catalogue card number is almost always on the copyright page, as is, when applicable, a statement that the book was manufactured in the United States of America (this is not part of the copyright notice, but it is important). The printer's name frequently is added, as well as a credit for the designer. Acknowledgments that involve copyrights (as in anthologies) should appear on the copyright page. If there are too many to fit on this page, they should begin on it and run over to the next page. (There is a divergence of legal opinion in this matter.)

The copyright notice is not meant for the reader and may be set very small. As in credits on pictures, legibility is all that is required. Only a few people need to read the type on the copyright page, and they are likely to be librarians concerned with the Library of Congress number rather than the copyright notice itself. Occasionally, more important credits are included, and they are set larger.

Although the copyright-page content is usually of little interest, the type on it is a graphic element of the book no less important than any other. (In design, there are no unimportant parts. Everything must be on the same level of quality or the whole looses its wholeness.) The copyright notice may be greatly subordinated in *emphasis*, but it must be entirely consistent in *style* with the rest of the book. It is necessary to stress this point because it is so common to see copyright pages that are badly at odds with the general scheme. Even in many otherwise well-designed books, one sees the copyright notice set as though it had not been given a thought. The most frequent fault is the use of a centered arrangement in a book that has an asymmetrical pattern, or vice versa. The effect is

* The present (1965) copyright law requires that the notice be printed "on the title page or the page immediately following it". The proposed revision of the law would be less specific.

jarring. (Some publishers insist on a uniform arrangement of the copyright notice for all their books, even though this results in some grotesque clashes in style.)

The copyright page is part of a spread that includes the facing page, and should be designed as such. However, try to back up elements of the title page with copyright-page copy, to avoid the latter showing through in open areas. To accomplish this, the copy may be set in any reasonable and suitable arrangement—line for line, centered, flush left or right, run-in in a block, all together, or in 2 or more parts.

A spread with copyright notice poorly related.

COPYRIGHT, 1946, BY JAMES M. CAIN

All rights reserved. No part of this book may be reproduced in any form without permission in writing from the publisher, except by a reviewer who may quote brief passages in a review to be printed in a magazine or newspaper.

FIRST PRINTING, MAY, 1949
SECOND PRINTING, NOVEMBER, 1949
THIRD PRINTING, DECEMBER, 1949
FOURTH PRINTING, MAY, 1955

Preface

THIS STORY goes back to 1922, when I was much under the spell of the Big Sandy country and anxious to make it the locale of a novel that would deal with its mine wars and utilize its "beautiful bleak ugliness," as I called it at the time, as setting. I went down there, worked in its mines, studied, trudged, and crammed, but when I came back was unequal to the novel; indeed, it was another ten years before it entered my mind again that I might be able to write a novel, for I had at least learned it is no easy trick, despite a large body of opinion to the contrary. But then I did write a novel, and the earlier idea began recurring to me—not the part about labor, for reflection had long since convinced me that this theme, though it constantly attracts a certain type of intellectual, is really dead seed for a novelist—but the rocky, wooded countryside itself, together with the clear, cool creeks that purl through it, and its gentle, charming inhabitants, whose little hamlets quite often look as they must have looked in the time of Daniel Boone. And then one day, in California, I encountered a family from Kentucky, running a roadside sandwich place. Certain reticences about a charming little boy they had led me to suspect he was the reason for the hegira from Harlan County, and the idea for a story began to take shape in my mind

v

A well-designed spread.

Library of Congress Catalog No. 63-13496
Copyright © The Joseph H. Hirshhorn Foundation

All rights reserved. No part of this book may be reproduced in any form without permission in writing from The Joseph H. Hirshhorn Foundation, except by a reviewer who may quote brief passages in a review to be printed in a magazine or newspaper.

Distributed simultaneously in Canada by McClelland and Stewart, Ltd.
Manufactured in the United States of America by H. Wolff, New York

The pine tree, used on flags during the American Revolution, was the official emblem of the Armory Show. The lettering used for the title on the title-page and the initials at the beginning of each chapter is adapted from the cover of the March, 1913 issue of Arts and Decoration that featured the original Armory Show.

To
The members of the
Association of American Painters and Sculptors,
in memory.

DEDICATION

If there is a dedication, it usually appears on the page facing the copyright, although the first page seems a more logical position. When frontmatter is being compressed to save pages, the dedication is sometimes placed on the copyright page itself.

The dedication should dominate the spread, but it should not be too large. Text size is about right under most circumstances. Names can be given added importance by setting them in small caps with letterspacing.

Authors frequently type their dedications in quite definite patterns (usually centered) but the arrangement should be made to follow sense and the typographic style of the book. After copyright notices, dedications are the most commonly incongruous elements.

ACKNOWLEDGMENTS

How acknowledgments are set will depend on their nature and importance. Some are routine (such as the anthology credits mentioned in connection with copyrights) and some are virtually recognition of co-authorship. In many cases, the acknowledgments are not so important to the book as they are to the author, who may use them to gain good will or repay obligations. At other times, an acknowledgment may be so sincerely felt as to constitute almost a dedication. The typographic treatment may range from the 8 or 9 pt. of the copyright notice to text size. One size smaller than text is usually appropriate. On extensive acknowledgments, the heading may be set in chapter-opening style; on brief copy, a subhead style will do. When only a few lines are involved, the heading may be omitted.

PREFACE & FOREWORD

There is some confusion about what is a preface, a foreword, and an introduction. The terms are often exchanged without any apparent reason. To some degree, the confusion is justified, because most dictionaries give about the same definition for all 3. The only useful distinction is that a preface is about the book as a whole, while an introduction discusses the text itself. A preface is most often either a background note by the author about the writing of the book or a comment on the book and/or the author by another person. An introduction may contain such matter, but it is primarily a preparation for, or explanation of, the content. These would seem to be editorial questions, but they are of concern to the designer in that they affect the placement of the copy in the frontmatter. (Foreword would seem to be interchangeable with preface.)

It is logical to put prefaces *before* the contents because they are not part of the text. (Also, when the preface is written by a prominent person, commercial considerations indicate a position up front.) An exception is made, sometimes, when the preface is so long that it pushes the contents page too far into the book.

In most cases, prefaces are set in text size, with the heading treated as a chapter opening. Occasionally, an exception is made when a brief but very important preface is set more prominently than the text, or one is set in another size in order to adjust the length of the book. However, the readability of a preface should not be reduced excessively unless there is an editorial reason.

CONTENTS

The contents page has been the least satisfactorily solved problem in book design from the beginning. The early printers got off on the wrong foot and stayed there. In this matter, convention is of no help and is best disregarded. Logic and instinct must be the guides.

Especially in a complex book, the contents page is a major problem in typographic design. A good one is an efficient tool, but it must also be closely integrated with the typographic scheme of the book. In addition, the contents page has a role in selling the book, and this must be played well too.

Primarily, the contents is an aid in using the book. Its function is to simplify finding material and to clarify the organization.

☞ **CONTENTS**

A complicated contents

When the contents will not fit on 1 page but will fit on 2, it is better to run it on facing pages rather than on a right-hand page and its back-up. This eliminates the inconvenience of turning the page, and enables both reader and buyer to see all of it in a glance. (There is always the danger that a browser will think the book contains only what is shown on the first page of contents.)

Contents

Since the main purpose of a contents is to show where each item may be found, the most practical place for the page numbers (folios) is directly *following* the item titles. It is sufficient to separate title and folio with an em space in most cases, although a punctuation mark or ornament may be preferable when the items are crowded or, as sometimes happens, the titles end with figures (for instance dates). The folios may be placed *before* (to the left of) the titles if there are no chapter numerals, and they will function well enough placed immediately *below* the titles in a centered arrangement with not too many items. The important point is that the folios should be *adjacent* to the titles.

In the past, it was customary to place the titles flush left and the folios flush right, with a row of periods (*leaders*) joining one to the other. Not so many years ago, it was recognized that leaders look awful, so, instead of eliminating the need for them by moving the folios close to the titles, the leaders were eliminated, thus making it more difficult to find the page numbers. In some books with a wide text page and short chapter titles, it is almost impossible to tell which folio belongs to each title without using a ruler to align them. This arrangement is still used in some books, although it would appear to have no advantage except in making it convenient to add up the folios, if anyone should care to do so. The practice

CONTENTS

CONTENTS.

CONTENTS

Left, *a contents page with leaders;* right, *folios aligned but close.*

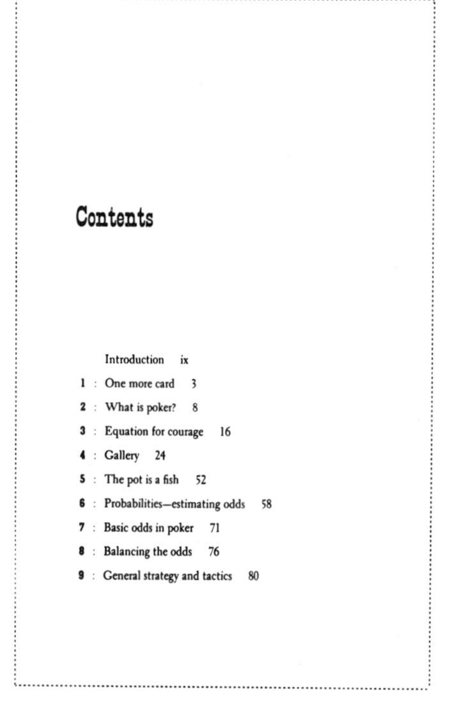

Contents

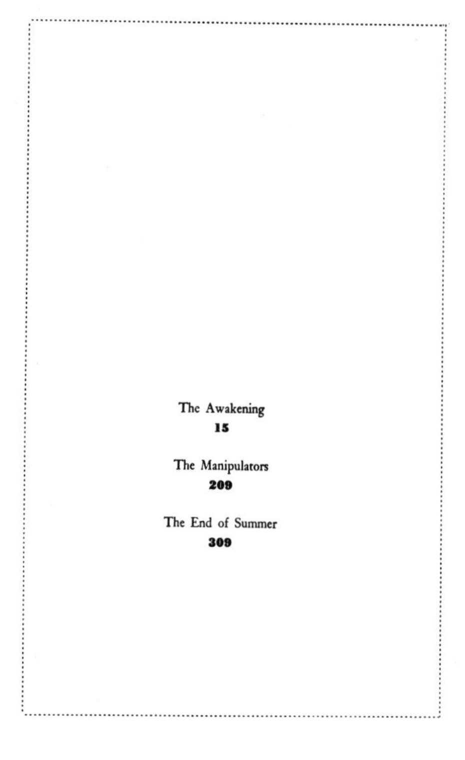

Left, *folios adjacent to titles;* right, *folios centered under titles.*

can be used successfully if the titles are all of about the same length, and the line of folios is moved so it is no more than about an em to the right of the longest title.

The contents should be extremely legible—which requires careful spacing as well as proper choice of type face and size. A judicious use of leading and indentions can set off a line of quite small type so that it is clearly visible, whereas a crowded page of larger type may be more difficult to read. In a complicated contents, a variety of sizes, italics, caps, small caps, boldface, and even other faces should be used as necessary to make a clear and practical page. Economy should not be maintained at the expense of usefulness in a contents page.

Normally, there is no need to set the word "chapter" above the chapter numbers, or to set the word "page" above a column of folios, if there is one. It is perfectly obvious what these numbers are. Also, there is usually no value in putting running heads and folios on contents pages, as these only add to the problem of simplifying and clarifying. Occasionally, a contents running head is desirable in a book that contains much material similar to a contents in appearance, and folios might be called for on a long contents that is preceded by a long, folioed preface.

It can be assumed that the book will be read from front to back, so there is no need to make reference on the contents page to items that precede it. If, however, there is a preface by a prominent person, it may be commercially desirable to list it, with the author's name.

LIST OF ILLUSTRATIONS

The functional problem of a list of illustrations is about the same as that of a contents. The titles should be legible and the folios should be adjacent to them.

One problem is how to refer to illustrations on unfolioed inserts and wraps. A practical solution is to use the term "facing page . . ." for single pages, and "following page . . ." where a group of such pages occur together. The reader is thus directed to the group of illustration pages containing the picture he wants to find, and he finds the picture itself by using the sequence in the list.

INTRODUCTION

An introduction is almost always set like the text and has an opening in the style of the chapters. When it is considered part of the frontmatter, it may be set differently from the text in order to adjust the length of the book. When it is part of the text, it would be rather awkward to set it differently, but this may be done in some circumstances. For example, if the introduction is by a different writer than the text (as in anthologies) it may be desirable to set it in another style to emphasize this fact.

A question of style arises when the introduction (or preface) is signed by its author. If he is the author of the text, no signature is really needed, but it is not uncommon to use his initials at the end, often with a dateline. The latter is usually set on the left, in a small size. An introduction by another author should probably have his name at the beginning, particularly if he is a prominent person whose name adds stature to the book. More often, however, the name will appear at the end.

In this connection, it is worth mentioning an odd and unexplained phenomenon. Almost invariably, and even though there may not be another style indication anywhere in the Ms, the signature on the preface or introduction will be marked for cap and small cap. It is never marked for even small caps, all caps, or italics, and it is rarely unmarked. The mystery is double—what fascination causes this particular item to be singled out for marking? and what universal force impels every author and/or editor to choose this particular style? The answer would be simple if we had one school in which all editors were trained uniformly, but alas, this is not so—and the mystery remains.

SECOND HALF-TITLE

The second half-title has, unlike the first, a real function—to mark the end of the frontmatter and the beginning of the text. It is usually called p.1, being considered part of the text. Ordinarily, the pages that precede it are numbered in a sequence of Roman numerals (i, ii, iii, etc.). This enables the text to be made up into pages independently of the frontmatter, which is more subject to last-minute changes in copy and length. Many books, especially brief ones, are folioed all through in Arabic numerals.

If a first half-title was set, the second may be an exact repetition of it. Otherwise, the book title may be set, or some other material may be used on this page such as was suggested for the first page.

When the book is divided into parts, it is not necessary to have a second half-title, as its function is performed by the first part-title. However, when the introduction is considered part of the text, it is preceded by a second half-title and is folioed in the sequence of arabic numerals. The first part-title, if any, follows.

Backmatter

The backmatter, though not part of the text, continues in the sequence of arabic folios, as changes in it will not affect the text pagination.

Whether or not there are part-titles in the text, they are generally used to divide the various parts of the backmatter, provided these are reasonably long—say, 6 pages or more. Such part-titles may be omitted to save space, but then it is desirable to begin each part of the backmatter on a right-hand page.

Backmatter may contain almost any kind of material, but it can all be encompassed under the following headings, listed in the order usually followed:

(1) Appendix
(2) Notes
(3) Bibliography
(4) Glossary
(5) Index
(6) Colophon

The sequence is not especially important. In general, it is best to put material to which the reader may want to refer at the end, where it is most accessible. Thus, if there is an index, it is invariably the last item (except for the colophon which, if it appears at all, takes only 1 page). Sometimes a glossary or list of abbreviations should be used while reading. If these cannot be placed at the end, it may be possible to print them on the endpapers.

Some publishers include a brief note about the author at the very end of the book. It is rarely more than 1 page.

APPENDIX

The appendix is really a catchall for any material that neither is part of the text nor falls under one of the other backmatter headings. Appendixes (or appendices, take your choice) may be letters, lists, tables, documents, charts, forms, speeches, etc.; anything that supplements or supports the text. The nature of the copy may vary from straight text to very complicated tabular material, so there is no way to indicate how it should be set.

The design of appendixes must, however, be based on their use. Don't set them very small just because they are not very important. If they are expected to be read, make them reasonably readable.

NOTES

Notes in the backmatter are likely to be references of interest to the scholar and researcher rather than the reader. Even if they are extensive, they are not meant for continuous reading so they may be set very small (usually 8 pt.). If they are explanatory in nature, they should be set larger and made quite readable.

Reference notes should be made easy to use, so the subheads and running heads on these pages should be treated as they would be in reference books (CHS.18,28).

BIBLIOGRAPHY

There are some variations in bibliography style, but generally the author comes first, followed by the book title, publisher's address (city), publisher's name, year of publication. Often, 1 or more of the last 3 items are omitted.

There is not much need for rapid reference in a bibliography so it isn't very important to use a distinctive way of setting the authors' names. They may be set in small caps, with a deep indent (usually 3 ems) for turnovers, or simply in roman upper and lower case with the book titles in italics. Bibliographies may be set quite small if necessary, but if the list of books is very brief, it is just as well set in text size, or any other size that is being used elsewhere in the backmatter. Sometimes there is a paragraph of description for each title, and these are usually set in a smaller size.

GLOSSARY

A glossary is essentially a dictionary. The items should be set so as to stand out from the definitions, especially if the latter are lengthy. Caps work well, but if the definitions do not turn over, the caps may look too crowded one under the other. Small caps work better in this case; they are just as distinctive, but have more space around them. Boldface upper and lower case is satisfactory, but involves expense if a Mixer is needed (CHS.5,12). Most italics do not make sufficient contrast unless the definitions are long, in which case the turnovers may be indented (hanging indent) so that the items stand out. Use a generous indent—at least 2 ems. A colon or dash after the items helps set them off.

There is no reason to capitalize the items unless they would ordinarily begin with a capital. To cap *all* the words eliminates the distinction between proper nouns and others.

abhyāntara vṛitti—that variety of *prāṇāyāma* in which the inhaled breath is held at maximal or near maximal lung capacity for as long as possible.
Aham Brahmāsmi—one of the great Vedic utterances used by a meditator as an aid in reaching the supreme state. It means "I am *Brahman*."
ahamkāra—universal ego, of which the individual sense of "I-ness" is a manifestation.
ahiṃsā—noninjury by body, speech, and mind, and the general attitude of welfare for the entire world. It is one of the yamas.
ājñā cakra(m)—the sixth of the seven *cakras*. It is located in the midbrain and is represented by the thalamus, which is the center of individual consciousness.

INDEX

The index is a unique typographic problem because the copy does not appear until after pages have been made up (except when the book is being reset from another edition). Its length must be a guess (CH.16) unless, after makeup, you calculate how many lines will fit in the space available and tell the editor how many items can be used.

To do this, allow for sinkage on the first page and make a liberal allowance for turnovers (25% should be enough). Thus, if you have 8 pages, and there is room for 50 lines per column, with 2 columns per page you will have 100 lines per page or a total of 800 lines, less whatever is used for sinkage. If this is 70 lines (actually 35 lines x 2 columns), there will be 730 lines available. To leave some room for error, drop half of the last page (50 lines), leaving 680. If 25% of the lines (170) are turnovers, there will be room for 510 items. This might work.

The index does not have to be set large, but the more legible it is the better. If necessary, however, the type size may go down to 7 or even 6 pt., with no leading. If the trim-size is large enough to take 3 columns of 9 or 10 picas in width, plus about 9 pts. between columns, this may be a better solution for a long index. If the index is too short, it may be padded out by using a type almost as large as the text size, with 2 or 3 pts. of leading. Another method is to insert space between the alphabetical breaks. This may be justified somewhat by using large initial letters in the spaces. Rather than making a ridiculously inflated index, it might be better to add a part-title, or find another means of using the extra pages (CH.20).

The organization of index copy is quite standardized, as there is not much choice. The problem is to indicate the relative value of sub-items, sub-sub-items, etc. by indention, without getting them confused with turnover lines. In a simple index having only 1 class of sub-items, the main items are flush, the sub-items are indented 1 em, and the turnovers of both are indented 2 ems. When there are 3 or 4 classes of sub-items, each with turnovers, matters become more difficult. However, the problem is purely mechanical and will submit to a little thought aided by some rough diagrams.

There is a matter of choice in the use of "continued" lines. When sub-items or turnovers fall at the top of a column, some prefer to reset the main item, followed by (continued) or (cont.), above the first line. This is done mainly when the break comes at the top of the first column on a left-hand page; less often where the break is from a left-hand to a right-hand page (facing pages). The use of "continued" lines it not vital, and may be decided on the basis of available space.

COLOPHON

In the early days of printing, the colophon was the printer-publisher's signature, usually consisting of a trademark and some information—his name, address, patron, date, etc. This material became separated when the functions of printer and publisher divided. Today, the publisher's name and address are called the imprint, his trademark is often called the colophon, and sometimes a paragraph of information about the book's design and manufacture is called a colophon also. The imprint and trademark now appear on the title page, while the descriptive colophon—which contains the name of the designer, printer, etc.—is usually put on the last page, although it sometimes appears on the copyright page. In most books, there is no descriptive colophon at all. In some, it appears as a rather precious survival. There is, however, a proper place for a straightforward colophon in books of such quality as to justify pride on the part of all concerned with their making.

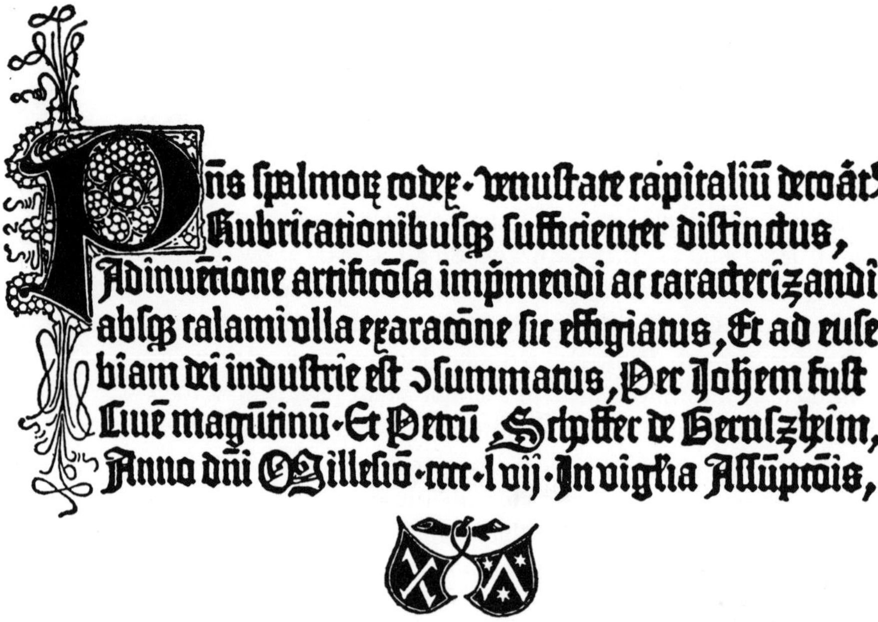
Pñs spalmoꝝ codex · venustate capitaliũ decoratꝰ
Rubricationibusq; sufficienter distinctus,
Adinuẽtione artificiosa imprimendi ac caracterizandi ·
absq; calami ulla exaracõne sic effigiatus, Et ad euse
biam dei industrie est cõsummatus, Per Johẽm fust
Ciuẽ magũtinũ · Et Petrũ Schoffer de Gernszheim,
Anno dñi Millesĩo · cccc · lvij · In vigilia Assũpcõis,

The colophon in Fust and Schoeffer's Psalter *of 1457.*

24 | Page makeup & proofs

Makeup

Page makeup (CH.5) follows the castoff (CH.20) to whatever degree is appropriate. If the castoff was unjustified, an attempt is made to arrive at the same total number of pages, but there may be variations within the total. A justified castoff can be followed exactly. The danger here is that an error in its paging will throw off the entire makeup.

Most problems are solved in a justified castoff, but there is 1 matter remaining—the handling of running heads. The questions are: (a) Should running heads appear on pages that have run-in chapters or subheads at the top? (b) What copy shall be used for running heads? (c) How shall the copy be cut if it will not fit in the space and style provided?

■ *Run-in heads at top of page*—This question is largely esthetic. An important factor is the amount of contrast between the running head and the title. If they are at all similar in style they are less acceptable together than if they are very different. Usually, the running head, if not the folio, is omitted over chapter titles and retained over subheads. A practical consideration is the copy involved. When the running head repeats the title immediately beneath it, the repetition seems needless.

■ *Running-head copy*—The sample pages establish a general pattern, but many books have elements that do not conform. The scheme may call for part-title left and chapter title right, but what if there should be an untitled introduction after a part-title, or an epilogue after the last part, or some other such problem? There is no stock answer. In each case, the answer must fit the circumstances. Sometimes, the solution may be elimination of 1 running head; at other times, repetition of the same head on both sides. If the latter is chosen, and the left- and right-hand running heads are set in different styles, which style will be used?

▪ *Cutting running-head copy*—This is an editorial function, of concern to the designer mainly in that the necessity for such cutting should be minimized (CH.8). If titles *must* be cut, give the editor the maximum number of characters.

Where a dummy has been made, makeup is a routine matter of following instructions (CH.5)—presuming that the dummy has been properly marked (CH.21).

If the book is set in metal type to be printed by letterpress from type or duplicate plates (CHS.5,7), no further choice is necessary. When photomechanical plates are to be made, the page makeup may be accomplished by (a) making a mechanical, (b) stripping-up film, (c) a combination of these, or (d) a combination of metal type makeup and one or both of the other methods. The considerations are both technical and economic (CHS.5,7,11,12).

Page proofs

Because of the high cost of making corrections in pages, the checking of page proofs should involve no changes in layout except, perhaps, when an exceptionally complicated page fails to work out properly. (Even this will not occur where a dummy has been made.) Otherwise, it should be enough to make certain that the makeup instructions were followed properly. Where the makeup follows an unjustified castoff, some unfortunate breaks may occur, but these are probably unavoidable and cannot be corrected without major changes.

Changes in metal-type pages are usually most expensive. Pages in film, particularly where the elements have been stripped up, often can be corrected with somewhat less difficulty.

In books consisting mainly of text, there will be little to check in page proofs other than running heads, the handling of run-in breaks, folios, and the makeup of chapter-opening pages. The latter can be a problem when uniform sinkage is desired. The number of text lines on the opening pages may increase or decrease because of run-in breaks or widows. It is important that instructions be given to provide for the disposition of space in such cases. It it usually best to maintain the sinkage and the space between items of display, letting the space between the display and text vary as necessary. However, where chapters begin on right-hand pages only, it is possible to maintain all of the spacing, letting the foot margin vary. This will not usually be noticed since there is no facing full page.

When the pages consist of many illustrations and only some or no text, page proofs are crucial and must be examined carefully, especially where bleeds are involved. The checking of *all* spaces and dimensions would be excessively tedious, and it is usually sufficient to compare the page proofs visually with the dummy, measuring only those spaces that appear to be incorrect. It is helpful to draw the outlines of the trim-size on tracing paper or acetate and lay this over the proof. Litho and gravure printers supply page proofs in the form of folded and trimmed blueprints, which greatly facilitates checking.

Unless letterpress page proofs (instead of galleys) are being used for book club submission or reviews (which sometimes occurs with illustrated books) the only copies pulled, usually, are the author's set and two duplicates, one of which is kept by the compositor. Lithographers charge separately for page blueprints and normally only 1 set is ordered. The customs of the cold-composition houses (CH.5) vary according to the kind of product and proof involved.

When page proofs are returned, indicate whether corrected pages are wanted or not. If photomechanical plates are involved, indicate whether or not plate proofs are to be pulled. With metal-type duplicate plates being made, specify whether foundry or plate proofs are wanted.

Foundry & plate proofs

In letterpress, the checking of foundry proofs (CH.5) should be solely for the purpose of detecting any errors made in correcting the pages, or any damage to type or engravings that may have occurred in the lockup. Plate faults are likely to consist of broken characters, light or heavy areas, black spots due to type-high background, and white spots caused by damage to the type or finished plate. Bad faults will probably be caught by the printer, but if a very high standard of quality is desired, it is best to check plate proofs carefully yourself.

Foundry and plate proofs are rarely sent to the author, so only 2 sets are pulled—1 for the publisher and 1 for the compositor. Sometimes, when the schedule is tight, plating proceeds while the foundry proofs are being read. If this arrangement is desired, there should be a clear understanding with the compositor to this effect, otherwise plating will begin only after foundry proof has been OKd.

In lithography and gravure, plate proofs are not usually made, for 2 reasons: (a) as the plate is an entire form, the cost of proofs pulled on the large press sometimes required is very high and (b) there is little likelihood of damage in photomechanical plates made from negatives that have been checked in blueprints. However, the lack of such proofs has been a distinct disadvantage of these printing methods, and there is an increasing demand for them.

25 | Ordering printing

The book is ready to go to press when (a) all proofs have been finally corrected and approved, (b) the plates, if any, have been made and checked for quality, errors, and damage, (c) the paper is on hand, and (d) the printer is in possession of complete instructions and a written, signed order to proceed. In order to arrive at this point, it is necessary to select a printer.

Selecting a printer

In choosing a plumber or shoemaker, the only considerations are their competence, reliability, and prices, plus your personal convenience and preference. Presumably, any of them can do what you require. When selecting a printer, all of the same considerations are involved, but in addition you must find a printer who is equipped with the plant and experience to match the specific job in question. Printers vary tremendously in the kind of work they can do—and do well.

A man with a platen job press is a printer, and so is one with a dozen 4-color web-offset presses with synchronized folders. If you need 300 letterheads, the first man is the best printer for you. Should you want 100,000 copies of a book illustrated with full-color photography, it is strongly suggested that you select the second man. The economical printing of *any* job requires selection of a printer specializing in that kind of work. The job-press man *could* print your book, and the man with the web-fed press *could* print your letterheads—but in both cases the cost would be astronomically higher.

Until you have had enough experience to find the right printer yourself, it is best to ask the advice of an expert. A direct approach to a printer may be successful—if he happens to be the right one himself or if he sends you to a suitable shop. However, there is always the chance that he may take the job himself even though he is not a good choice for it. He may need the work badly or he may not know enough to realize that another printer could do the job better.

There are many considerations involved in matching printer to job, but the main ones are:

(a) the *kind* of presses he has (letterpress, offset lithography, gravure),

(b) the *size* presses he has,

(c) the *number* of presses he has (this relates to capacity to produce),

(d) the kind of work he has done,

(e) the quality of his work,

(f) his schedule, and

(g) his prices.

The printing order

All the information needed by the printer should appear on the printing order except details relating to individual pages, and at least a reference to those details should be included. For example, if it is necessary to provide a dummy giving individual margins for each page, the printing order should have a note indicating that such a dummy is being supplied. This insures that no directions will be overlooked because they are separate from the order.

The printing order should constitute both the official instructions and the official authorization for doing the job. The latter requires only (a) a statement to the effect that the job is to be done according to the instructions thereon, (b) the number of copies to be printed, (c) the place to which the sheets are to be delivered, and (d) the buyer's signature with the date.

The instructions should be complete, and it is best to use a printed form—if only to be sure that nothing is overlooked. On the next page is a sample form which could be used for any kind of printing.

DIFFERENT KINDS OF PRINTING

There are basic differences between ordering (a) letterpress and (b) offset lithography or gravure. (a) When ordering letterpress, the job is ordinarily ready to go on press, using type or plates produced in another shop (or another department). (b) In lithography or gravure, the plates will be made by the printer (CH.7). (This distinction is beginning to disappear, as letterpress printers use more photomechanical plates, but few of them have their own photoplatemaking facilities at this time.)

(a) In letterpress, it is necessary to arrange for delivery of type or plates to the pressroom, and to inform the printer of those arrangements (unless the composition was done in his own shop or was ordered through him). (b) For lithography or gravure, com-

Print Order

NO. ____________

DATE ____________

TO: ____

TITLE ____

AUTHOR ____

TEXT

QUANTITY ____________ TRIM SIZE ____________

________ PAGES, TO PRINT AS ____________, CANCEL ________ PAGES.

PRINT FROM ____________ YOU WILL RECEIVE FROM ____________

MARGINS: ____________ IN GUTTER; ____________ IN HEAD AFTER TRIM.

GET FOLDING IMPOSITION FROM ____________

IMPOSE FOR ____________

PAPER ____________

____________ FROM ____________

ILLUSTRATIONS

QUANTITY ____________. PAGES, AS ____________

COLOR(S): ____________ PRINTED ONE SIDE. PRINTED TWO SIDES.

PAPER ____________

____________ FROM ____________

LAYOUT

DELIVER SHEETS TO ____________

TO BE AT DESTINATION BY ____________

____

PRODUCTION DEPARTMENT

pleted mechanicals (CH.11), a dummy with marked copy (CH.21), or a combination of both must be delivered.

As lithography or gravure require ordering plates, your order must specify the kind of plates wanted and your proof requirements. It is a good practice to establish in advance who will own the plates and/or the negatives from which they are made. There has never been any question but that the customer owns letterpress plates, but in offset lithography in particular there has always been ambiguity on this point. The matter is important in determining who has the right to order the negatives *killed* [destroyed] and in establishing the customer's right to have them used by another printer.

INFORMATION REQUIRED

Regardless of the method of printing, the dimensions of the job must be clearly indicated. The trim-size, basic margins, total number of pages, and *layout* [the sequence and numbering of the pages] are the essential facts, and to these should be added any pertinent information about binding that would affect the imposition. The placement of all wraps and inserts should be indicated so that the printer will be aware of the need for any unusual arrangement of signatures. Although he will get his imposition from the binder, giving the printer the primary information is extra insurance against error.

Not only the name, size, weight, and quantity of the paper, but its source should be on the printing order. This enables the printer to make direct contact with the supplier in case any trouble with the stock should appear while on press. The paper is ordered in terms of weight and number of sheets (CH.8) but the printer keeps his records in *reams*, so it is best to indicate the quantity in that measure. Parts of reams are expressed in fractions, using twentieths as the unit (1 ream = 500 sheets, 200 sheets = 8/20 ream).

DUMMIES REQUIRED

- *Lithographic or gravure printing*—It is necessary to supply either (a) a dummy indicating the exact position of every element on every page in the book, (b) mechanicals on which everything is pasted in correct position, or (c) a combination of these. Often, a mechanical is supplied with some of the elements (usually the text, running heads, and folios), while the other material (usually illustrations and captions) is supplied separately with a dummy to indicate their position or with directions written on the mechanical. If the makeup is simple, the type elements may be supplied as loose page repros, with the illustrations again separate. As there would then be no mechanicals, a dummy must be provided. No dummy is needed for the text pages of books in which all have the same head and inside margins.
- *Letterpress*—Even when the margins vary there is usually no need

for a dummy if all pages are made up to the same size, and the plates, if any, are all the same size. The head margin is then measured to the top of the *page or plate*, so no distinction need be made between pages on which something appears at the top and those in which the highest element is further down the page. Even when the page layouts are quite irregular, it is necessary to indicate only 2 margins on each page in the final proof, as all the elements are already positioned in relation to each other.

It is good practice to provide for *any* printer a dummy showing the frontmatter and the first 3 pages of text, with margins indicated. This has several virtues: (a) the dummy enables the designer (and others) to see how the book will appear when printed —at least with respect to the positions of frontmatter and text pages in relation to the trim-size and, sequentially, in relation to each other, (b) the exact position of each item of frontmatter can be indicated, and (c) there is less chance of an error in pagination.

In ordering the printing of jackets, a dummy should be provided on which the positions of flap copy and back ad, as well as the front and spine, are indicated (CH.11).

COLOR SWATCHES & PROOFS

On printing orders, specify the color of ink to be used and, if there is to be a color other than black, provide a substantial swatch or specify a standard ink that can be ordered by the manufacturer's number. Swatches should be at least 2 square inches and solid in tone. Watercolor or pencil swatches that vary in color may be difficult to match. The ink should be specified as transparent or opaque, and the sequence of colors should be indicated where any question exists (CH.7).

When a letterpress job contains illustrations—particularly halftones—an engraver's proof of each cut should be sent with the printing order. This gives the printer a standard to work toward and enables him to determine if any blemishes on the cut are newly made or were in the original. In color printing, progressive proofs should be supplied.

If possible, the printing of separate sections of illustrations should be done after the text is off press. This enables the printer to adjust the illustration run to the actual net number of text sheets—which may be somewhat more or less than the quantity ordered.

Bear in mind that the printing order is a purchasing order; it should have a number and be treated as are other financial records.

26 | Binding design

The binding design as such has not been mentioned so far, although some binding factors have been considered in connection with the illustration arrangement (CH.17). In practice though, the binding design is ordinarily dealt with while the rest of the work is in progress, but it has been bypassed until now to avoid interrupting the discussions of text and illustration.

The first attention given to binding is in the creative visualization (CH.15). Then it is customary to provide some specifications on which to base a cost estimate, probably at the time of making the basic decisions (CH.16). Ideally, the actual binding design is made immediately after the sample pages, title page, etc. are designed, so that the entire book will be planned in 1 period without interruption or lapse of time. Unfortunately, it is rarely possible to work this way, but the main benefit of the procedure—a unity of concept—can be realized through the initial visualization. In any case, the general outlines of the binding design should be established by this stage.

To understand the problem of binding design (which refers to all features of the book other than the planning and printing of its pages) it is necessary to realize that a bookbinding has several functions.

The functions

Originally, the only purposes of a binding were to hold the pages together and protect them. The sheets were sewed together along the folded edge and wooden or leather boards were placed at the beginning and end of the book, to be held in place by leather thongs joined to the threads or cords holding the pages together. Later, leather or vellum covered the boards and extended around the spine, concealing the threads and cords.

Books were precious objects at that time (about the 9th century

A.D. in the Middle East and parts of Europe), so they were decorated—usually with gold tooling, sometimes with inlays of semi-precious stones. Except for the possible sales value in the marketing of a particularly handsome volume to a prince or merchant, it is unlikely that the decoration served any but an esthetic or devotional purpose. To a large extent, the books produced then were religious in nature, and the binding designs, as well as the illuminated pages, were acts of glorification. (If they were incidentally acts of vanity we should not object, because the results are so wonderful.) But, if binding decoration was not at first of practical value, the techniques developed were useful when they became needed a thousand years later.

Until printing spread through Europe, books were so few in number that it was unnecessary to have titles on their covers for identification. With a few exceptions, libraries of manuscripts were small, and their contents well known to their proud owners or custodians. When books became numerous, the binding acquired an additional function—identification of the content.

In the 19th century, competition among publishers resulted in the decoration of book bindings to attract buyers. At this point then, the binding had 4 distinct purposes:

(a) construction,
(b) protection,
(c) identification, and
(d) attraction.

To these is now added a 5th function. The binding must be *expressive* of the content. With the technical facilities that have become available in the past 30 years, it has become possible to create virtually any graphic effect on a book binding. Now the binding design may be integrated with the design of the text to produce an expressively unified entity. It is now possible to raise book design to a level of expression comparable to the other ancillary arts, such as architecture, stage design, or theatre music.

VARIATIONS

The functions of binding apply not only to the casebound book, but to paperbacks and mechanical binding, although not in exactly the same way. To these variations must be added the problem of the jacket.

■ *Jackets*—The introduction of book jackets (CH.10) has complicated development of binding design in particular and book design in general. To a large extent, the jacket is a superfluous cover, performing some of the functions which should—and now could—be performed by the real cover of the book.

Having begun life as a plain paper wrapper meant to prevent soiling, the jacket was given a sales role when the marketing of books became more aggressive (in the 1890s). When publishers wanted to apply the new techniques of advertising design to their books, it was not possible to achieve the desired effects on book covers, nor were there many artists capable of such design then working in the book field. The solution was to use the wrappers as posters, and call in advertising artists to design them.

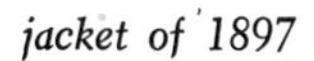

jacket of 1897

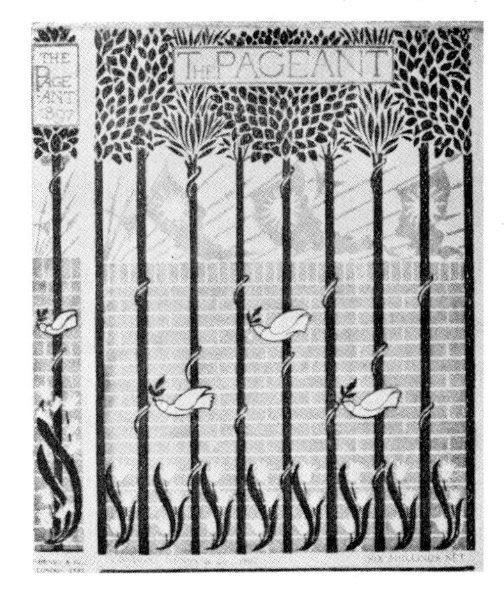

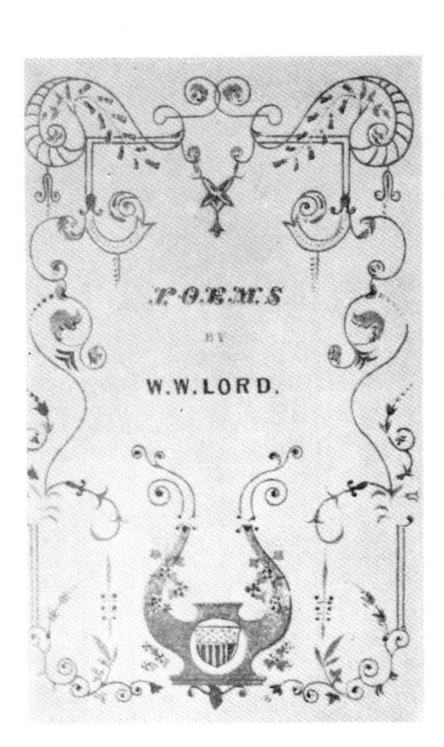

book jacket of 1845

Today, the wrapper is not needed for its original purpose of protection. The application of plastics to binding can provide much better resistance to soiling and abrasion. The jacket's role in identification and attraction, as well as its ability to be expressive, are now well within the possibilities of the book cover, due to modern printing and binding techniques.

In cost, the conventional binding plus a jacket is not less—and may be more—than the kind of cover that needs no jacket. In fact, a book with a jacket actually has 2 covers.

That this is unnecessary is demonstrated by the millions of paperbacks in existence—particularly the trade paperbacks. These lines, one of the most successful parts of book publishing today, have no jackets, sell to a considerable extent on the attractiveness of their cover designs, and provide less protection for their pages than any unjacketed hard-bound book. A place in them is found for advertising copy, even though there are no "flaps"—and book buyers seem to find and read this copy.

Why do jackets continue to be used? Well, for one thing, by the time they became unnecessary they were a "tradition"—and traditions die very hard in the book business. More important is the legitimate doubt that covers can succeed in serving the poster requirements of a jacket and also maintain a pleasing aspect in keeping with the restrained character of some books. Certainly it is easier to design a jacket or a paper cover if there is no need to integrate it with the design of the text, which means that there is no compromise in the quest for maximum display effect. This fact, combined with a few relatively minor advantages, such as their value in library display and their usefulness in showing favorable comments, etc., will probably keep jackets in use for a long time to come, despite their anomalous role and economic impracticality.

▪ *Paperbacks*—For a paperback binding, somewhat lower standards of construction and protection generally prevail. In the other 3 respects—identification, attraction, and expression—the paperback covers, can, and often do, perform superlatively, although here, as on jackets, the expressive function is sometimes slighted in favor of the poster needs.

▪ *Mechanical binding*—The mechanical binding is used in lieu of either case or paperback binding when its particular structural features are required, and these are quite unique. As far as identification, attraction, and expression are concerned, it functions as any external cover (mechanical bindings rarely have jackets).

Functional factors in binding design

Each decision in binding design must take into account all the functional factors. Consideration of the functions is not separated in practice because almost all decisions involve more than 1, but it is useful here to think of the binding design elements in terms of the individual functional problems for which they are the solutions.

The manufacturing processes and materials are described in CH.10. Binding costs in general are discussed in CH.12 Here we deal only with the influence of these factors on binding design decisions.

For visual purposes, the design of jackets, paper covers, and hard covers will be considered varying aspects of 1 problem—cover design. A distinction will be made only when a point peculiar to 1 aspect is discussed. However, bear in mind that cover design is only 1 of the visual factors in binding.

CONSTRUCTION

The aspects of construction that most affect binding design are: (a) the method of holding the pages together and (b) the endpapers.

■ *Method of holding pages*—The choice of method (sewing, stapling, gluing, or mechanical binding) depends on the nature of the book and the costs.

The advantages of perfect-binding are obvious. No sewing or utilitarian considerations prevent folding larger (and thus fewer) signatures. Single leaves may be inserted without concern for the weakness or cost of tipping, and the book is ready to be joined to its cover with several fewer operations than is a sewed book.

It is not price but function that indicates the use of a mechanical binding. With some of these, a book can be made to not only lie perfectly flat when open, but to stand up like an easel or to fold back on itself so that it is no larger when open than closed. Others enable pages to be removed, inserted, or changed around. When such attributes are wanted, a mechanical binding of some kind is required.

Some of the spiral wire kinds are fairly inexpensive, while the loose-leaf ring or post bindings can run into large sums. Generally, mechanical bindings cost more than the standard case binding.

The cost of materials in a mechanical binding is more significant than in other binding methods. This cost varies not only with the trim-size of the book and the kind of apparatus used, but with the book's thickness. As the bulk increases, the strength—and therefore the weight—of the wire or plastic used must increase also. In fact, it is not generally feasible to use a spiral or plastic binding on books over about 1″ in bulk.

Because of the way mechanical bindings are made, this is a practical method to use when only a few copies are needed. There is little of the high cost of setting up automatic machines, so the unit cost for a few hundred copies (or 1 copy!) is not very much more than for several thousand.

If sewing is used, the choice between Smyth and side stitching will probably be made for you. Side stitching holds the pages together so well that it is quite difficult to keep the book open, so it is used only where utility and appearance must be sacrificed to strength. This method is now required for almost all school uses below the college level, and is almost essential for library sales of children's books.

Saddle-wire stitching is used mainly for pamphlets, where there is only 1 signature and a paper cover. Side-wire stitching is probably the strongest and cheapest method of holding pages together, but it is more objectionable than side sewing with thread.

The kind of text and illustration paper used has a bearing on the choice of binding method. This is discussed in CHS. 8 and 10.

▪ *Endpapers*—A book with many pages of heavy coated paper needs a stronger endpaper than another of the same trim-size but printed on a bulking antique. Two books of identical specifications call for different endpapers if one has an ephemeral subject and the other is a reference book. The heavy book needs a paper of good edge and tensile strength, while the reference book needs a stock with good folding or flexing strength. In general, the choice of endpaper from the structural standpoint depends on the book's characteristics.

These varied considerations could cause confusion, except for the practice of making all paper sold specifically for endleaves strong enough to meet the BMI standards for textbooks. Very few books require stronger paper; and most of the 80 lb. text papers, and even some of the 70 lb. weights, are perfectly safe for tradebooks of average size where no strenuous use is involved.

The least expensive endpaper is the regular white stocked by the binder. Although it is about the same quality as the colored endpapers available, its price is slightly lower. On an average-sized book, however, the difference comes to only about ¼¢ per copy. If one of the finer text papers is used, the difference may be around ¾¢ (unless the paper cuts out badly for the trim-size, in which case it may be almost twice as much).

Self-lining is a relatively weak construction, suitable for small- to average-sized books of which repeated use is unlikely. The advantages are (a) a saving of about 1½¢ and (b) the opportunity to print on all parts of the endleaves at no cost, these being part of the text sheets themselves.

PROTECTION

To protect a book effectively, the binding must be resistant to numerous hazards such as flexing, abrasion, soiling, tearing, impact, etc. The burden of providing such protection is shared by various features of the book: (a) cover material, (b) board, (c) headbands, (d) edge stain, and (e) the jacket.

▪ *Cover material*—The most important protective features of the case-binding cover material are resistance to flexing and tearing. In both cases, the strength is needed at the joint or hinge.

Flexing is involved in the opening and closing of the book. Since the cover material bends each time this occurs, it is necessary to use one that can stand the probable number of flexings required by the particular book. Certainly a reference book will receive more flexings in its life than a topical work, so the former will require a stronger hinge; but the question of use is somewhat complicated by library practices. A title which might be expected to get no more than 1 or 2 readings (say, a novel), may get many times that number in a library—but some libraries will rebind the book upon purchase and others may not.

BMI specifications settle the question for textbooks. Children's books meant for library use are usually given special bindings by the publisher. They are not only side stitched but are bound in a cloth usually up to BMI specs or better. The problem of hinge strength is given consideration also for reference books, manuals, etc., but for most general books the cover material is selected on the theory that it will be strong enough for normal use and libraries will rebind.

The problem of tearing at the hinge concerns generally the same kinds of books (particularly elementary textbooks) that can expect much flexing. The choice of material is not affected when BMI standards are required, but there may be a question when using some papers and plastics. Many of these materials are likely to have relatively better flexing qualities than tearing strength.

Abrasion and soiling are hazards to which all books are subjected in varying degrees. Again, school and library books are most vulnerable and the materials required for them are made to take considerable abuse. Abrasion is usually more of a problem on the bottom edges of the cover than anywhere else, although reference books can expect exceptionally heavy wear on the sides. Any material used for cases should either be dyed-through, to avoid having another color show as the material wears thin, or be heavily coated, or both. Soiling is an important consideration in cookbooks and other manuals whose users may have dirty hands (CH.28). To prevent soiling, materials should be coated or impregnated with a resistant compound such as pyroxylin.

Since (a) the strains of flexing and tearing are only at the hinge and (b) there are relatively inexpensive materials that provide adequate protection for the sides of most tradebooks, it is a common practice to use 3-piece covers on such books. A strong, flexible material—usually cloth or plastic—is used for the spine and hinges and a weaker but abrasion-resistant material—usually paper—is used on the sides. A soil-resistant paper can be used at a little higher cost.

When a 3-piece cover is made on an end-feed, web-fed casemaker in 1 operation—provided the edition is large enough to absorb the longer setting-up time (5000 is about the minimum) and there are no special running problems—the cost is about the same as making a 1-piece cover. If, for example, a 37¢ per yard cloth is used for the spine and hinge and extends the minimum amount onto the side boards (about ⅜"), the cost of the cloth will be about ¾¢ on a book of average size. A 10¢ per yard material on the sides will add about 1¢, for a total of 1¾¢. Using 37¢ material all over would cost about 4¢ per book.

If the run is too short to warrant setting up a web-fed machine, the cover can be made in 2 operations and may still be somewhat cheaper than the 1-piece cover, but the cost difference will probably be so small that the loss of time and efficiency might not be justified.

In general, the qualities of book cloth can be determined by reference to the grade or price range. The decision to use a particular quality for a book should be taken in consultation with the binder or another experienced person.

The use of plastics is less certain but very promising. Just as cloth replaced leather, plastics may replace cloth. Plastics can equal and surpass cloth in almost all performance tests, and are completely impervious to liquids and other kinds of damage to which cloth is vulnerable. The indications are that plastics with such properties can be marketed at lower prices than comparable cloth.

Nevertheless, plastic cover materials have been accepted very slowly for book binding, except in such fields as looseleaf binders, diaries, checkbooks, etc., where they have almost completely replaced other materials.

The development of plastics and other non-woven materials—including augmented papers—for book binding was inhibited for many years by the fact that they could not meet BMI standards for schoolbooks, those standards being based on cloth characteristics (thread count, etc.). However, during the latter part of 1965 the standards were revised to permit use of any material that can perform satisfactorily.

The protective aspects of *mechanical-binding cover* materials involve only the resistance to abrasion and soiling needed for sides, as the flexing and tearing hazards are borne mainly by the mechanical device. The same considerations apply to the cover material here as in casebound book sides.

For *paperback covers* almost any stock may be used, provided it has sufficient folding strength, tear strength, rigidity, and abrasion resistance. How much is sufficient? This depends on what is expected of the book. If *maximum* protection is required, a hard cover is the answer. If maximum protection *for the price* is the object, the answer is the regular 10 pt. coated stock being used.

As paperbacks become more generally accepted, and are purchased even by libraries and schools, there is greater demand for cover durability. This demand, combined with a search for economy in hardbinding, has created a trend toward a midpoint at which the distinction between softbound and hardbound virtually disappears. Certainly, where the trade paperback is concerned, such a disappearance is conceivable, as the differences in production and distribution between these books and their hardbound counterparts is minor. The possibilities in this direction probably lie in plastics, for no paper product alone is likely to have all of the requisite features.

▪ *Boards*—Damage from impact—usually in dropping the book (or in using it as a missile in school)—is borne mainly by the boards. If a good and heavy-enough board is used, the book will not ordinarily suffer too badly, but a light board may crumple and the book will probably be ruined. Remember that the heavier the book the harder it falls, so a heavier, tougher board is needed. No material short of textbook specifications is likely to fare well under the stress of severe impact, but few books used outside the elementary schools are likely to receive such blows.

▪ *Headbands*—Headbands have no structural value, but they do provide a bit of protection for the spine. In pulling a book off a full shelf, the common practice is to apply pressure at the top of the book near the spine and pull down and out. The headband takes some of this strain, which might otherwise rip the spine.

▪ *Edge stain*—The protective function of the edge stain is real—it protects the edges from a soiled appearance caused by handling or the accumulation of dust and soot. This concerns the top edge mostly, and it is the top that is generally stained. The other edges *can* be stained, but this would be for esthetic reasons only. An interesting effect is obtained by staining the top and the fore-edge different colors, but it is a relatively expensive operation. Another possibility is to color only the fore-edge, but this also costs more than staining the top.

▪ *Jacket*—The protective factor in choosing jacket material is important because jackets do get relatively hard use. Of course, if the cover is sturdy enough, one has a right to assume that the jacket will not be needed by the reader and is justified in using material adequate only for distribution purposes. But the jackets *are* used by readers (and libraries), so the tendency has been to provide materials that will stand considerable handling.

For most tradebooks, a 70 lb. text stock is sufficient, although 80 lb. is better. In coated papers, 80 lb. is the minimum. Heavier books and those that get exceptionally hard use, such as dictionaries, cookbooks, etc., usually get 100 lb. coated stock, often with a plastic lamination added.

Actually, protection of the book has 2 aspects: (a) keeping the book intact during use and (b) preservation of the book's bindery-fresh appearance in the bookstore and warehouse. The jacket is not adequate for the former but it is of great help in the latter—and its material should be chosen with that function in mind.

The acetate jacket provides good protection and gives a luxurious, glossy finish to a book, like the cellophane wrapping on a package of cigarettes, but it is not inexpensive. The cost is about the equivalent of a 4-color process jacket for an average-size book. The cost goes higher as the size gets larger, but goes down for larger quantities. Wrapping books with acetate jackets is somewhat slower than with paper jackets, which adds to the cost. Acetate has a tendency to become cloudy from the abrasion of normal use and sometimes cracks or tears. Despite these drawbacks, the acetate jacket is effective packaging, usually worth its cost for books expected to sell on visual appeal—provided the cover design is really good.

IDENTIFICATION

The strongest visual necessity in cover design is identification. The title, author's name (last name, at least), and publisher's imprint should appear on the spine in any case. (An exception might be a new edition of a classic so well-known that the author's name can be omitted without loss of identification.) Inclusion of the author's first name is preferred by some publishers.

The title's position on the spine is the subject of considerable disagreement. Some insist that the title read horizontally on all but the narrowest spines. Others insist that it read from top to bottom when it must be vertical. In England, they prefer the title running from bottom to top. The choice in each case is presumably concerned with legibility, but there are several factors affecting the legibility of titles on spines, so that no one position is best in all circumstances.

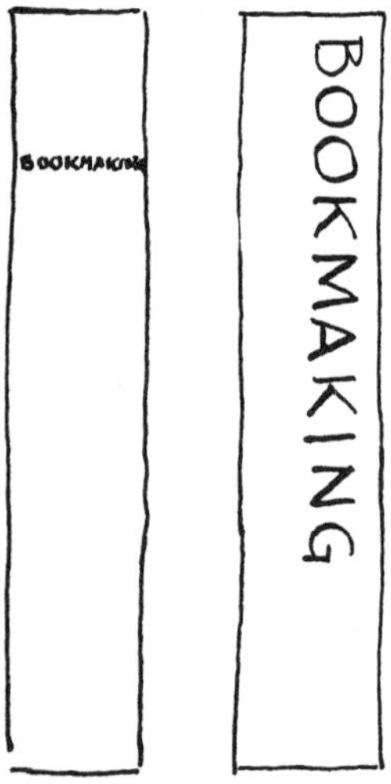

BOOKMAKING

BOOKMAKING

All other things being equal, a horizontal line is certainly easiest to read. However, a word which can be made no larger than 14 pt. across the spine would be much more legible set vertically in 48 pt. type. This is true of thick books as well as thin ones.

Legibility is affected by the contrast and clarity of the type also. A poorly chosen color combination or typeface can kill the legibility of *any* arrangement. Conversely, a change in color can make an otherwise unsatisfactory arrangement work quite well.

Whatever may be said about the relative merits of bottom-to-top vs. top-to-bottom titles, it is a fact that italics and cursives are much more easily read from bottom to top. This position is actually less of a departure from the normal horizontal arrangement for them than it is for roman type, the latter being perpendicular to the normal angle, whereas italics are turned considerably less than 90°.

When italics run down the spine, they are much *more* than 90° from the usual axis and require a twist of the neck to be read. Whether this disadvantage is worse than the inconvenience of reading 1 title up on a shelf of down titles is a matter of personal choice. It is probably best to avoid the problem by not using italics on spines at all.

The need for having the title and author's name on the front cover varies with circumstances. They are of prime importance when the book is to be displayed and sold in stores—but this applies only to jackets, paperback covers, and hard covers of books having no printed jackets. When the book has a printed jacket, there is usually no reason to put the title on the front of the cover, unless it is expected to be used as a schoolbook also, in which case the jacket will not be used. The title is considered essential on the front cover of textbooks, not for the ultimate user, but for sales purposes at conventions and other places where such books are displayed for buyers.

ATTRACTION

For display purposes, the cover design problem is to attract attention and hold it long enough for the title and author to be read. There is much room for variation in method.

It is not absolutely necessary that the title be the attracting element. A striking illustration or even a particularly effective abstract pattern may be used to catch the eye, while the title itself may be quite small and/or restrained. In such cases, the design must be sufficiently intriguing to lure the shopper close enough to read the title. Occasionally, the latter has been omitted entirely, with a very

familiar illustration (usually a well-known personality) carrying the entire burden of identification. This practice is not being recommended, but it does demonstrate that use of the title as the primary element of display is not essential, and it emphasizes the value of a highly relevant illustration.

The competition for attention in bookstores today is terrifying—and getting worse. Not simply because the number of titles published is multiplying rapidly, or because there are so many other things diverting the public's attention, but because the proportion of effective design on books is increasing. A generation ago, an outstanding jacket design stood out easily in a desert of mediocrity. Today, it is less noticed. This is really a good thing. The pleasure of browsing is heightened, and the quality of publishers' output is constantly under pressure to improve. There is still (and always will be!) bad design on books, but the publisher is aware of the competitive disadvantage he risks if he buys it.

All this points to 2 principles. First, the effectiveness of a design is relative to its background—"effectiveness" meaning, primarily, the ability to be noticed, which in turn implies being different from the others. Thus, no practice is more effective than another under all conditions. A red cover may be successful if no others are red, but probably not if surrounded by red ones. A photographic design may stand out on a shelf of typographic jackets, but might become lost in a display with all photographic designs. This is not to say that the designer should strive to be "different" at all costs, but design trends should be taken into account, if only to avoid repeating the current fads.

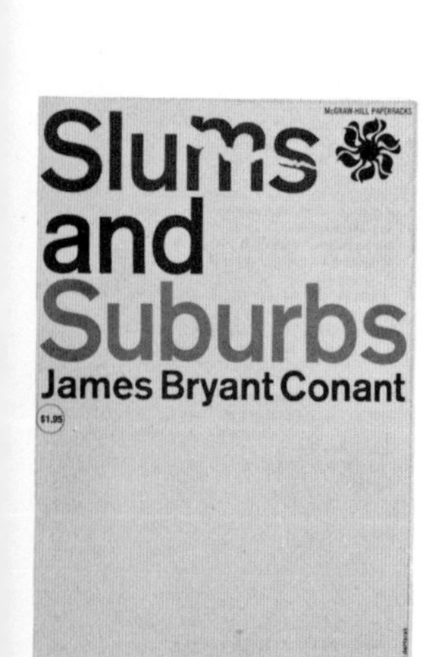

The second principle is in some ways a contradiction of what has gone before—now it must be said that use of the title as the attracting device is probably best. The title is *the* identifying element —not just graphically, but aurally and psychologically. The title usually has overtones of meaning and association more specific than any illustration or pattern can have. Particularly when it is brief and descriptive ("Horses", "Play Ball!", etc.) it offers graphic opportunities which, combined with its literal values, make a powerful effect possible. The poster value of the title diminishes as it becomes longer and less descriptive (unless it is sufficiently odd).

On the other hand, when the book is by a very popular author it may be best to emphasize his or her name, and give the title a secondary or equal place. This choice must be made with care. Consult with the sales and editorial departments before proceeding along this line.

EXPRESSION

For some books, putting the title on the cover is sufficient for sales purposes. Titles like "Algebra for Beginners", or "Operating a Drill Press" reveal enough for a prospective buyer to decide if he should

look into the book. On the other hand, a title such as "Out of the Blue" may concern aviation, meteorology, psychology, music, fishing, an unexpected visit, romance, or fortune, retirement from the Navy, an invasion from another planet, or any number of other subjects, so it becomes necessary for the binding design to indicate what the book is about.

The binding, as well as the rest of the book, must indicate the content also because the design should be a reflection of the text. The degree of literalness or subtlety appropriate is discussed in CH.15, but it is obvious that the binding—if it has a sales role—is the place for a rather direct expression. If it has *no* poster requirement, the principles of expression are the same as for the book as a whole. The elements of a binding design that concern expression are: (a) subject, (b) illustration, (c) typography, (d) material, and (e) color.

■ *Subject*—Even when the cover is used for display, it must not hold the viewer's attention too long. If he becomes too intrigued with an intricate or detailed cover design, the time spent in this examination will be taken from the precious few seconds allottable to the book—seconds which could otherwise be spent reading the flap copy or perusing the content. The cover design should attract attention and arouse interest in the content, not satisfy the curiosity it stimulates.

Designs should be general as to the content of the book, but very specific and individual about the subject. For example, a book about exploration of the Pacific Northwest is not just about exploration, or about exploration of a wilderness in America, but about an expedition by a *particular group of people* to an area with *specific characteristics* in a *certain period* of *American history*. All of these and other salient features should be evident in the design because they give the book its unique character. On the other hand, it is not especially desirable to illustrate an actual incident from the text. To do so would not reveal any more about the nature of the book, and it might divert attention from further examination. Sometimes, of course, an incident in the book is so graphically dramatic that it can be illustrated on the cover with good effect, but even then it should be a simple occurrence that can be grasped in an instant.

■ *Illustration*—Illustrations for covers may be taken from inside the book or elsewhere. In any case, their use follows the principles discussed in CHS.9,15,16 and 21. On covers, the purpose is likely to be entirely suggestive, although it may be considered partly reproductive in the case of art books. Here there is also the display consideration—which may affect their treatment. Indeed, the distortion of values required by the poster needs of cover design tends to separate the (display) cover esthetically from the rest of the book, making it difficult to maintain a feeling of unity.

■ *Typography*—Unity is a problem also in the choice of lettering or typography. A single spirit should prevail, yet the needs of display may indicate a quite different kind, weight, or size of letter from that inside the book. However, remember that not only harmony but contrast can create unity (CH.6).

■ *Material*—The cover and endpaper materials will be chosen partly on the basis of technical and economic considerations discussed earlier. The visual factors follow the principles indicated in CH.15 and the conception visualized at that stage. Color and texture are the esthetic components of this choice, and these may be selected tentatively for their suitability, but the final decisions must take the practical factors into account.

■ *Color*—On paperbacks and hard covers on which there is to be no printed jacket, color choice is entirely open, if there is no color in the text. Where there *is* color in the text, cover colors should be effectively related to those already used. Otherwise, any suitable colors can be chosen.

When a book has 2 covers, i.e. a case binding and a printed jacket, a controversial situation arises. One view has it that the jacket is merely a promotion piece wrapped temporarily around the book, so there is no need to consider its colors in designing the book itself. Another school holds that this is unrealistic, because in fact the jacket almost invariably remains on the book, so a harmonious relationship between them is as essential as it is between any 2 of the book's parts.

It can be argued thus: (a) On paperback books and unjacketed hardbound books the design of the cover and pages *must* be integrated, even though a permanent cover performs the sales function. (b) The only difference between these and jacketed books is that a jacket *can* be discarded, but (c) if it is not, and usually it is not, then there is really *no* difference, and the jacket should be treated as though it is a permanent part of the book. It would be another matter if, by making the jacket clash with the book, the purchaser would be induced to discard it, but this doesn't seem to work that way. The ideal solution would be to make the jacket conform to the book's design, but this might involve a limitation of sales, which is not likely to be accepted at all.

Besides the cover, there are 4 other binding elements that involve color: endpapers, ink or leaf, edge color, and headbands. These may be used to bridge over a poorly related jacket and binding color combination, but in any case, they provide an opportunity to use a considerable range of color in the service of both attraction and expression.

Cover graphics

Whereas the production of jackets and paper covers requires no special techniques, making designs on cloth and the other binding materials involves some unique problems.

PREPRINTED COVERS

Printing on cloth, plastic, or plastic-coated cloth is almost always done by offset lithography, and requires experience in this work. The material must have a surface suitable for lithographic printing, and sometimes special inks are required. The printing is on the surface rather than impressed (as in stamping) so it must usually be locked in by a transparent finish.

The cost of printing on binding materials is considerably more than printing on paper, and the special finishes make the difference even greater. Except where very long runs make coordinated web-printing and web-casemaking feasible, the high cost of preprinting covers is made higher by the necessity of making the cases on a sheet-fed machine. However, no stamping is needed and, if *no jacket* is needed, the cost becomes comparable to that of a stamped cover with a printed jacket.

Preprinted covers are relatively more economical for short-run titles which would require sheet-fed casemaking anyway. The ideal situation might be an edition of less than 3000 of a fairly small book of minor importance—say, a routine mystery or western story. This would probably go on a sheet-fed casemaker anyway, and the saving in stamping dies would be relatively high per unit. The size and nature of the book would permit the use of paper cover material, thus simplifying the printing (CH.7). If a soft-finish paper were used, no coating would be required.

It may be even more practical in some instances to preprint the covers by silk screen (CH.7). The process is suited to short runs and can produce excellent results if suitable copy is used. Although nothing comparable to halftone printing by lithography is possible, the silk screen technique is now capable of printing quite detailed subjects. Also, the ink used is resistant enough so that no other finish is necessary, and the process can be used on the roughest materials.

What is described above is, in effect, a paperback with hard cover. The cost of a jacket is saved, and the saving in stamping would about equal the cost of printing the cover—depending, of course, on the kind of stamping and printing involved. This is not only the most economical way to bind a hardbound book (of these characteristics), it is very little more expensive (perhaps 10¢ per copy) than a paperback binding. The economic advantages diminish as the quantity increases enough to make web-fed casemaking feasible.

A variation of the preprinted cover is a 3-piece binding on which a cloth spine is stamped and the sides are a preprinted material. There is no economic advantage in this arrangement unless the design permits elimination of a printed jacket. However, if the sides can be printed in rolls and run with the cloth backstrip in a single casemaking operation, this is not likely to be more expensive than the 1-piece preprinted cover made on a sheet-fed machine.

STAMPED COVERS

The stamping processes are described in CH.10. The cost of stamping depends on the combination of labor and materials used. With several factors to juggle, it is possible to spend a little for a lot, or vice versa.

The labor cost of stamping is relatively uniform: about 1½¢ per impression. Price differences are in the kind and size of die, and the amount of ink or leaf used. Ink is a negligible cost factor unless an unusually large amount is used. Leaf varies somewhat according to color, but the main difference is between the cost of pigment leaf (colors) and the various forms of metallic leaf. The former cost about 1¢ for 20 square inches, while the metallics range from about 5 square inches for 1¢ for genuine gold to about 28 square inches for 1¢ for imitation gold. In between are the anodized metallics.

From this it may be seen that the cost of stamping is affected considerably by the design. It may range from 1¢ for a simple type layout stamped in ink with a plastic plate costing $2, to 7 or 8¢ for 2 impressions of leaf covering the full area of an average-sized book (say, 50 square inches each impression) with brass dies costing $200.

Labor costs can be held down by reducing the number of impressions required. This can be done by utilizing the stamping presses' ability to run more than 1 roll of leaf at a time. There is room for considerable ingenuity in this area, but there are also mechanical limitations (CH.10). Before planning this kind of operation, check with the bindery for their requirements and practices.

Economies in the amount of leaf used can be realized by careful placement of the elements to be stamped. For example, if 2 small elements in the same color are placed far enough apart so that the leaf can be "jumped" between them, you will pay for only the amount of leaf they use. If they are a little too close, you may have to pay for the leaf covering all the space between—even though it is not used. This could easily be twice as much as the amount actually used. In fact, if you stamp a border of leaf around the edge of the cover, you must expect to pay for all the leaf in the middle. Again, until you are experienced enough, check with the bindery.

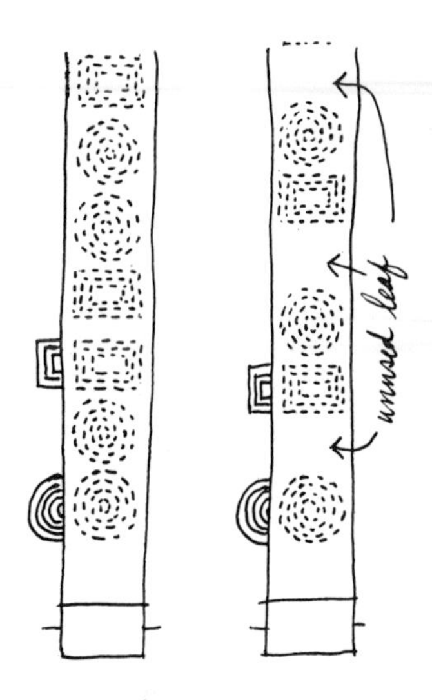

Don't overlook the value of blind stamping. There is no cost at all for materials, and some very handsome effects are possible. True embossing requires expensive dies, but the effect of embossing can be obtained by the use of reverse (negative image) dies (CH.10). This requires a design that includes the necessary background in a logical way. For example, see the colophon stamped on the cover of this book.

In planning designs with leaf, remember that colors are not entirely dependable from one run to another, nor are paper or cloth colors. For this reason, it is not wise to use color combinations of such subtlety that a small color variation will spoil them.

Sketches

There are 2 reasons why it is important to make very comprehensive sketches for hardcover binding designs. First, these arrangements involve very distinctive textures and colors which are usually not subject to adjustment. That is, having decided on a particular cloth, leaf, etc., the designer can rarely make small corrections of color and texture in the proof stage, as there are relatively few choices in these lines. Therefore, it is desirable to see in the sketch exactly how the end result will look. Second, once a sketch has been approved, the commitment of time and money necessary to see a proof is usually so large that a major change due to dissatisfaction with the proof may be impossible, and will almost certainly be awkward.

The same principles apply to the preparation of sketches for jackets, paper covers, preprinted covers, etc., but with a lesser degree of necessity. The materials are rarely as significant in color or texture as cloth, and it is possible to modify colors or even plates without too much difficulty. However, changes are not desirable, and the best practice is to make all sketches as near as possible to the finished appearance.

▪ *Material*—Hardcover sketches should be made same-size on the actual material being proposed. The suppliers will be pleased to provide sample sheets for this purpose. It is not necessary to make a cover with boards, etc., as you will probably have sample covers made later. It is sufficient to trim the material to the size of the front cover plus the spine (CH.11). Bear in mind that it is not feasible to stamp in the ¼″ alongside the spine, since this is the hinge and there is no board there.

▪ *Layout*—The arrangement of type, illustration, etc. to be stamped should be carefully drawn on tracing paper. Particularly on the spine, care must be taken to trace the type to make certain that it will fit. (By this time, the bulk of the book should have been definitely established.) Presumably, if the sketch is approved, the copy for dies and plates will follow the arrangement exactly, so it is important to place everything properly.

▪ *Transferring the design*—The means of transferring the pencil layout to the material will depend on whether leaf or ink is to be used. For ink stampings, rub the back of the layout with a pencil or chalk similar in color to that desired, tape the layout in position on the material, and go over the letters or illustration with firm pressure of a fairly hard pencil. This will transfer a reasonably accurate facsimile, which may be refined as necessary by using colored pencil or a brush with opaque water colors (tempera). Note that wax-base pencils or crayons will not transfer.

Whereas the ink color can be made to match your sketch, the leaf you specify cannot be modified, so it is best to use the actual leaf in making the sketch. To transfer gold leaf, simply use the pressure-sensitive leaf sold in stationery stores. Place the sheet of gold face down underneath the layout and apply fairly hard pressure with a very hard pencil or stylus. This is genuine gold and is quite expensive, but it is very simple and quick to use, and can be applied with great accuracy. To apply pigment leaf, or other metallic leaf, heat is required. For this, obtain a tool sold in art supply and hobby shops for burning designs in wood and leather. This is an electric pencil-like device. Place a piece of the leaf face down under the layout and, when the tool has heated to the proper degree, apply light pressure with the point. Until the point is hot enough, it won't release the pigment; when it is too hot, it will burn through the tracing paper. It takes a bit of practice to use this instrument well, but anyone can do it. This may sound like a lot of trouble, but don't forget that there is only 1 tracing involved. Once the leaf is transferred there is no need to go over it as with the other method—and the color is exact. Samples of leaf may be obtained from the suppliers. Warning: the point of that tool gets

very hot, so don't leave it plugged in or forget where you put it.

Blind stamping can be indicated by tracing the design with the burner without any leaf. For larger areas this is not too satisfactory, and sometimes a better effect is obtained by using a leaf slightly darker than the material.

To make blank or colored panels or large areas it is easiest to find a piece of cloth or paper of the proper color, cut it, and glue it down.

▪ *Endpapers*—When colored endpapers are being suggested, get a sheet of the actual paper, fold it, trim it to the trim-size, and glue it to the inside of the cover sketch. This will leave the ⅛″ borders (*squares*) around the edges of the glued-down half, and will leave the other half free, as it would be in the book.

▪ *Edge stain*—Edge stain can be indicated by cutting a piece of colored paper the proper size (width of trim-size x paper bulk) and taping it on the back to the back of the free leaf of endpaper. One edge of the "topstain" will then be hinged to the top of the endsheet, so it can be bent over at right angles to it.

When the spine of the cover is folded back at the hinge, a 3-sided box will be formed, showing the parts of the binding design in their correct relationship to each other. (The design is actually 3-dimensional and should not be judged in only 2 dimensions.) A length of headband cut to the paper bulk may be taped to the back edge of the "topstain" to complete the sketch.

For the preparation of copy for dies and plates see CH.11.

Sample covers

When the binding design has been approved, it is desirable to make *sample covers*—which are the equivalent of proofs. Sample covers are made by hand, using the actual materials specified, and are stamped with the dies to be used for the edition. Besides providing a final opportunity to approve or modify the design, they reveal any problems in stamping and materials. If a particular leaf or ink doesn't show up or will not take well on the cover material, it is better to find out on sample covers than when the edition is being run. However, sample covers are rather costly to make and they may be omitted when the design is very simple. For example, if the dies are being stamped in gold foil on a black cloth, there can be no surprises when the job is run, so there is no need for sample covers.

It is comforting to see the completed cover in advance, and sometimes alternate colors of leaf or material may be tried, but in general, all of the design decisions should have been made in the sketch stage. Trial and error is uneconomical and, except in unusual circumstances, unprofessional.

Besides its value for the publisher, the sample cover is a useful guide for the binder, who uses it as a model for stamping. An OKd cover with any corrections noted serves as the binder's "Author's Proof". It should be returned to him with the binding order or earlier.

27 | Ordering binding

Schedule

The binding order may have to be delayed for some reason that does not affect the cover materials or stamping—perhaps because of some uncertainty regarding the jacket or illustrations. Where the schedule is tight (as it usually is by binding time), it may be best to return the approved sample cover to the binder with instructions to order the necessary materials and leaf. If these orders are delayed until the binding order is ready, it may turn out that an item is not in stock and there is not time enough to wait for it.

The binding order

As is true of composition and printing orders, the binding order is both instruction and authorization. The latter frequently indicates that only part of the edition printed is to be bound, and should specify what is to be done with the sheets being held. Most binders prefer to hold sheets in the form of folded, gathered, and sewed books, partly because it is much more economical to process the whole edition together, and partly because it is more convenient to store the unbound books that way than as *flat sheets*.

The order should contain, also, instructions for the disposition of the bound copies—whether they are to be held at the bindery or shipped, and if so, to where—and an authorized signature with a date. Here, too, a printed binding order form saves time and reduces the likelihood of important omissions. A typical order form appears on the following page.

Space is usually a problem in a bindery and it is very awkward if a partly finished job cannot be shipped out because something is missing. For this reason, few binders will schedule a job unless everything—text sheets, illustrations, dies, cover materials, and jackets—is on hand.

To prevent a mix-up, indicate on the binding order where the printed sheets and jackets or covers are coming from. This also enables the binder to act directly when there is a delay or discrepancy in shipment.

The items listed on the specimen order form are generally self-explanatory, but there are a few points worth mentioning:

Where illustration inserts, wraps, and tips are not clearly identified by captions or folios, it is best to order a set of folded and gathered sheets for checking their position.

Presumably, your dies and jacket or paper cover were made to fit a bulk calculated from the paper bulking tables or derived from a dummy. As there is a considerable amount of leeway in smashing antique book papers, it is a good idea to specify on the binding order the bulk you used, so the smash can be adjusted accordingly.

Provide a good color swatch to match for the edge stain if any.

Attach a printed copy of the jacket and indicate how it is to be placed on the book. This is best done by marking the point at which the front joint is to come.

Date ____

Title ____
Author ____

Binding Order

PLEASE BIND ____ (Quantity)

FROM ____ PRINTING OF ____ HOLD BALANCE OF SHEETS ____

SHEET SIZE ____ FROM

TRIMMED SIZE ____ wide ____ high FULL TRIM ☐ SMOOTH TOP, ROUGH SIDE & FOOT ☐

MARGINS FOR TEXT: Gutter ____ Head ____ TOTAL PAGES ____

PRINT AS ____ FOLD AS ____ SEWING ____

BULK ____ ENDPAPERS:

LINING: super & paper ☐ other ____ STAIN ____

HEADBANDS ____ REINFORCEMENTS ____

INSERTS/ILLUSTRATIONS: ____ pp. TO BIND AS ____

BACK: ROUND ☐ other ____ BOARDS ____

COVERS ____

STAMPING: Spine ____ FRONT ____

Verso ____ DIES FROM ____

JACKETS FROM ____

SPECIAL INSTRUCTIONS:

PACKING ____

BOUND STOCK READY ____ *Signed* ____

28 | Special design problems

Except in a few instances, the discussions of design in this book have been general in nature. It has not been feasible to elaborate each point in terms of the many different kinds of books there are. But there are categories of books with specific and unique problems which need to be discussed. Some of the most common of these are dealt with in this chapter.

Cookbooks

A large number of cookbooks are published each year, and they vary considerably in their content. A few are narrative in form and present no special problem. We are concerned here with the recipe book, which has design problems unlike any other.

The use of a cookbook is basically the same as other "How to" books that deal with manual operations, but there are few that require such intimate involvement with such messy work. Most manuals give instructions which are referred to less and less as the worker gains experience. In cooking, each recipe is a unique operation to be followed step by step. It is this feature that makes cookbooks a special problem in design.

As a workshop guide, the cookbook requires: (a) a high degree of legibility, (b) an arrangement that minimizes the amount of handling needed, (c) resistance to soiling, and (d) a format and construction suitable to its use.

Legibility here means a size of type large enough to make reading possible while the book lies on a table or counter and the cook stands. This requires 12, or even 14, pt. type in most faces. The leading should be at least 2 pts. and preferably 3 or more. This ideal usually conflicts with a desire to keep down the number of pages, but it remains the ideal.

A large type size suggests a large page size also. In theory, a large book is less practical where work space is limited, but it is probably better in practice to sacrifice a few square inches of space than to require the bending, squinting, and handling caused by small type.

The necessity for handling a cookbook in use can be reduced by placing the complete instructions for each recipe on a single spread. (If, in the middle of a crucial sentence, the cook must turn the page with greasy or floury little fingers or else suffer a culinary disaster, the book is not doing a good job.) The difficulties of achieving such an arrangement are great, especially if the text is crowded. It is almost impossible to manage without shifting recipes around. Such shifts are much easier to make in Ms than in galleys, so the ideal situation is a page-for-page arrangement by the author that provides the most practical breaks. Even this may not succeed, as shifting recipes in sequence is impossible when they are in alphabetical order, and sometimes extremely awkward when they are arranged by subject. Also, with such an arrangement, it is usually difficult to avoid wide variations in spacing to achieve pages of uniform depth. However, there is really no reason why the pages *must* be uniform in depth, so this is not a problem.

To avoid having to flatten the pages while the book is lying open on a table, the text should be kept well out of the gutter. A gutter margin of 7/8″ is the minimum, and more is better. A mechanical binding enables the book to lie perfectly flat, which eliminates this problem. If the book can also be folded back all the way, this saves space too.

The text paper for cookbooks should be as dark as possible, consistent with readability, to minimize the effects of soiling. The standard buff or tan available in many lines are satisfactory, although any other color of suitable value and intensity (low) may be used. When using tinted stock, remember that the type must be chosen with consideration for the lower contrast between ink and paper. Lighter colors, even the regular off-whites, are satisfactory if the paper is waterproof or water resistant so that it can be cleaned. Truly washable paper is too expensive for most cookbooks, but some water resistance is found in all litho papers, even the least expensive (CH.8).

Materials used on the covers of cookbooks should and can be washable (most washable materials are relatively soil resistant anyway, which is good, as few people take the trouble to wash them). The cost of plastic impregnated or coated materials is not significantly greater than others, and pure vinyl, which is totally impervious to water and most other liquids (CH.10), is in the medium range of binding material prices. Lacquer coating and plastic lamination—both liquid and sheet—are useful on preprinted covers, although they are not always entirely satisfactory (CH.10).

There are other important special factors in the design of cookbooks, such as the need for structural strength, ease of reference, etc., but they are not peculiar to cookbooks, being common to others of this nature.

Art books

Generally, the problem is to present the pictures in the best possible way without sacrificing too much in the layout and typography. In some books, however, the text is primary and the illustrations are merely adjuncts, as in many histories of art. These illustrations are informative rather than representative (CH.9), and it is probably not correct to call such books art books at all.

Where the purpose of the illustration is clearly representative, the closer to actual-size (of the original picture) the reproduction can be made, the better—so, the larger the book the better. However, there *is* a point of diminishing returns in relation to both reading convenience (and shelf space) and manufacturing economy. This limit is about 10 x 13″. Art books can be, and are, made larger, but the disadvantages of such size must be outweighed by some vital consideration to warrant it. Usually, the consideration is a desire to make a big splash. This is a good enough reason if (a) the retail price can stand the much higher manufacturing cost (in large sizes, many bindery operations no longer fit on machines and must be done by hand) and (b) the book consists almost entirely of reproductions, so that reading inconvenience is a minor factor. (There are skeptics who doubt that the texts in art books are read at all.)

The large size of even an average art book page creates typographic difficulties. To begin, 30 picas is the maximum width of the standard slug machine line. Butted slugs, special machines, or other means of adding to the width are available (CH.5), but not much may be added before readability is seriously impaired. A 30-pica line of 11 or 12 pt. type has about 70 characters—which is enough (CH.6). On the other hand, 30 picas is not much on a page of, say, 9″ width. Esthetically it can be made to work, especially if the arrangement is asymmetric, but it may not provide enough text on the page. One alternative is double (or triple) column makeup. If it is not necessary to have much text on the page, another solution is to set the type by photocomposition, which can set large sizes on wide measures economically.

Books in which full-page pictures are faced by a descriptive text present a problem when the amount of text varies considerably. If most units of text are short but some are long, the typography must accommodate the large units and will look awkward with the small ones. Rather than using very small type to get the large units on 1 page, it might be better to run long sections over at the back of the book (as in magazines) or to the following page. The latter will work only when the text unit will make an odd number of pages. Another possible solution is to continue the runover text at the bottom (or top) of the new text that follows. This can be done only where the next unit of text is short enough to fit on the page *with* the runover material. Otherwise, the new text will have to run over, etc., etc.

Putting all the text in one section and all the pictures in another has 2 advantages: (a) each section may be printed with the process and paper most suited to it and (b) the pictures may be arranged without the complication of fitting them to a text. From an editorial standpoint, this arrangement is usually unsatisfactory, as the reader cannot conveniently see the pictures while reading the relevant text.

A basic creative problem in art books is the relationship of the style of design to the style of art in the book. There are 3 alternatives: the design may be (a) unrelated to the art, (b) related to the period of the art, or (c) related to the spirit of the art.

The use of period design is probably the least valid, except where the subject *is* a period or style of art. In books on the work of a particular artist or school, it is more reasonable to reflect the spirit and character *of the work* than the time in which the work was done. A dynamic and radical artist who lived during a conventional era would be badly served by a period treatment, as would an academic artist living today be misrepresented by a radical design. Something can be said for using a moderate contemporary style for all art books, thereby avoiding the hazards of choosing an appropriate expression in each case. Such a solution is definitely indicated in omnibus works (such as a museum collection) in which there is no single style or character.

Poetry

The problem of style in the design of poetry books is very much the same as for art books—only more so. Again, unless the book is an anthology of no single style, the significant feature to which the design should relate is *the essence* of the poet's work. The need for harmony between the design and that which is characteristic in the content is more vital here because the poems are an attempt at direct communication between author and reader, and the designer must not produce a false note that might break the spell. An entirely neutral design is virtually impossible, as *some* character will become evident in any work in which so many choices are made. It is better to try to make appropriate choices, and fail somewhat, than to try to be neutral and arrive accidentally at something unsuitable. Here too, it is the nature of the work that is important, not so much the period in which the work was done. This does not mean that national or period style elements should not be used, it means simply that such features are secondary to the central one—which is the spirit of the individual work.

As a practical typographic problem, poetry is unique but has several variations, depending on the form of the poems and the organization of the book. The latter is largely a question of whether the poems run in or begin on new pages—usually a matter of space. If there are so many poems that they must run in, the only associated problem is how to break stanzas at the end of a page. It is best not to break them at all, and full use of the available space is warranted to avoid such breaks. If this fails, keep a minimum of 2 lines on both pages. Beyond this point, breaking is a matter of judgment in individual cases. Each poem is a unique thing—especially the less formal modern poetry. But, formal or not, a poem is a most delicately balanced expression, and its physical arrangement is very important.

When the poems begin on new pages, breaking can be controlled somewhat. Make and tabulate a line count of each poem, allowing for turnovers as accurately as possible (CH.17). In deciding on a maximum number of lines per page, avoid a figure that would result in frequent breaks 2 or 3 lines from the ends of poems. For example, if most poems have less than 36 lines, only a few have between 37 and 40, and the remainder are well over 40 lines, then a 36-line page will leave very few problems. On the other hand, a page of 34 or 35 lines might be extremely awkward.

A similar procedure is useful in avoiding turnovers on the width. Ideally, all lines in poetry should be printed exactly as written, with no turnovers due to accident of page size. This is not always possible, but it should be attempted by making the text page the maximum feasible width. There is no justification for using a measure too narrow to accommodate the longest lines of poetry until margins have been reduced to the limit. This limit will depend partly on the nature of the poems. Where they consist mainly of long lines, the right-hand margin should be somewhat larger than is necessary for poems with only occasional long lines. The latter require no more than about 1/4″ on right-hand pages and about 9/16″ on left-hand pages. For poems with mostly short lines, a small outside margin and a fairly large inside margin on right-hand pages are necessary to bring the main body of type out of the gutter toward the middle of the page. On left-hand pages there is no such problem, as the short lines will fall naturally on the outer part.

To determine the best measure, calculate the width of the longest lines and the shorter long lines to arrive at the number of characters in the *average* long line. If possible, the measure should accommodate the average long lines, leaving only the longest to turn over. If *all* lines will fit, so much the better, but try to avoid a measure that will result in frequent 1-word turnovers.

Poetry is by nature aligned at the left, so it does not lend itself to centering. The only way it can be centered is optically, which is very awkward if there are any long lines. Such a situation presents

2 alternatives: (a) breaking the long lines, which is not justified merely to achieve centering, or (b) moving the type mass to the left to accommodate the long lines, which is no longer centering. It is better design to respect the essential form of the material than to force it into an unnatural arrangement. For most poetry, this means alignment at the left. Optical centering is feasible only for poems of formal construction with uniformly short lines. Actual centering is meaningless (unless all lines are short) as it is not apparent.

I had read and thrown.
Oh, but not to boast,
Ever since Nag's Head
Had my heart been great,
Not to claim elate,
With a need the gale
Filled me with to shout
Summary riposte
To the dreary wail
There's no knowing what
Love is all about.
Poets know a lot.
Never did I fail
Of an answer back
To the zodiac
When in heartless chorus
Aries and Taurus,
Gemini and Cancer
Mocked me for an answer.
It was on my tongue
To have up and sung
The initial flight
I can see now might –
Should have been my own –
Into the unknown,
Into the sublime
Off these sands of Time
Time had seen amass
From his hourglass.

42

10

THE QUESTIONER

WHEN EVENING bows its head so does the farmer,
I have seen him do it, haggard with sweat and fatigue
As he limps his way home to the daily chores,
I have been the man myself.

I have come to the lane that leads off toward the barns
And leaves the fields, and the streams of growing,
If one can think of earth as a moving tide
Where the flow is vertical.

I have stopped at the gates where maples lean on my shoulder
As confidential friends with nothing to say,
Staying to keep me company while the sunset
Squats on a burning hill.

Is this really the way it looks or is it seeming,
A distortion of the eye to fool the heart,
Collector of imitations, but still believing
It does not beat for nothing?

This is what I ask myself, is there a ledger
That adds this work and sweat to my account?
I know I do not fill my barns with dreaming,
But what's the accounting for?

Some poets, particularly of our era, use typography to convey meaning. In typescripts, it is important to watch for indentions, groupings, or other arrangements that are meant to be followed exactly in setting and makeup. These are often indistinguishable from vagaries due to irregular typing, so it is a good idea to check with the editor where special requirements are suspected. In some cases, the words may be arranged to take curved forms, etc. (this has been done by Appolinaire, e.e. cummings, Norman Mailer, and others). A practical procedure is to have the type set without regard for position, paste up repro proofs in the desired arrangement, and have a line cut or film made.

96

LITTLE OLD LETTER

It was yesterday morning
I looked in my box for mail.
The letter that I found there
Made me turn right pale.

Just a little old letter,
Wasn't even one page long—
But it made me wish
I was in my grave and gone.

I turned it over,
Not a word writ on the back.
I never felt so lonesome
Since I was born black.

Just a pencil and paper,
You don't need no gun nor knife—
A little old letter
Can take a person's life.

97

CURIOUS

I can see your house, babe,
But I can't see you.
I can see your house,
But I can't see you.
When you're in your house, baby
Tell me, what do you do?

A basic problem in books of verse that do not run in is to achieve a sense of order and continuity, as the type area varies in shape, width, and depth on each page. For this reason, it is desirable to establish some constant relationships. Aligning the poems flush left helps by creating a uniform left-hand margin. Placement of poem titles and folios in a fixed relationship to the beginning of the poems is effective. By setting these units flush left or slightly indented from the left, a structural order is created in the upper left corner of each page. The poems then become variations on this order, rather than a chaotic succession of unrelated forms. Order can be achieved also by the use of recurring devices, such as rules, ornaments, etc., and it helps to use strongly positive typography—large or bold titles and/or numbers.

Plays

The question of style in designing plays, as in poetry and art books, is better resolved in favor of the spirit and essence of the work than the period. The use of this approach in stage productions is an interesting parallel. Some of these have been notably successful, but there have also been some misuses of the approach; modern-dress productions of old plays which *belong* to their period. The indiscriminate use of contemporary style and dynamics is just as bad as blind application of period trappings according to date of composition.

Typographic considerations in play composition begin with the question: For what use is the volume intended primarily—for reading or for performance?

Where the book is to be used by actors, the text should have a higher degree of legibility than is otherwise necessary. The performer should be freed as much as possible from the need for close attention to the type, so that he can use his mind and body for acting. For example, consider the type used in television prompting. If half the size were used, the effort required to read it would distract the performers and diminish their effectiveness. The same principle holds for a performing copy of a play. True, the book is not used during a public performance, but it *is* used for tryouts and other occasions during which the actor should be at his best.

Not only must the text be more legible in a performing edition, but there should be more emphasis on the names of the characters, as it is important that the actors quickly recognize their own lines. This means that the names of speakers should stand out clearly, with both typographic style and position contributing.

It makes little difference whether the speaker's name is abbreviated or spelled out. The performer identifies his part with whatever is used, once he has seen it. Indeed, it is possible that a single abstract symbol for each character might be less distracting and more readily recognized than a name. Particularly on a first reading, an actor might have an easier time if he knew that his lines were preceded by a triangle or a circle rather than an unfamiliar name.

Where the conventional identification is used, there are several alternatives. If all the speeches are long, centering the speakers' names may work. However, if there are some short (less than half a line) speeches, centered names are very awkward—practically, because the eye must shift repeatedly from center to left and back again; visually, because the centered names frequently will hang out in space with no type directly under them. Also, where the speeches are brief, the lines occupied by the speakers' names become a very large percentage of the total, and add substantially to the length of the book. This is true even when the names are flush or slightly indented from the left on separate lines. The most satisfactory solution then is to place the names at the beginning of each speech.

With the name on the first line of the speech, it is important to make it visually distinctive. The usual method is to use caps, small caps, or caps and small caps. Boldface is effective also, but may involve expense. In performing editions, it is best to further set off the speakers' names by adding a colon, a dash, or a space at the end. In reading editions, a period is sufficient. Italics are not a good choice, as there is often italic within speeches (sometimes at the beginning). Then too, italics are generally used for stage directions. It is helpful to indent turnover lines, but this device cannot do the whole job because it is not available where a succession of single-line speeches occurs.

Sometimes a distinction must be made between (a) stage directions for the actors (*enters left, laughs,* etc.) and (b) information for the reader (setting, time, background of action, etc.). The relative emphasis will depend on whether the edition is for performance or reading.

Anthologies

The special problem in anthology design is the sometimes very diverse material to be set in a single typographic style. The text matter rarely presents difficulties, but it is often quite difficult to devise an arrangement for headings that will encompass all the selections. The style chosen must provide unity, yet it must be flexible.

A practical procedure is to set a sample page using the most complicated selection heading, and then let the editor mark up the Ms, keying each element to one of those in the sample. In extreme cases, it may be necessary to make an individual layout for each selection heading.

Reference books

To a certain extent, all books are tools—but a reference book is *entirely* a practical instrument and its design is concerned with the problem of use almost to the exclusion of anything else. This does not mean that reference books cannot be handsome. On the contrary, a particularly well-thought-out reference work is likely to have a distinct functional beauty, even if no conscious effort is made toward this end.

There are basically 2 kinds of reference books: (a) those that give *facts* and (b) those that give *instructions*.

▪ *Fact books*—The main consideration here is convenience in locating items, so the running heads and/or folios are of primary importance (CH.18). Subheads and alphabetical indicators should be made prominent also, as they are the guides followed by readers who are not inclined to use running heads or folios.

In directories, encyclopedias, and other reference books in which the user will be reading brief passages, the text type may be quite small, particularly where 2- or 3-column composition results in a narrow measure (CH.6).

▪ *Instruction books*—These are essentially the How-to books. In design, they follow most of the principles applicable to cookbooks, combined with those indicated above for other reference works.

Learning usually requires considerable effort, which most people naturally resist, so the instructional book should be designed to *appear* simple in organization even if it is not. This is not always easy to accomplish, but when it *is* managed, it is a distinct contribution to the value of the book. The designer should study the Ms until its organization is *thoroughly* understood. Only then is it likely that it can be made understandable to the reader.

One particularly useful device is to give the various classes of headings and subheads quite contrasting treatment. The more nearly similar they are, the more confusion arises. A distinctly different treatment in type face, size, space, position, and/or weight tends to establish an order that reassures the prospective user. Space around subheads, charts, etc. reduces the forbidding aspect of a page of difficult text. There is an unfortunate tendency to set professional-level technical books without consideration for the reader's comfort—mainly on the theory that he *must* read the book so why bother—but this is unfair and, in the long run, impractical. One may be technically talented and lazy at the same time, so the unreadable text might scare away some potentially great discoverers.

Textbooks

Although textbooks are one of the major subdivisions of book publishing, they are not really a separate category of book design. They are unique in the *method* by which they are created—usually being a collaboration of author, editor, designer, and illustrator—but even in this respect they differ from other books only in that they, textbooks, are produced as books *should* be, whereas most books are created by authors, editors, designers, and illustrators who never see or speak to each other.

It is also true that schoolbooks sometimes have features not often found in other books, such as tests, summaries, foot glosses, etc., but these are typographically little different from similar material used elsewhere, and represent no fundamental departure. Essentially, textbooks fall into the functional category of reference books and their problems may be approached accordingly.

The schoolbooks with the most special character are those for elementary grades, especially the earlier ones. The design problems in these books are not so much *different* from instructional material for adults as they are more *acute*. A greater effort must be made to simplify matters and present them effectively. To this end, illustration, color, particularly legible typography, and careful layout are required. These devices are just as useful in adult books of instruction, but they are rarely used because they are thought to be unnecessary, and they involve extra expense. The principles, in any case, are the same. All graphic devices must be brought together to achieve maximum clarity and arouse maximum interest. The latter is thought to be more important in books for children, because motivation is weaker, but this is true only in the sense that school children are *required* to learn what is in their books, whereas the only adults who use instructional material are those who have decided that they want to learn the subject. However, learning is a chore at any age and at any level of motivation. Textbooks (and all books) should always be made as interesting as possible.

The specific design problems of mathematics texts, literature, social studies, etc. cannot be covered in detail here. In many respects, the material will be similar to the various kinds discussed in CHS. 17

and 18, but some situations will be so special that their solution must be devised without the aid of anything but previous experience with the same or similar matter. In general, the basic principles of design apply—analyze the problem, consider possible solutions, select the best one.

The difficulties of discussing textbook design are heightened by the changing aspects of instructional material. There is, indeed, a new category of book design coming into view as programmed texts introduce new techniques of learning. As these materials employ more mechanical devices they become less like "books" and more like machines, but it would be foolish for book designers to form too rigid or limited a concept of what is a book. Ultimately, the designer's job is to facilitate the transmission of thought from author to reader, and it is relatively unimportant what form the *means* of transmission takes as long as it is effective. It is reasonable to assume that the book designer will be concerned with all such means short of those that are in areas now served by other technicians, such as radio, television, and electronic devices in general.

brought 1451	We (*brought, took*) **our dog to the veterinarian today.** 1452	drugstore closes 132	Many sentences are built upon the framework of a *subject* and a ______ 133
prompt 1670	**The company answered my letter very** (*prompt, promptly*). 1671	two 352	A subject complement either *describes* or *identifies* the subject. When the subject complement *identifies* the subject, both words mean the *same* person or thing. 1←——1 **Mr. Jones is our postman.** **Mr. Jones** and the **postman** are (*one, two*) person(s). 353
they 1889	**Peggy and** (*she, her*) **are always together.** 1890	adverbs 572	We have been working with special words that control the "power" of other modifiers. These words are **adverbs.** These special adverbs can modify both ______ and other adverbs. 573
a 2108	a. **Paul works at a garage.** b. **Paul works at the Fuller garage.** In which sentence should **garage** be capitalized because it is part of the name of a particular business? ____ 2109	verb 792	WHERE? **Connie works** *where Helen works*. Because *where Helen works* has a subject and a verb and does not make sense by itself, it is a (*phrase, clause*). 793
bargain, 2327	**Columbus had expected to make a fortune but died a pauper.** 2328	adjectives 1012	Lesson 25 **Using Appositives to Combine Ideas** [Frames 1014–1059]
ha 2546	**I'll** (= *I will*) **tell you a secret.** In this sentence, the apostrophe takes the place of the two letters ____. 2547 *page 264*	come 1232	The form of **come** that should be used after **have, has,** or **had** is ______. 1233 *page 265*

programmed textbook

D

USEFUL INFORMATION

Sources of information

The list of sources is divided into 3 parts—(a) *Books* (which includes pamphlets, annuals, special numbers of periodicals), (b) *Periodicals*, and (c) *Other sources* (associations, libraries, films).

Books

This list is divided by subject, but many titles contain some material on subjects other than those under which they are listed. Those that cover all or most aspects of bookmaking are included under the heading *General;* the *Miscellaneous* list contains books *about* rather than *on* bookmaking, and others of special interest. Out-of-print publications are included but are not so marked, as the in-print status of books changes from time to time.

GENERAL

Methods of Book Design—Hugh Williamson. Oxford University Press. 1956. (Excellent on British bookmaking.)

The Making of Books—Sean Jennett. Faber & Faber. 1951. (British book.)

Helpful Aids in Book Production—BMI. 1953. (Contains tables and other data.)

Pages, Pictures, and Print—Joanna Foster. Harcourt, Brace & World. 1958. (For children, but useful as an introduction to bookmaking.)

The Story of Printing—Irving B. Simon. Harvey House. 1965. (For teenagers, but has particularly good technical explanations.)

How Books Are Made—David C. Cooke. Dodd, Mead. 1963. (Good picture story although also a juvenile.)

Printing and Promotion Handbook—Daniel Melcher, Nancy Larrick. McGraw-Hill, 2nd ed. 1956. (An alphabetically arranged encyclopedia of practical information, including much related to bookmaking. A new edition is in preparation.)

An Encyclopedia of the Book—G. A. Glaister. World. 1950.

Trade Customs—Book Manufacturers' Institute. (A pamphlet that every bookmaker should have and read. Revised occasionally.)

Official Minimum Manufacturing Standards and Specifications for Textbooks—Book Manufacturers' Institute, American Textbook Publishers Institute, Assn. of State Textbook Directors. (The BMI specs. Revised occasionally.)

Penrose Annual—Herbert Spencer, ed. Hastings House. (A British survey of the graphic arts.)

The Fleuron: A Journal of Typography—Oliver Simon, Stanley Morison, eds.

Doubleday, Page. 7 numbers. 1923–30. (Each number is a very well made hardbound book containing articles on the bookmaking of that time.)

The Dolphin: A Journal of the Making of Books—The Limited Editions Club. No. 1: 1933, No. 2: 1935, No. 3: 1938, No. 4: (magazine) 1940–41. (Similar to *The Fleuron*, the first 3 numbers are hardbound books, of which the third is listed separately below.)

A History of the Printed Book—Lawrence C. Wroth, ed. Limited Editions Club (The Dolphin, vol. 3). 1938. (A large and well-illustrated study by experts on various aspects.)

The Annual of Bookmaking—1938. (This special number of *The Dolphin* surveys the preceding decade of bookmaking in America.)

Chronology of Books and Printing—David Greenhood, Helen Gentry. Macmillan. 1936. (Important events from the beginning to 1936.)

The Book—Douglas C. McMurtrie. Oxford University Press. 1943. (A history of bookmaking from the beginning.)

Fine Books—Alfred W. Pollard. Cooper. 1964. (An historical survey of bookmaking, originally published in 1912.)

The Book in America—Hellmut Lehmann-Haupt, Lawrence C. Wroth, Rollo G. Silver. Bowker. 1952. (A history of American book publishing, bookmaking, and bookselling.)

Life of the Book—Hellmut Lehmann-Haupt. Abelard. 1957. (For young people, but a good general introduction.)

PUBLISHING

What Happens in Book Publishing—Chandler B. Grannis, ed. Columbia University Press. 1957. (Chapters by experts in each area of publishing. Indispensable.)

The Structure of Publishing—William Jovanovich. NYU (pamphlet). (A brief but valuable explanation. Written in the 1950s.)

Now Barabbas—William Jovanovich. Harper & Row. 1964. (Essays on the principal varieties of publishing and on reading, writing, and learning.)

The Truth About Publishing—Sir Stanley Unwin. Macmillan. 7th ed. 1960. (Primarily about British publishing, but gives vital insights into publishing in general.)

The Adventure of Publishing—Michael Joseph. Wingate (London). 1949. (A British book and somewhat dated but full of publishing knowledge.)

The Bowker Lectures on Book Publishing—Bowker. 1957. (A collection of essays by leading figures.)

Publishers on Publishing—Gerald Gross, ed. Grosset & Dunlap (paperback). Bowker (hardcover). 1961. (An anthology of pieces by outstanding publishers. Very enlightening.)

Editors on Editing—Gerald Gross, ed. Grosset & Dunlap (paperback). 1962. (A good source of information on the editorial function of publishing.)

The Paperbound Book in America—Frank L. Schick. Bowker. 1958. (A broad and thorough study of paperbound book publishing.)

This Was Publishing—Donald Sheehan. Indiana University Press. 1952. (Mostly about 19th century American publishing.)

Library Trends (magazine)—July 1958 Issue on Book Publishing. (A survey of American publishing in the decade 1947–57.)

Publishing and Bookselling—F. A. Mumby. Bowker. 4th ed. 1956. (A history.)

COMPOSITION, PLATES, & PRINTING

Printing Progress—International Assn. of Printing House Craftsmen (Cincinnati). 1959. (A survey of the graphic arts in general.)

Modern Illustration Processes—Charles W. Gamble. Pitman. 1947. (Thorough explanation of all reproduction processes.)

Production Yearbook—Colton Press. 9 numbers from 1934 to 1950. (Contains many good explanations of production processes. A new number is in preparation.)

L'Imprimerie et les Métiers Graphiques—M. Valotaire, ed. Arts et Métiers

Graphiques. 1947. (Contains very good photographs of bookmaking operations.)

General Printing—G. U. Cleeton and C. W. Pitkin. Taplinger. Rev. ed. 1958. (A well-illustrated textbook of printing.)

Modern Photoengraving—L. Flader, J. S. Mertle. Modern Photoengraving Publishers (Chicago). 1948. (Definitive.)

Line, Halftone, and Color—American Photoengravers' Assn. (Chicago). 1961.

Photoengraving Specifications Manual—Printing Industry of America.

Lithographer's Manual—Victor Strauss, ed. Waltwin. 2 vols. (Encyclopedic coverage.)

Survey of Lithography—H. C. Latimer. Graphic Arts Technical Foundation. 1954. (Brief but clear explanation of offset lithography.)

Screen Process Methods of Reproduction—Bert Zahn. Drake. 1950. (Detailed description of silk screen methods, materials, etc.)

Graphic Arts Procedures—R. R. Karch. American Technical Society. 2nd ed.

The Printing Industry—Victor Strauss. Printing Industry of America. (In preparation.)

DESIGN & TYPOGRAPHY

GENERAL

Paragraphs on Printing—Bruce Rogers. Rudge. 1943. (Informal commentary by a master bookmaker.)

Notes on Modern Printing—Merle Armitage. Rudge. 1954. (An important work by a pioneer of modern book design.)

Mss. by WAD—W. A. Dwiggins. The Typophiles. 1947. (Amusing, incisive essays.)

Typography—Francis Meynell. Pelican Press (London). 1923. (Cogent remarks by the Director of Nonesuch Press.)

Typography—Eric Gill. Sheed & Ward (London). 1931. (Opinions and outlook of the versatile designer and craftsman.)

A Psychological Study of Typography—Sir Cyril Burt. Cambridge University Press. 1959. (A thorough examination of readers' reactions.)

SURVEYS

Books For Our Time—Marshall Lee, ed. Oxford University Press. 1951. (A survey of the modern approach to book design. 150 books illustrated.)

Four Centuries of Fine Printing—Stanley Morison. Benn (London). 1924. Rev. ed. Barnes & Noble. 1960. (The original edition is a large folio with 272 reproductions of book pages from 1465 to 1924. The revised edition is much smaller.)

The Art of the Book—Charles Holme, ed. 1914; Bernard Newdigate, ed. 1938; Charles Ede, ed. 1951. *The Studio* (London). (3 well-illustrated surveys of European and American book design.)

Modern Book Production—*The Studio* (London). 1928. (A survey of bookmaking, 1915–28.)

The Nonesuch Century—Nonesuch Press. 1936. (Descriptions and specimens of their first 100 books.)

Quarto Millenary—Limited Editions Club. 1959. (Descriptions and illustrations of their first 250 books.)

Biblio-Typographica—Paul Johnston. Covici-Friede. 1930. (A survey of book typography of the 20s.)

Book Design and Illustration: Modern Trends and Developments—John Lewis. Studio Vista (London). (In preparation.)

The Growth of the Book Jacket—Charles Rosner. Harvard University Press. 1954. (A brief history and many illustrations of jackets from all over the world.)

HISTORY

The Shaping of Our Alphabet—Frank Denman. Knopf. 1955. (A particularly interesting and well-illustrated history of typography.)

The 26 Letters—Oscar Ogg. Crowell. 1948. (The development of the Roman alphabet. For young people, but a very clear introduction to the subject.)

Printing Types—D. B. Updike. Harvard University Press. 2 vols. 3rd ed. 1951. (The definitive history of type.)

Five Hundred Years of Printing—S. H. Steinberg. Pelican. 1962.

Modern Book Design—Ruari McLean. Essential Books (Oxford University Press). 1959. (A British study of bookmaking in the 20th century.)

The Typographic Book,. 1450–1935—S. Morison, K. Day. University of Chicago Press. 1964.

INSTRUCTION

Introduction to Typography—Oliver Simon. Harvard University Press. 1949. (A sound exposition of book typography by the English authority.)

Printing Types and How to Use Them—Stanley C. Hlasta. Carnegie (Rutgers). 1950. (A study of some standard display faces.)

Designing Books—Jan Tschichold. Wittenborn, Schultz. 1951. (Rules of typography from a conventional viewpoint.)

The Design of Books—Adrian Wilson. Reinhold. (In preparation.)

Typography—A. Burns. Reinhold. 1961.

TYPE SPECIMENS

ATA Type Comparison Book—Frank Merriman. Advertising Typographer's Assn. 1965 (Shows one line specimens related by visual characteristics. A valuable book.)

Encyclopedia of Type Faces—W. Turner Berry, A. F. Johnson, W. P. Jaspert. Pitman. 3rd ed. 1962. (Very useful, particularly for European faces. Grouped by visual characteristics.)

Type and Typography—Ben Rosen. Reinhold. 1963. (Good specimen book with complete alphabets. Interesting essays.)

Graphic Arts Typebook—Reinhold. 1965. (A projected series of 7 type specimen books, each covering a separate category. The first 2—serifed text type and sans serif text type—were published in 1965. Large and well done.)

Wood Type—Morgan Press (catalogue). (A broad selection of these vanishing types.)

Lettera—A.Haab, A.Stocker. Teufen (St. Gall). 2nd ed. 1963. (An inspirational collection of type and lettering.)

Typographic Variations—Hermann Zapf. Museum Books. 1964. (Examples of the author's work in type design and typography.)

Kingsport Type Specimens—Kingsport Press. 3 vols. (Text and display types. Many complete alphabets.)

NOTE: Many typesetting and book manufacturing companies issue substantial specimen books. The typefounders and typesetting machine manufacturers also have specimen books of their own faces. Most of these are available on request or are for sale.

ILLUSTRATION

USE

Picture Sources—Helen Faye, ed. Special Libraries Association. 1959. (Invaluable lists with addresses and useful information, divided by subject and indexed.)

Illustrators Annual—The Society of Illustrators. (Examples of the work of outstanding illustrators, both young and well-established.)

Illustration: Aspects and Directions—B. Gill, J. Lewis. Reinhold. 1964.

Guide to the Special Collections of Prints and Photographs in the Library of Congress—Paul Vanderbilt. Library of Congress. 1955.

Directory of Professional Photography, 1958–59—Professional Photographers of America (Milwaukee). 1958.

British Sources of Photographs and Pictures—G. W. A. Nunn, ed. Cassell (London). 1952.

HISTORY AND SURVEYS

The Illustrated Book—Frank Weitenkampf. Harvard University Press. 1938. (A thorough, scholarly history. Excellent bibliography.)
500 Years of Art in Illustration—Howard Simon. Garden City. 1949. (Mostly illustrations.)
A History of Book Illustration—David Bland. World. 1958. (Comprehensive.)
An Introduction to a History of Woodcut—A. M. Hind. Dover. 2 vols. 1963. (Originally published by Houghton Mifflin in 1935, this definitive work is now available as an inexpensive paperback.)
Book Illustration—R. W. Ellis. Kingsport Press. 1952. (A brief series of vignettes of illustrators from the beginning of printing to 1950.)
The Artist and the Book, 1860–1960—Museum of Fine Arts, Boston. 1961. (Excellent survey of book illustration.)
Illustrators of Children's Books, 1744–1945—B. Mahony, L. P. Latimer, B. Folmsbee, eds. *The Horn Book*. 1947. (A supplement edited by R. H. Viguers and others covers 1946–56.)
Modern Book Illustration in Great Britain and America—F. J. H. Darton. Special Winter number of *The Studio* (London). 1931.

PAPER

The Story of Papermaking—Edwin Sutermeister. Bowker. 1954. (A technical but readable explanation of the process.)
Pulp and Paper: Science and Technique—C. Earl Libby, ed. McGraw-Hill. 2 vols. 1962. (A definitive work.)
Paper Making—Dard Hunter. Knopf. 2nd ed. 1947. (The history and technique, by a master of the art.)
Paper and Paper Making—F. H. Norris. Oxford University Press. 1955.
Lockwood's Directory of Paper and Allied Trades—Lockwood Trade Journal Co., New York.

BINDING

Bookbinding—Edith Diehl. Rinehart. 2 vols. 1946. (The definitive work.)
Bookbinding in America—H. Lehmann-Haupt, H. D. French, J. W. Rogers. Anthoesen. 1941.
Modern Bookbinding—Douglas Leighton. Oxford University Press. 1935.
Library Binding Manual—American Library Association. 1951.
Bookbinding—James B. Blaine. Book Production Industry Magazine. (This pamphlet gives a brief but clear illustrated explanation of edition binding processes.)

PREPARATION OF CAMERA COPY

Preparing Art for Printing—B. Stone, A. Eckstein. Reinhold. 1964.
New Techniques in Practical Art Reproduction—J. Bourges Mayfield. Bourges. 1951. (Explains the use of Bourges transparent color sheets, etc.)
How to Prepare Art and Copy for Offset Lithography—W. J. Stevens, J. McKinven. Dorval. 1948.
Illustration and Reproduction—John R. Biggs. Farrar, Straus & Cudahy. 1952.

MANUSCRIPT PREPARATION

Words into Type—M. E. Skillin, R. M. Gay. Appleton. Rev. ed. 1964.
Manual of Style—University of Chicago Press. 11th ed. 1949.
Elements of Style—W. Strunk, Jr., E. B. White. Macmillan. 1962.
Proofreading and Copy-Preparation: A Textbook for the Graphic Arts Industry—Joseph Lasky. Mentor Press. 1954.
Manuscript and Proof—John Benbow. Oxford University Press. 1938.
Dictionary of Modern English Usage—H. W. Fowler. Oxford. 1937.

MISCELLANEOUS

Books and Printing—Paul A. Bennett. World. 1951. (Paperback, 1963.) (Anthology of pieces interesting to bookmen.)
The Printing of Books—Holbrook Jackson. Cassell (London). 2nd ed. 1948. (Essays including observations on bookmaking by famous writers.)

The Look of the Book—AIGA. 1960. (Articles on bookmaking from a variety of professions)

The Author Looks at Format—R. A. Freiman, ed. AIGA (pamphlet). 1951. (Comments on book design by authors.)

Graphic Forms—Harvard University Press. 1949. (Essays by prominent bookmen and designers.)

One Hundred Books About Bookmaking—Hellmut Lehmann-Haupt. Columbia University Press. 1949.

The Reader's Adviser—H. R. Hoffman, ed. Bowker. 10th ed. 1964. (Contains bibliographies of books about books.)

Bibliotheca Typographica—Horace Hart. Leo Hart, publisher (Rochester, N.Y.). 1933. (An annotated list of books about books.)

Literary Market Place—Anne J. Richter, ed. Bowker. (Annual containing names and addresses of interest to book people.)

Names & Numbers—Bowker (annual). (Alphabetical directory of individuals in book trade.)

Bowker Annual—Phyllis B. Steckler, Wyllis E. Wright, eds. Bowker. (A compendium of statistics and information about libraries and the book trade.)

Economic Survey of the Book Industry—O. H. Cheney. 1932. (Reprinted by Bowker in 1960 with introduction by Robert Frase. The basic study in this area.)

Books for All—R. E. Barker, UNESCO, Columbia University Press. 1957. (A study of international book trade.)

The American Reading Public. A Symposium—Roger Smith, ed. Bowker. 1964.

Golden Multitudes—Frank Luther Mott. Bowker. 1960.

How and Where to Look it Up—R. W. Murphey. McGraw-Hill. 1958. (For any kind of research.)

How and Where to Find the Facts—William Sunners. Arco. 1963. (Same as above.)

The Bookman's Glossary—Mary C. Turner. Bowker. 1961.

The Printer's Terms—R. Hostettler. Wittenborn. 3rd ed. 1959. (5-language dictionary.)

So You Want to Get into Publishing—Daniel Melcher. Bowker (pamphlet). 1964.

Manual of Copyright Practice—Margaret Nicholson. Oxford University Press. 2nd ed. 1956.

Copyright Guide—Harriet F. Pilpel, Morton D. Goldberg. Bowker, 1963.

Copyright Law of the United States of America—1960. (Can be obtained from Superintendent of Documents, U.S. Govt. Printing Office. Wash. 25, D.C. 25¢.)

An Introduction to Color—R. M. Evans. John Wiley. 1948. (A study of the properties of color in its physical and psychological aspects.)

Color by Overprinting—Donald E. Cooke. Winston. 1955. (An exhaustive guide to the techniques and effects of superimposing transparent inks.)

Periodicals

Publishers' Weekly—1180 Avenue of the Americas, New York, N.Y. (News of publishing activity, people, books, etc. A monthly section is devoted to bookmaking.)

Book Production Industry—201 East 42nd Street, New York, N.Y. (A monthly with articles and features of general publishing interest but with emphasis on bookmaking.)

Book Design and Production—Blomfield House, London Wall, London, EC 2. (A British quarterly covering bookmaking in England, but including some material on activities on the Continent and in America.)

Print—527 Madison Avenue, New York, N.Y. (Concerned with graphic design in general, including books.)

Graphis—15 East 48th Street, New York, N.Y. (A monthly devoted to graphic design around the world. Produced in Switzerland but printed in 3 languages including English.)

Saturday Review—380 Madison Avenue, New York, N.Y. (While this weekly does not deal with bookmaking directly, it carries articles and features of book interest—as well as material on music, art, science, education, travel, and affairs in general.)

Quill and Quire—Toronto. (Canadian book trade journal.)

The Bookseller—London. (British equivalent of *Publishers' Weekly*.)

Other sources

ASSOCIATIONS

The institutions listed are private agencies from whom information may be obtained to a limited degree, but in most cases they have neither staff nor facilities for extensive informational activities. Addresses can be found in the current *Literary Market Place* (Bowker).

Organizations concerned with standards and appreciation of the book arts.

American Institute of Graphic Arts (AIGA)—New York
Bookbuilders of Boston
Society of Printers—Boston
Philadelphia Book Clinic
Chicago Book Clinic
Typophiles—New York
Book Club of California—San Francisco

Business and technical associations

American Book Publishers Council—New York
American Booksellers Association—New York
American Photoengravers Association—Chicago
American Textbook Publishers Institute—New York
Association of American University Presses—New York
Book Manufacturers' Institute—New York
Canadian Book Publisher's Council—Toronto
Canadian Booksellers Association—Toronto
Edition Bookbinders of New York
Graphic Arts Technical Foundation (formerly Lithographic Technical Foundation)—Pittsburgh
Gravure Technical Association—New York
Printing Industry of America—Washington, D.C.
Research and Engineering Council of the Graphic Arts Industry—Washington, D.C.
Technical Association of the Pulp and Paper Industry—New York

Special interest groups:

American Library Association—Chicago
Children's Book Council—New York
Child Study Association—New York
Copyright Society of the U.S.A.—New York
Library Binding Institute—Boston

Professional and craft associations:

Association of Printing House Craftsmen—Cincinnati
Society of Illustrators—New York
Guild of Bookworkers (Professional and amateur hand binders, calligraphers, etc. Affiliated with AIGA)—New York
New York Publishing Society (Mostly editors)
The Permissions Group—New York
Women's National Book Association—various cities

LIBRARIES

Any large library contains items of bookmaking interest, but the following have specialized collections and/or permanent exhibits.

Harvard University—Cambridge, Mass.
Brown University—Providence, R.I.
Columbia University—New York
Grolier Club—New York
New York Public Library—New York (Bookmaking exhibit)
Yale University—New Haven, Conn.
Dartmouth College—Hanover, N.H.
Williams College—Williamstown, Mass.
Rochester Institute of Technology—Rochester, N.Y.
Princeton University—Princeton, N.J.
National Museum (Smithsonian Institution)—Washington, D.C.
Toledo Museum—Toledo, Ohio (Bookmaking exhibit)
University of Kentucky—Lexington, Ky. (Dwiggins materials)
Newberry Library—Chicago
R. R. Donnelly Company—Chicago
Book Club of California—San Francisco

FILMS

These are produced by individual suppliers or associations and are generally available for loan or rent to groups. Most may be obtained through the lending library of The Graphic Arts Industry, Inc., 5728 Connecticut Ave. N.W., Washington 15, D.C.

Making Books—Encyclopedia Britannica Films, Wilmette, Ill. Sound, 11 min. (The entire book manufacturing operation.)
Making a Book—Eastman Kodak, Rochester, N.Y. 17 min. (The bookmaking process from beginning to end.)
Bound to Last—William J. Ganz, New York. Sound, 18 min. (Covers book-manufacturing process from typesetting through binding.)
Printing Through the Ages—Encyclopedia Britannica Films, Wilmette, Ill. 1950. Sound, 13 min. (History of printing, type, and paper.)
Printing—Educational Council of Graphic Arts Industry. Sound, color, 22 min. (Career opportunities in graphic arts.)
A New Era of Printing—International Typographical Union, New York. Sound, color, 28 min. (Survey of composition and printing.)
Photocomposition—International Typographical Union, New York. Sound.
A Better Run for Your Money—Harris-Intertype Corp. Sound, color, 20 min. (Describes offset lithography and compares it with gravure and letterpress.)
Lithography—Graphic Arts Technical Foundation, Pittsburgh, Pa. (Series of training films.)
Art and Technique of Photoengraving—Horan Engraving Co., New York. 1954. Color, sound, 28 min.
Bindery Operations—Western Printing and Lithographing Co., Racine, Wis. Silent with titles, 45 min. (Describes operations at the company's own plant.)
Paper Work—Champion Paper & Fibre Co., Hamilton, Ohio. Sound. (Papermaking)
Color—International Printing Ink Co. Sound, color.

Typeface widths

The tables on the following pages give the average number of characters per pica for 6 sizes of 86 machine-set text types (roman only). Included are many of the phototypesetting machine faces—the first time they have been listed with this information in one place.

Note that some names are used for faces of more than one machine. However, while the names are the same, the typefaces and their characteristics are not necessarily so (CH.5). On the other hand, some faces having different names are almost identical.

The average number of characters per pica is not always simply an arithmetical computation based on the length of the lower case alphabet, but may be an actual average found in setting and counting a large amount of average prose. This takes into account the varying widths of frequently-used letters in relation to the alphabet length of each font. That is why the average characters per pica may differ for fonts of the same alphabet length.

The number of characters per pica may be affected by several other factors: texts with mostly Latin-origin words tend to have a higher percentage of vowels than those with more Anglo-Saxon words; technical and other non-fiction texts usually have many capitals; narrow measures will average fewer characters per pica because of wider word spacing; computerized composition will set tighter than manual setting.

Allowance should be made for these variables. The importance of accurate character-per-pica figures for book calculations is generally underestimated. In a small amount of copy for an ad or a newspaper column an error of 2% is not significant; in a 416-page book such an error represents 8 pages—a substantial amount indeed. For this reason it is desirable to use character-per-pica figures carried to 2 digits past the decimal point. For example, the difference between 2.1 and 2.2 is almost 5%, which is much too wide a spread.

Metal typefaces

LINOTYPE & INTERTYPE

	8	9	10	11	12	14
Baskerville (L)	3.15	2.9	2.6	2.43	2.32	2.05
Beton Medium (I)	3.48	2.97	2.65	2.36	2.14	1.91
Bodoni (I, L)	3.07	2.83	2.55		2.36	2.14
Bodoni Book (I, L)	3.23	2.95	2.75	2.6	2.47	2.27
Caledonia (L)	3.07	2.83	2.57	2.43	2.28	2.04
Caslon (I, L)	3.1	2.95	2.78	2.41	2.21	1.94
Century Expanded (I, L)	2.83	2.63	2.4	2.31	2.15	1.81
DeVinne (I)	3.13	2.92	2.61	2.29	2.1	1.79
Electra (L)	3.2	2.88	2.68	2.5	2.4	2.18
Fairfield (L)	3.15	2.95	2.75	2.58	2.43	2.23
Garamond 3 (L)	3.23	3.03	2.85	2.68	2.58	2.3
Granjon (L)	3.35	3.07	2.88	2.67	2.47	2.26
Helvetica (L)	3.07	2.74	2.46		2.06	
Janson (L)	3.03	2.75	2.57	2.43	2.33	2.11
Metromedium (L)	3.4		2.78		2.36	2.07
Monticello (L)	2.95	2.73	2.55	2.4	2.3	2.13
News Gothic (I)	3.02	2.87	2.61	2.44	2.21	1.88
Old Style 7 (L)	3.27	3.05	2.78	2.52	2.33	
Opticon (L)	2.58	2.52	2.38	2.26	2.18	
Optima (L) *	3.3	3.1	2.77		2.52	
Palatino (L) *	3.	2.77	2.57		2.21	
Primer (L)	2.75	2.55	2.42	2.28	2.17	
Scotch (L)	3.05		2.68	2.52	2.24	1.89
Times Roman (L)	3.08	2.85	2.68	2.5	2.33	2.15
Waverly (I)	3.11	2.73	2.56	2.34	2.13	1.8
Weiss (I)	3.9	3.45	3.2	2.97	2.62	2.31

MONOTYPE

	8	9	10	11	12	14
Baskerville 353	3.2	3.05	2.72	2.48	2.28	2.12
Bulmer 462	3.3	3.05	2.8	2.62	2.5	2.24
Caslon Old Style 337	3.33	2.98	2.68	2.42	2.22	1.96
Century Expanded 20	3.05	2.72	2.52	2.42	2.22	1.9
Garamont 248	3.4	3.02	2.7	2.43	2.22	1.97
Janson 401	3.27	3.1	2.78	2.58	2.33	2.08
Modern 8	3.12	2.98	2.68	2.41	2.22	1.9
News Gothic 206	3.08	2.7	2.42	2.3	2.2,	1.78

* For this face the sizes listed are U.S. equivalents of the European (Didot) sizes. However, this is a confused area. Approach with caution.

Photo typefaces

LINOFILM

	8	9	10	12B*	12A	14
Baskerville	3.2	2.83	2.56	2.13	2.13	1.83
Caledonia	3.1	2.74	2.46	2.28	2.06	1.96
Electra	3.27	2.92	2.62	2.41	2.18	2.07
Garamond 3	3.34	2.97	2.68	2.48	2.23	2.12
Palatino	3.13	2.76	2.5	2.11	2.08	1.81
Primer	2.83	2.52	2.27	2.13	1.89	1.83
Times Roman	3.24	2.9	2.6	2.38	2.16	2.03
Trade Gothic	3.1	2.74	2.46	2.28	2.06	1.96

FOTOSETTER

	8	9	10	11	12	14
Baskerville	3.24	3.1	2.7	2.46	2.31	1.94
Bodoni Book	3.34	3.06	2.95	2.74	2.53	2.15
Bulmer	3.82	3.42	2.95	2.74	2.53	2.15
Century Expanded	2.92	2.81	2.43	2.3	2.11	1.81
Garamond	3.32	3.1	3.03	2.89	2.61	2.22
Goudy Old Style	3.47	3.11	2.71	2.52	2.31	2.
News Gothic	3.3	2.93	2.54	2.41	2.21	1.84
Times Roman	3.33	3.	2.61	2.42	2.22	1.91

MONOPHOTO

	8	9	10	11	12	14
Baskerville 169	3.33	2.94	2.67	2.41	2.22	1.91
Bodoni 135	3.33	2.99	2.67	2.41	2.2	1.89
Garamond 156	3.51	3.08	2.74	2.56	2.33	1.98
Imprint 101	3.23	2.86	2.53	2.35	2.13	1.83
Perpetua 239	3.57	3.28	2.94	2.74	2.47	2.15
Plantin 110	3.23	2.86	2.53	2.35	2.13	1.83
Times Roman 327	3.28	2.99	2.6	2.38	2.18	1.87
Univers Light 685	3.08	2.7	2.44	2.25	2.04	1.72

ATF PHOTOTYPESETTER

	8	9	10	11	12	14
Baskerville	3.25	3.05	2.75	2.49	2.33	1.97
Bodoni Book	3.59	3.28	2.92		2.58	
Caledonia	3.18	2.92	2.65	2.46	2.27	
Century Schoolbook	3.	2.56	2.25	2.2	1.94	1.62
Elmora	2.89	2.58	2.43	2.2	2.01	
Garamond	4.1	3.72	3.51		3.	2.69
Spartan Book	3.98	3.42	3.03		2.48	2.22
Times Roman	3.23	2.99	2.75	2.54	2.27	

* Equivalent to about 11 pt.

PHOTON		8	9	10	11	12	14
	Baskerville	3.4	3.1	2.7	2.5	2.3	2.
	Bodoni	3.6	3.2	2.9	2.6	2.4	2.
	Century Expanded	3.2	2.8	2.5	2.3	2.1	1.8
	Concord	3.9	3.4	3.1	2.8	2.6	2.2
	Garamond	3.8	3.4	3.	2.8	2.5	2.2
	Highland	3.4	3.1	2.7	2.5	2.3	2.
	Times Roman	3.3	3.	2.7	2.4	2.3	1.9
	Univers Light	3.8	3.3	3.	2.7	2.5	2.1

ALPHATYPE		8	9	10	11	12	14
	Baskerline	3.42	3.	2.69	2.43	2.31	1.96
	Bodoni	3.12	3.02	2.71	2.46	2.27	1.94
	Caledo	3.23	2.87	2.59	2.35	2.14	1.98
	Century X	3.05	2.73	2.52	2.25	2.17	1.86
	Clarendon Wide	2.43	2.27	2.02	1.8	1.69	1.48
	English	3.35	2.97	2.66	2.43	2.23	1.91
	Musica	3.22	2.87	2.6	2.36	2.07	1.93
	Uranus	3.16	2.82	2.56	2.34	2.07	1.79

Glossary-Index

This index was planned to be used in conjunction with the detailed Contents pages—which are, in effect, a subject index.

With a few exceptions, definitions are given here only for terms occurring on more than one page in the text, as the meaning of each term is made clear where it first appears.

C

N

O

P

BOOKMAKING: *The illustrated guide to design and production*

This book was designed by the author and
produced by BALANCE HOUSE.
Composition and binding were done by
H. Wolff Book Manufacturing Company, New York.
The text type—10 on 13 Electra—was set on a
Linotype Elektron No. 1 activated by a punched tape
produced on a Teletypesetter and justified by a Linasec computer.
The printing was done by offset lithography by Mahony & Roese, New York.
The text paper is Bergstrom Thor Cote Hi-Bulk, 60 lb.
For the cover, Bancroft's Arrestox was lithographed
by Reehl Litho, New York. The front endpaper was
printed by Chroma-Philips, New York. The back
endpaper is Canfield's Colortext.